Prentice Hall Brief Review

The Living Environment

John Bartsch / Mary P. Colvard

Ordering Information

Send orders to:
  Pearson Customer Service
  P.O. Box 2500
  Lebanon, IN 46052-3009

or call toll free:
  1-800-848-9500
  (8:00 A.M.-6:00 P.M. EST)

School orders:
  k12.oasis.pearson.com

Individual orders:
  pearsonschool.com/nybriefreviews

PEARSON   ALWAYS LEARNING

About the Authors

John Bartsch and **Mary Colvard** each have taught high school biology for over 30 years. Their many professional activities include working for the New York State Education Department as Education Specialists and serving the Science Teachers Association of New York State (STANYS) as officers, on the Board of Directors, and on various committees. They were also coordinating biology mentors for the Biology and Chemistry Mentor Network.

Mr. Bartsch has written a chemical safety manual, worked on several writing projects for Pearson, attended and worked as a consultant/instructor for the Cornell Institute for Biology Teachers (CIBT) program, and is a long-time member of both the National Association of Biology Teachers (NABT) and the National Science Teachers Association (NSTA).

Ms. Colvard has developed activities for CIBT, the Howard Hughes Medical Institute Holiday Lectures, and the Cold Spring Harbor Dolan DNA Learning Center. She has also served on the Board of Directors for NABT and on several National Research Council Committees.

Teacher Reviewers and Contributors

Anthony (Bud) Bertino
Canandaigua Academy
Canandaigua, New York

Patricia L. Nolan
Scotia-Glenville High School
Scotia, New York

Elise Russo, Ed.D.
Administrator for Secondary Curriculum
Amityville Union Free School District
Amityville, New York

Content Reviewer

Jerry Sanders

Acknowledgments begin on page I-4 and constitute an extension of this copyright page.

ISBN-13: 978-0-32-887050-9
ISBN-10: 0-32-887050-1

2 3 4 5 6 7 8 9 10 V011 19 18 17 16

Brief Review in
The Living Environment

New York Standards

KEY

Standard   Key Idea

4.2.1

Performance Indicator

4.1 Intro	4.1.2d	4.1.2h
4.1.2a	4.1.2e	4.1.2i
4.1.2b	4.1.2f	4.1.2j
4.1.2c	4.1.2g	4.1.3a

4.1.2c	4.5.1f	4.5.2g
4.1.2d	4.5.1g	4.5.2h
4.5 Intro	4.5.2a	4.5.2i
4.5.1a	4.5.2b	4.5.2j
4.5.1b	4.5.2c	4.5.3a
4.5.1c	4.5.2d	4.5.3b
4.5.1d	4.5.2e	
4.5.1e	4.5.2f	

4.2 Intro	4.2.1g	4.2.2c
4.2.1a	4.2.1h	4.2.2d
4.2.1b	4.2.1i	4.2.2e
4.2.1c	4.2.1j	4.3.1c
4.2.1d	4.2.1k	4.3.1d
4.2.1e	4.2.2a	
4.2.1f	4.2.2b	

4.4 Intro	4.4.1e
4.4.1a	4.4.1f
4.4.1b	4.4.1g
4.4.1c	4.4.1h
4.4.1d	

4.3 Intro	4.3.1f	4.3.1l
4.3.1a	4.3.1g	
4.3.1b	4.3.1h	
4.3.1c	4.3.1i	
4.3.1d	4.3.1j	
4.3.1e	4.3.1k	

4.1 Intro	4.6 Intro	4.6.1g
4.1.1a	4.6.1a	4.6.2a
4.1.1b	4.6.1b	4.6.2b
4.1.1c	4.6.1c	4.6.3a
4.1.1d	4.6.1d	4.6.3b
4.1.1e	4.6.1e	4.6.3c
4.1.1f	4.6.1f	

New York Standards

4.7 Intro	4.7.2b	
4.7.1a	4.7.2c	
4.7.1b	4.7.3a	
4.7.1c	4.7.3b	
4.7.2a		

1.1.1a	1.2.1	1.3.2
1.1.1b	1.2.2a	1.3.3
1.1.1c	1.2.3a	1.3.4a
1.1.2a	1.2.3b	1.3.4b
1.1.2b	1.2.3c	1.3.4c
1.1.3a	1.2.4	1.3.5a
1.1.3b	1.3.1a	1.3.5b
1.1.4a		

Appendix A: Bullets 5, 9–17

Appendix A: Bullets 1–8

Separate Teacher Answer Key Contents:

Teacher Strategies/Explanations of Topic Openers

Diagnostic Tests with Answers

Topic Quizzes with Answers

Answers to Review Questions

Answers to Regents Exam Practice Questions

About This Book

This book is designed to enhance review of the concepts, skills, and applications of The Living Environment Core Curriculum that may be tested on the Living Environment Regents Examination. For nearly all students, passing this examination will be a requirement for graduation from high school.

Features

Content Review

The Regents Examination will be based entirely on the content and understandings specifically addressed by The Living Environment Core Curriculum. For the most part, any material *not* addressed in the core curriculum is not included in this book.

Vocabulary Many exam questions require an understanding of the language of biology.

Bold Words Bold-type terms listed at the beginning of a topic are defined within that topic. These terms are likely to appear on the exam.

Underlined Words Underlined terms are either words that appear as bold in other topics or that describe basic biological concepts, or are words commonly used in discussions of science concepts.

Real-world Examples Many real-world examples are included to reinforce content understandings. Use these examples or others of your choosing to answer questions on the exam. The examples you choose demonstrate your understanding of the content as well as your ability to apply these understandings to the real world.

Sidebars

Memory Jogger Recalls relevant information covered elsewhere in this book or previous science courses.

Digging Deeper Goes beyond what you need to know to help you better understand the required material.

Review Questions Questions similar to those on the exam, totaling more than 400, appear throughout each topic to clarify and reinforce understanding.

Practice Questions for the New York Regents Exam

A total of more than 300 practice questions are written and organized for each topic in the format of the exam.

Part A Multiple-choice questions test knowledge of concepts.

Part B Both multiple-choice and constructed-response questions test understandings and skills.

Part C These questions often require extended constructed responses with more detailed answers supported by applications or examples. Numbers in brackets tell how many points the question is worth on an actual exam.

Reference and Support

Strategies for Answering Test Questions Support to help you interpret and answer the range of exam questions.

Appendix *NY State Required Laboratory Activities* Information regarding the skills, content, and types of questions you can expect to find on Part D of the Regents Examination.

Glossary Defines all bold vocabulary words and underlined words appearing in the topics.

Index Cross-references concepts in the topics.

Regents Examinations

The most recent released Regents Examinations are reproduced at the end of this book to provide practice in taking actual Regents Examinations.

Answer Key with Diagnostic Tests A separate Answer Key includes all answers to the Review and Practice Questions plus topic-by-topic Diagnostic Tests to help determine which concepts require more intense review and Topic Quizzes for quick assessment with different questions.

Strategies for Answering Test Questions

This section provides strategies to help you answer various types of questions on The Living Environment Regents Examination. Strategies are provided for answering multiple-choice and constructed-response questions as well as for questions based on diagrams, data tables, and graphs. For each type of question, practice questions are provided to show you how to apply the strategies to answer specific questions.

Strategies for Multiple-Choice Questions

Multiple-choice questions account for more than 50 percent of The Living Environment Regents Examination. Part A is totally made up of multiple-choice questions, and Parts B and D include some. Therefore, it is important to be good at deciphering multiple-choice questions. Here are a few helpful strategies. For any one question, not all strategies will need to be used. The numbers are provided for reference, not to specify an order (except for Strategies 1 and 2).

1. Always read the entire question, but wait to read the choices. (See Strategy 4.)

2. Carefully examine any data tables, diagrams, or photographs associated with the question.

3. Underline key words and phrases in the question that signal what you should be looking for in the answer. This will make you read the question more carefully. This strategy applies mostly to questions with a long introduction.

4. Try to think of an answer to the question before looking at the choices given. If you think you know the answer, write it on a separate piece of paper before reading the choices. Next, read all of the choices and compare them to your answer before making a decision. Do not select the first answer that seems correct. If your answer matches one of the choices, and you are quite sure of your response, you are probably correct. Even if your answer matches one of the choices, carefully consider all of the answers, because the

obvious choice is not always the correct one. If there are no exact matches, re-read the question and look for the choice that is most similar to your answer.

5. Eliminate any choices that you know are incorrect. Lightly cross out the numbers for those choices on the exam paper. Each choice you can eliminate increases your chances of selecting the correct answer.

6. If the question makes no sense after reading through it several times, leave it for later. After completing the rest of the exam, return to the question. Something you read on the other parts of the exam may give you some ideas about how to answer this question. If you are still unsure, go with your best guess. There is no penalty for guessing, but answers left blank will be counted as wrong. If you employ your best test-taking strategies, you just may select the correct answer.

Practice Questions

1. Most of the oxygen that enters the atmosphere results from the process of
   (1) respiration   (3) excretion
   (2) photosynthesis   (4) digestion

Explanation of Answer Use strategy 5. Eliminating choices 3 and 4 may be easy, but think about the other two choices carefully before choosing your final answer. Be sure that you are not confusing respiration with photosynthesis. The correct answer is choice (2), photosynthesis.

---

2. Cellular respiration in humans occurs in
   (1) red blood cells, only
   (2) the cells of the lungs, only
   (3) the cells of the digestive system, only
   (4) all the cells of the body

Explanation of Answer Use strategy 4. Note that the question is asking where cell respiration occurs in humans. Your answer before reading the choices should say that respiration occurs in all of the cells of the body or that respiration occurs in the mitochondria. All of the choices are different types of cells. Think about what cell respiration is, and why cells respire. Lung cells and red blood cells help obtain and carry oxygen, but cell respiration is a process that releases energy in *all* cells. Therefore, the correct answer is choice (4), all the cells of the body.

---

3. A number of white potato plants are grown by placing pieces of one potato in the ground. This method of reproduction is most similar to

(1) sexual reproduction
(2) cloning
(3) genetic engineering
(4) zygote formation

Explanation of Answer Use strategy 5. You should be able to eliminate choices 1 and 4, since both are related to the same form of reproduction. The fusion of sex cells results in the formation of a zygote. Since there can be only one correct answer, these will not work. Genetic engineering refers to the manipulation of genes leading to the development of new combinations of traits and new varieties of organisms. Since only one parent (potato) is involved, the genetic makeup of the new potato plants will be the same as the original plant. Therefore, cutting up a potato and planting the pieces is most like choice (2), cloning. This is a form of asexual reproduction in which all offspring are genetic copies.

---

4. Overexposure of animals to X-rays is dangerous, because X-rays are known to damage DNA. A direct result of this damage is cells with

(1) unusually thick cell membranes
(2) no organelles located in the cytoplasm
(3) abnormally large chloroplasts
(4) changes in chromosome structure

Explanation of Answer Use strategy 3. As you read this question, underline key words: Overexposure of <u>animals</u> to <u>X-rays</u> is dangerous, because X-rays are known to <u>damage</u> <u>DNA</u>. A <u>direct</u> <u>result</u> of this damage is cells with (4) changes in chromosome structure. You should know that chromosomes are composed of DNA molecules and that X-rays can cause mutations, which are changes in DNA and/or chromosome

structure. Choices 1, 2, and 3 can be eliminated, since even if they could occur, it would not be a <u>direct</u> <u>result</u> of the <u>DNA's</u> being <u>damaged</u>.

Strategies for Constructed–Response Questions

Some questions in Parts B and D, and all questions in Part C of The Living Environment Regents Examination require a constructed response. Some of these questions require you to write one or two words, while others require much more. Students who use complete sentences when appropriate tend to have more organized answers. As a result, they usually get higher scores.

No matter which type of answer is requested, the following strategies will help you write constructed responses.

1. Always read through the entire question.

2. Underline key words and phrases in the question that signal what you should be looking for in the answer. This will make you read the question more carefully.

3. Write a brief outline, or at least a few notes to yourself, about what should be included in the answer.

4. Pay attention to key words that indicate how to answer the question and what you need to say in your answer. Several of these words are very common. For example, you might be asked to identify, describe, explain, state, compare, contrast, or design. The table on the next page lists key words and directions for your answers.

5. When you write your answer, don't be so general that you are not really saying anything. Be very specific. You should use the correct terms and clearly explain the processes and relationships. Be sure to provide details, such as the names of processes, names of structures, and, if it is appropriate, how they are related. If only one example or term is required, do not give two or more. If one is correct and the other is wrong, your answer will be marked wrong.

Using Key Words to Direct Your Answers

Key Word	What Direction Your Answers Should Take
Analyze	• Break the idea, concept, or situation into parts, and explain how they relate. • Carefully explain relationships, such as cause and effect.
Compare	• Relate two or more topics with an emphasis on how they are alike. • State the similarities between two or more examples.
Contrast	• Relate two or more topics with an emphasis on how they are different. • State the differences between two or more examples.
Define	• State the exact meaning of a topic or word. • Explain what something is or what it means.
Describe	• Illustrate the subject using words. • Provide a thorough account of the topic. • Give complete answers.
Discuss	• Make observations about the topic or situation using facts. • Thoroughly write about various aspects of the topic or situation.
Design	• Plan an experiment or component of an experiment. Map out your proposal, being sure to provide information about all of the required parts.
Explain	• Clarify the topic of the question by spelling it out completely. • Make the topic understandable. • Provide reasons for the outcome.
State	• Express in words. • Explain or describe using at least one fact, term, or relationship.

6. If a question has two or three parts, answer each part in a separate paragraph or bullet. This will make it easy for the person scoring your paper to find all of the information. When writing your answer, don't shortchange one part of the question by spending too much time on another part.

7. Whenever it is appropriate, answer in complete sentences. A sentence should always have a subject and a verb, and a good answer should not start with the word *because*. Note that you will not lose points for incorrect grammar, spelling, punctuation, or poor penmanship. However, such errors and poor penmanship could impair your ability to make your answer clear to the person scoring your paper. If that person cannot understand what you are trying to say, you will not receive the maximum number of points.

Practice Questions

5. State a safety precaution that a student should use when heating liquid in a test tube. [1]

Sample Answer When heating liquid in a test tube, the student should wear safety goggles.

6. The diagram below shows the setup of an experiment.

Setup in light   Setup in dark

State a problem that could be investigated using this experimental setup.

Sample Answer Is light needed for photosynthesis?

Tip Note that "State a problem" here really means to state a question. You are not expected to describe a fault with this setup.

---

7. The diagram below shows two ways in which grains, such as wheat or corn, can provide food for humans.

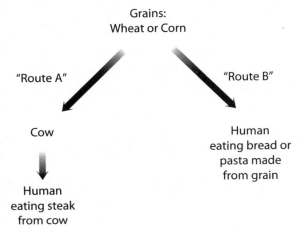

Grains:
Wheat or Corn

"Route A"   "Route B"

Cow   Human
                   eating bread or
                   pasta made
                   from grain

Human
eating steak
from cow

Select which "Route ," A or B, involves the least energy loss and explain why this is true. [2]

Hint Note the key words that have been underlined to indicate two things you must do: (1) select a route and then (2) explain why it is your choice. Note that this question is worth two points, one point for each correct answer.

Scoring Guide Teachers are provided with Scoring Guides and Sample Answers to use when rating your answers. Often there are several correct answers to a question. Here is an example of what teachers would use to score question 7:
Allow a maximum of 2 credits: 1 credit for identifying Route B as the one with the least energy loss and 1 for a correct explanation. Acceptable responses include, but are not limited to the following:
• Route B involves the least energy loss because some energy is lost at each step on a food chain.
• Route B because the energy goes directly from the corn to the human. That is not the case with Route A.

8. Provide two reasons why it is important to preserve biodiversity. [2]

Scoring Guide and Sample Answers Award one point for each correct reason given for a maximum of two points. Possible answers include, but are not limited to, the following:
• Biodiversity ensures the availability of a variety of genetic material.
  OR
• Biodiversity may allow us to find plants or animals that could be used as new medicines.
  OR
• Biodiversity helps an ecosystem remain stable.
  OR
• A lot of tropical plants may contain chemicals people can use to cure cancer or HIV.
  OR
• Loss of species from an ecosystem could disrupt the food web.

Base your answers to questions 9 through 12 on the information in the paragraph below and on your knowledge of biology.

It is possible to collect human sperm and to use this sperm later to fertilize eggs in a process called *artificial insemination*. The collected sperm samples are frozen and stored in a sperm bank until needed. When a woman makes use of a sperm bank, she requests sperm from a donor with the physical features she wants for her baby. The name of the donor is not revealed. The artificial insemination process involves placing the sperm in the woman's body and allowing fertilization to occur in the normal manner.

9. Suppose a woman whose husband cannot produce sperm becomes pregnant through artificial insemination. Explain how the baby's DNA will compare to the DNA of the woman and her husband. [1]

10. If a woman were given sperm from the same donor for three different pregnancies, and she had three daughters, would the three girls look alike, or would they be different? Provide at least one scientific fact that supports your answer. [1]

11. The production of a normal baby also involves protecting the developing embryo from harmful environmental factors. Identify three ways in which the pregnant woman could avoid exposing the developing embryo to environmental risks. [3]

12. Artificial insemination is also used on animals. State two benefits farmers or animal breeders gain from using artificial insemination. [1]

Scoring Guide For questions 9 through 12:

9. Award one point for an answer that recognizes that the baby received DNA from the mother, but none from the mother's husband. A possible acceptable answer would be: The baby's DNA sequence would have much (one half) in common with the mother's DNA sequence, but it would have no specific resemblance to the DNA of the woman's husband.

10. Award one point for an answer that states the girls would not look alike, and one point for a correct explanation of why they would not look alike. Award no credit for stating they would all look alike. A possible correct answer: The girls would look different from each other, since they came from different eggs and sperm, each containing unique DNA information. (Equivalent correct answers are also acceptable.) Maximum of two points.

11. Award one point for each correct way the pregnant woman could avoid environmental risks to the embryo. Fully correct answers should include three of the following (or other equivalent correct ways to avoid environmental risks to the embryo): The woman should not drink alcohol, smoke, take drugs, expose herself to a disease such as HIV, or eat an unhealthy diet. Maximum of three points.

12. Award one point for an answer that identifies one benefit that artificial insemination provides to farmers or breeders. Correct responses could include reference to being able to breed animals that live far apart without transporting them to the same location, being able to select desirable traits from animals you do not own and cannot afford to buy, not needing

to maintain large numbers of both sexes on a farm (bulls along with cows, or roosters with chickens), or that one male individual with very desirable characteristics being able to father many, many offspring in many locations, and so on.

Strategies for Questions Based on Diagrams

Both multiple-choice and constructed-response questions frequently include diagrams or pictures. Usually the diagrams provide information needed to answer the question. The diagrams may be realistic, or they may be a schematic. Schematic drawings show the relationships among parts and sometimes the sequence of events that occur in a system.

Practice Questions

Base your answer to questions 13 and 14 on the diagram below and on your knowledge of biology.

The diagram illustrates one possible scheme of evolution among various groups of organisms.

- **First, study the diagram.** Ask yourself what the diagram is about and what it shows you. Read the title or description provided, if there is one.

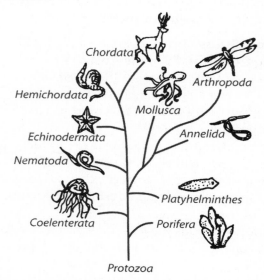

You are told that the diagram represents a possible sequence of events in the evolution of a number of organisms. Based on the illustration, you see that *Protozoa* are the common ancestor of all the other animals shown. It also indicates that *Porifera*, *Platyhelminthes*, *Nematoda*, and *Coelenterata* existed before *Echinodermata*, *Hemichordata*, *Chordata*, *Arthropoda*, *Annelida*, and *Mollusca*. The diagram also shows that *Platyhelminthes* and *Nematoda* are very closely related, as are *Arthropoda*, *Annelida*, and *Mollusca*.

You need to know that the closer the point of branching, the more closely related the organisms. The farther apart the point of branching, the more distant the relationship.

- **Second, read the question.**

13. Which inference does the diagram best support?

For this type of question, it is difficult to try to anticipate what the correct answer might be. Carefully read each of the choices, one at a time, and see if they make sense by looking back at the diagram. As you do this, eliminate any choices you can.

(1) Members of the animal kingdom are more complex than members of the plant kingdom.
(2) Members of the animal kingdom and members of the plant kingdom share common ancestry.
(3) Chordates are more closely related to arthropods than to echinoderms.
(4) Members of the group *Echinodermata* and the group *Annelida* share common ancestry.

Explanation of Answer There is no information provided about plants by the diagram; you can eliminate choices 1 and 2 based on what you see here or even on what you have learned during the year.

According to the diagram, chordates are more closely related to *Echinodermata* than they are to *Arthropoda*—the opposite of what choice (3) states—because *Echinodermata* branches off the same line that chordates are on. Arthropod ancestors branched before that.

The correct answer is (4), Members of the group *Echinodermata* and the group *Annelida* share common ancestry. All of the animals on this evolutionary diagram share a common ancestor—*Protozoa*.

14. Which two groups of organisms in the diagram are shown to be the most closely related?

Before reading the choices provided, think about how you could tell which organisms are most closely related (by two organisms being close together on one branch). Then apply this to eliminate obviously wrong choices. Do not select the first answer that seems correct.

(1) Porifera and Echinodermata
(2) Chordata and Platyhelminthes
(3) Mollusca and Annelida
(4) Arthropoda and Coelenterata

Explanation of Answer Choices 1, 2, and 4 have separate branches and are widely separated. Therefore, these choices can be eliminated. *Mollusca* and *Annelida* are the only two groups that share a common side branch on the diagram. Therefore, the correct answer is (3), *Mollusca* and *Annelida*.

- **First, study the diagram for Question 15.** This illustration shows a rabbit and a plant giving off CO_2 and taking in O_2 from the environment. This analysis of the illustration indicates that materials are being cycled through the environment.

- **Second, read the question.**

15. Which ecological principle is best illustrated by the following diagram?

Before reading the choices provided, think about the diagram and what the question is asking. It seems that the ecological principle illustrated here has something to do with cycles in the environment. As you read the choices, eliminate any choices that you can.

(1) In an ecosystem, material is cycled among the organisms and their environment
(2) In an ecosystem, the number of producers and consumers is equal.
(3) Competition within a species results in natural selection.
(4) An ecosystem requires a constant source of energy.

Explanation of Answer Since an ecosystem requires more producers than consumers, choice 2 is incorrect. Choices 3 and 4 are not addressed by the illustration. It does not show competition within the rabbit species. There is no energy source shown in the diagram, nor is the ecosystem requirement for a constant energy source illustrated. Therefore, you would probably select the correct answer as being choice (1), In an ecosystem, material is cycled among the organisms and their environment.

- **First, study the diagram for Question 16.** Ask yourself what the diagram is about and what it shows you. It shows CO_2 and H_2O entering, and sugar and O_2 leaving. The illustration seems to have something to do with photosynthesis, since CO_2 and H_2O are raw materials and sugar and O_2 are products.

- **Second, read the question.**

16. The diagram represents some events that take place in a plant cell. With which organelle would these events be most closely associated?

Before reading the choices provided, write what you think the answer should be on a separate piece of paper. Then compare your answer to the choices provided.

(1) mitochondrion   (3) ribosome
(2) chloroplast   (4) vacuole

Explanation of Answer Mitochondria are associated with cellular respiration, ribosomes with protein synthesis, and vacuoles with storage. Since this diagram illustrates photosynthesis, which occurs in chloroplasts in plant cells, the correct answer is choice (2), chloroplast.

Note: If you realized that the process was either photosynthesis or respiration but weren't sure which one, you at least could narrow your choices to 1 and 2 and improve your chances of guessing the right one.

Base your answers to questions 17 and 18 on the information below, and your knowledge of biology.

The map was drawn by an ecologist. It represents the vegetation around a small pond in a forest located in New York State.

KEY 🖾 Open water   🏕 Forest
     🐟 Shallow water containing   🌾 Wet area with grass
        pond plants   and cattails

- **First, study the diagram.** Think about what the diagram shows you. Did you read the information at the top of the illustration?

If you were approaching the pond from the forest, you would walk through trees, then wet areas with tall plants, such as cattails and grasses. The ground would be wet and squishy. Next, you would enter shallow water in which many rooted plants grow. From this point, open water would be visible. The water would be much deeper, and you would probably not be able to walk but would need to swim or use a boat. There are many different questions you could be asked about this diagram.

- **Second, read the questions.**

17. Describe one specific way this environment would be likely to change if it were left undisturbed by humans for 100 years. [1]

Sample Answers The pond environment will probably fill in, leaving mostly forest.

OR

The species present in the nonforest communities will disappear, and forest plants and animals will replace them.

Explanation of Answers Both answers relate to the idea of ecological succession. All ecosystems progress through a series of changes during which one community modifies the environment, making it more suitable for another community. The organic matter from decaying vegetation will gradually fill the pond.

18. Name two organisms in this ecosystem that are producers. [1]

Sample Answers and Scoring Guide Sample answers: cattails and grass. Scoring guide: Any two of the following or their equivalent are acceptable: cattails, pond plants, grass, or trees. Award one point for naming two correctly. Award no points for naming only one correctly.

Explanation of Answer Producers are organisms that are capable of taking inorganic raw materials from the environment and synthesizing their own food. Plants are producers.

Strategies for Questions Based on Data Tables

Most data tables contain information that summarizes a topic. A table uses rows and columns to condense information and to present it in an organized way. Rows are the horizontal divisions going from left to right across the table, while columns are vertical divisions going from top to bottom. Column headings name the type of information included in a table. Sometimes different categories of information are listed down the left-hand column of the table.

Examine the sample data table below. It provides information collected during an old study of the death rates of policy holders of a large life insurance company.

Before attempting to answer any questions based on the data, go through the following steps:

Deaths as a Result of Disease		
Cause of Death	Deaths per 100,000 People	
	1911	1957
Tuberculosis	224.6	6.7
Communicable disease	58.9	0.1
Cancer	69.3	136.2
Heart disease	156.4	256.2

1. Find the title of the table. It is usually located across the top. What is the title of the sample table? (Answer: Deaths as a Result of Disease)

2. Determine the number of columns in the table and their purpose. Do this for the sample table. (Answer: There are three columns. They show the causes of death and deaths per 100,000 people during the years of 1911 and 1957.)

3. Determine the number of rows and their purpose. Do this for the sample table. (Answer: There are four rows. The rows provide you with the number of deaths due to tuberculosis, communicable diseases, cancer, and heart disease.)

4. Read across the rows and down the columns to determine what the relationships are. Do this for the table shown. Notice how the numbers of deaths changed for each disease between 1911 and 1957. Some decreased and some increased.

Now you are ready to read the question with the sample data table and answer it.

19. The study most clearly indicated that during the time period examined

    (1) cancer of the lungs was increasing
    (2) people were living longer
    (3) children were safer from communicable diseases
    (4) better housing reduced deaths from tuberculosis

Explanation of Answer Choice 1 doesn't work because even though cancer death rates increased from 69.3 to 136.2 per 100,000, there is no way to tell what type or types of cancer caused the difference. Choice 2 is not correct because you have no information about how long people were living in either 1911 or 1957. Choice 4 is not correct because no information is provided about what caused the decrease in deaths due to tuberculosis. You only know that the death rate decreased from 224.6 in 1911 to 6.7 per 100,000 in 1957. The correct answer is choice (3), children were safer from communicable diseases. The number of deaths decreased from 58.9 per 100,000 in 1911 to 0.1 per 100,000 in 1957.

Practice Questions

Base your answers to questions 20 and 21 on the information below and on your knowledge of biology.

A dog was placed in a special room free of unrelated stimuli. On repeated trials, a tone was sounded for 5 seconds; approximately 2 seconds later, the dog was given food. Trials 1, 10, 20, 30, 40, and 50 were test trials; that is, the tone was sounded for 30 seconds and no food was given. The following data were collected:

Data Table		
Test Trial Number	Drops of Saliva Secreted	Number of Seconds Between Onset of the Tone and Salivation
1	0	—
10	6	18
20	20	9
30	60	2
40	62	1
50	59	2

20. The greatest increase in the number of drops of saliva secreted occurred between test trials

    (1) 1 and 10   (3) 20 and 30
    (2) 10 and 20   (4) 30 and 40

Explanation of Answer The increase for choice 1 amounted to 6 drops, since it increased from 0 drops to 6 drops between Test Trial Numbers 1 to 10. Choice 2 resulted in an increase of 14 drops, since Test Trial Number 10 resulted in 6 drops, while Test Trial Number 20 resulted in 20 drops. The difference is 14 drops. Choice (4) only resulted in an increase of 2 drops. The correct answer is choice (3), 20 to 30. The number of drops of saliva secreted increased from 20 in Test Trial 20 to 60 in Test Trial 30, for an increase of 40 drops of saliva.

21. At test trial 60, the number of drops of saliva secreted would probably be closest to

    (1) 75   (2) 55   (3) 35   (4) 25

Explanation of Answer Choice 1 is wrong, since it shows a large increase. Choices 3 and 4 are incorrect, because the decrease in number of drops is very large. These numbers do not fit the trend shown in the data table. The correct answer is choice 2, because the number of drops of saliva secreted between trials 30 and 50 has been changing slowly and at trial 50 has started to go down.

Strategies for Questions Based on Graphs

Graphs represent relationships in a visual form that is easy to read. Three different types of graphs commonly used on science Regents examinations are line graphs, bar graphs, and circle graphs. Line graphs are the most common, and they show the relationship between two changing quantities, or variables. When a question is based on any of the three types of graphs, the information you need to correctly answer the question can usually be found on the graph.

When answering a question that includes a graph, first ask yourself these questions:

- What information does the graph provide?
- What are the variables?
- What seems to happen to one variable as the other changes?

After a careful analysis of the graph, use these strategies along with the other strategies you have learned:

- Read the question.
- Read each of the possible answers and consider which is the correct choice by referring to the graph.

Practice Questions

Use the graph below to answer questions 22 and 23.

Genetic Diversity in Corn and Wheat Varieties

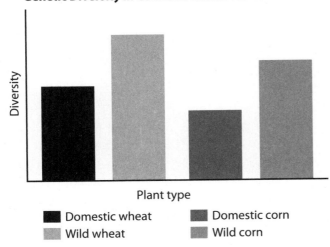

22. Which types of plants represented on the graph have the greatest diversity?
    (1) wild wheat and wild corn
    (2) wild wheat and domestic corn
    (3) domestic wheat and wild corn
    (4) domestic wheat and domestic corn

Explanation of Answer Choices 2, 3, and 4 do not work, because they each contain one or more of the domestic plant types that do not extend as high on the diversity scale. The correct choice is (1), wild wheat and wild corn. The bars for wild wheat and corn extend higher on the diversity scale than the others.

23. If the environment were to change dramatically or a new plant disease affecting both corn and wheat were to strike, which of the plant types would be most likely to survive?
    (1) wild wheat   (3) wild corn
    (2) domestic wheat   (4) domestic corn

Explanation of Answer To be able to answer this question correctly, you need to know two things. First, biodiversity increases the stability of an ecosystem. Second, the diversity of species increases the chance that some will survive in the face of environmental changes. Therefore, the bar representing the plant with the greatest diversity would be the best choice for an answer. For that reason, the correct answer is choice (1), wild wheat.

24. Which statement best describes the relationship between enzyme action and temperature shown in the graph below?

Remember to first study the graph in order to determine what it is about and what information it gives you about the variables. Then read the question and analyze the choices by referring to the graph.

(1) Enzyme synthesis begins at 30°C.
(2) Enzyme activity constantly increases with increasing temperature.
(3) The pH has a greater effect on this enzyme than temperature does.
(4) Enzyme activity increases as the temperature increases from 32°C to 34°C.

Explanation of Answer Choice 1 is not correct since the graph tells you nothing about enzyme synthesis. The graph starts to show data at 30°C, but shows nothing about synthesis. Choice 2 is wrong, because enzyme activity does not continue to increase. It starts to decrease rapidly at about 37°C. Choice 3 is incorrect, since there is no mention of pH anywhere on the graph. The correct answer is choice 4. If you follow the graph line, it does show an increase in relative rate of enzyme activity as the temperature increases from 32°C to 34°C.

Similarities and Differences Among Living Organisms

TOPIC 1

What do You Think?

Body Systems at Work

Blood vessels in organs of the digestive system pick up nutrients such as glucose, starch, and protein and transport them to cells.

Blood vessels in the respiratory system pick up oxygen and drop off carbon dioxide and water.

Blood vessels in organs of the excretory system drop off wastes from cells and food that was not digested.

1

Similarities and Differences Among Living Organisms

Vocabulary

active transport	excretion	organelle
amino acids	homeostasis	organic
cell	hormone	receptor molecule
cell membrane	immunity	reproduction
cell respiration	inorganic	respiration
chloroplast	metabolism	ribosome
circulation	mitochondria	simple sugars
cytoplasm	nucleus	synthesis
diffusion	organ	tissue
digestion	organ system	vacuole
enzymes		

Topic Overview

Earth's living environment is made up of millions of diverse organisms, from towering redwood trees, sleek antelope, and mushrooms that grow in huge circles, to microscopic bacteria, one-celled organisms that turn the tides red, and the students in your class.

These living organisms are both similar to and different from each other. They also differ from the nonliving parts of the environment. Although that difference may seem obvious, scientists have not been able to agree upon a simple definition of life.

The Characteristics of Life

Although there is no simple definition of life, most scientists agree that living things share certain characteristics that distinguish them from nonliving things.

- Living things are organized structures. All are made of one or more **cells,** which are the basic units of structure and function. They maintain their cellular organization throughout life.
- Living things use energy to maintain life and to grow and develop. These activities require that the cells carry out various chemical reactions. The combination of all the chemical reactions that occur in an organism is called **metabolism.**
- Living things maintain a fairly stable internal environment even when their external environment changes dramatically. The maintenance of this internal stability is known as **homeostasis.** To maintain homeostasis, organisms must respond and adapt to both their internal and external environments.

- Living things pass hereditary information to new organisms of the same type in the process of **reproduction.**

Only living things share the characteristics of life. Nonliving things have no functioning cells and no metabolic activity; they do not maintain homeostasis, nor do they reproduce.

Diversity Among Living Things

Although living things share the characteristics of life, there are differences among the many kinds of organisms. Throughout history, people have tried to bring order to all the varieties of life on Earth by grouping, or classifying, them. Several classification systems have been popular at different times. As we learn more about the similarities among organisms and how they carry out their life processes, classification systems change. Currently, biologists classify organisms into kingdoms, which are large groups of related organisms.

Similarities Among Living Things

Although living things have many differences, they are also alike in important ways. The first similarity is that they share the characteristics of life. They are made of cells, reproduce, maintain homeostasis, and carry out metabolic activities. They also share similar life processes, chemical composition, and organization.

Life Processes Living things are similar in that they rely on a variety of specific processes to maintain life. Organisms may differ in the way they carry out these processes, however. Some of these life processes include

- obtaining nutrients from the environment and breaking them down for transport
- transporting materials throughout the organism
- breaking nutrients into smaller units to release the chemical energy stored in them through the process known as **cell respiration**
- combining simple substances into complex substances during the process known as **synthesis**
- increasing the size or number of cells through the process of growth
- removing waste products from the organism through the process known as **excretion**
- responding to internal and external stimuli
- reproducing more of their own species

Chemical Composition All living things are made of four main elements—carbon, hydrogen, oxygen, and nitrogen—as well as many other elements in smaller amounts. The elements combine to form molecules.

Organic molecules contain BOTH carbon and hydrogen. Organic molecules include all of the major molecules of life: structural molecules, such as those in cell walls and membranes, as well as biologically active molecules, such as the enzymes that help carry out the chemical reactions of life. DNA, protein, fats, and carbohydrates—such as glucose ($C_6H_{12}O_6$) and starch—are **organic** molecules.

Digging Deeper

Many scientists do not include viruses with living things. The reason is that viruses are not cells. Instead they are made only of protein and genetic material. As a result, viruses do not independently carry out all processes of life. To reproduce, they must invade the cell of a living organism.

Inorganic molecules do *not* contain *both* carbon and hydrogen, but can contain any other combination of elements. Inorganic molecules include salts and minerals, most acids and bases, oxygen (O_2), carbon dioxide (CO_2), and water (H_2O), the most abundant substance in any organism.

Organization The shared organization of specialized structures that work together to accomplish a specific task is another similarity of living things. In other words, organisms share a similar "building plan." The basic structural and functional unit of living things is the cell.

Simple organisms may consist of just one cell; complex organisms may consist of billions of cells. Most cells contain specialized structures called **organelles,** which have specific life maintenance functions.

This organization of cells into increasingly specialized structures is the basis for much of the complex life on Earth. Complex organisms have several advantages over simpler organisms. For example, many complex organisms can explore their environment or gain energy in ways that simpler organisms cannot. In Figure 1-1, notice that the organizational structure of organisms resembles a pyramid with a base of cells.

In multicellular organisms, groups of specialized cells may be grouped into **tissues** to expand how they function. For example, a single muscle cell would not be strong enough to move any organism—not even one as light as a hummingbird. Grouped with other muscle cells, however, muscle tissue can move an elephant.

Different kinds of tissues may be combined to form an **organ** that performs one of the life processes. Several organs may work together as an **organ system** that also performs one of the life processes. For example, the heart is an organ with the function of pumping blood. The organ may be a simple "arch" like the heart of the earthworm, or it may be a complex four-chambered structure like the heart of a monkey. In either case, the organ's function is to pump blood. Each heart is part of an organ system that transports materials throughout the body.

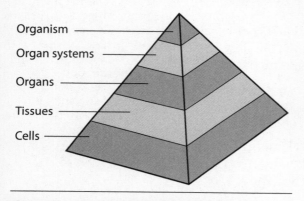

Organism
Organ systems
Organs
Tissues
Cells

Figure 1-1. The structural organization of organisms

Review Questions

1. State two ways in which a single-celled organism, such as an amoeba, and a human body cell are alike.

2. One characteristic of all living organisms is that they

   (1) make food
   (2) live on land
   (3) maintain homeostasis
   (4) move from place to place

3. Which sequence is listed in order from simplest to most complex?

   (1) tissue → cell → organ system → organ
   (2) cell → tissue → organ → organ system
   (3) cell → tissue → organism → organ
   (4) organism → tissue → organ → organ system

4. A student brings a specimen and claims it is a living organism. Explain how a microscope could be used to determine if the specimen is a living thing.

5. A biologist would most likely study all of the chemical activities of an organism to obtain information about the organism's

    (1) number of mutations
    (2) reproductive cycle
    (3) development
    (4) metabolism

6. Cells are to tissues as organs are to

    (1) organ systems   (3) genes
    (2) cells   (4) organelles

7. The ability of an organism to maintain internal stability is known as

    (1) metabolism   (3) circulation
    (2) homeostasis   (4) excretion

8. State two ways living and nonliving things differ.

9. Which statement about cells is *not* true?

    (1) One or more cells make up all living organisms.
    (2) Cells carry on the basic life functions of living organisms.
    (3) Cells contain structures that carry on life functions.
    (4) Most cells cannot reproduce.

10. Living things are made mostly of these four main elements:

    (1) hydrogen, oxygen, nitrogen, and protein
    (2) water, protein, carbohydrate, and fat
    (3) carbon, hydrogen, oxygen, and nitrogen
    (4) glucose, salt, mineral, and base

Cells: The Basic Structure of Life

Many of the world's organisms are made of only one cell, but all organisms—no matter how simple or complex—are made of cells. Each cell contains a jellylike substance surrounded by a thin membrane. Most cells also contain organelles that perform specific tasks for the cell. Despite their seemingly "simple" structure, cells carry out the processes of life and function together in a coordinated manner.

Inside the Cell

The jellylike substance inside the cell is known as the **cytoplasm.** The cytoplasm contains specialized structures, transports materials through the cell, and is the site of many chemical reactions associated with the cell's metabolism.

Organelles Organelles are formed of many different molecules and vary in size, shape, and function. They interact to transport materials, extract energy from nutrients, build proteins, dispose of waste, and store information. Figure 1-2 shows several vital organelles.

Nucleus The **nucleus** is a large structure that controls the cell's metabolism and stores genetic information (DNA in chromosomes). Many people think of the nucleus as the cell's "control center" because it directs the cell's activities.

Vacuoles The storage sacs within the cytoplasm are **vacuoles.** They may contain either wastes or useful materials such as water or food. Some vacuoles are specialized to digest food; others pump excess water out of the cell. Vacuoles in plant cells are usually a lot larger than the vacuoles in animal cells, as shown in Figure 1-2.

Ribosomes The cell contains many tiny structures, called **ribosomes,** that are important to the process of making protein. Some ribosomes are attached to membranes in the cell. Others float in the cytoplasm.

(A) A typical plant cell

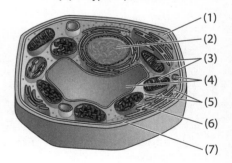

(B) A typical animal cell

Figure 1-2. Some parts of plant and animal cells: (1) cytoplasm, (2) nucleus, (3) mitochondria, (4) vacuoles, (5) ribosomes, (6) chloroplast, (7) cell membrane.

Mitochondria Mitochondria are pod-shaped structures that contain special proteins, known as **enzymes,** used to extract energy from nutrients. Mitochondria are sometimes called the cell's powerhouses because they release most of the cell's energy.

Chloroplasts The green structures found in plants and some one-celled organisms are **chloroplasts.** They contain the green pigment chlorophyll and capture light energy, which is then used to produce food for the plant. Animal cells do not contain chloroplasts.

Review Questions

11. Which structure is the boundary between a living cell and its environment?

(1) cell membrane
(2) cytoplasm
(3) vacuole
(4) ribosome

12. The structures labeled A, B, C, and D in the diagram below represent

(1) organelles
(2) organs
(3) nuclei
(4) mitochondria

13. The cell nucleus functions

(1) in obtaining energy for the cell
(2) in the storage of digestive enzymes
(3) as the center of control for cell metabolism and reproduction
(4) in the transport of materials throughout the cell

14. The genetic material of an animal cell is found in the

(1) nucleus
(2) cytoplasm
(3) ribosomes
(4) vacuole

15. In the diagram below, structure A is most probably a

(1) mitochondrion   (3) vacuole
(2) ribosome   (4) nucleus

16. Current evidence indicates that ribosomes are most closely associated with

(1) contraction of the cytoplasm
(2) production of DNA
(3) synthesis of protein
(4) regulation of mitosis

17. Mitochondria are organelles that

(1) store digestive enzymes
(2) package cell products
(3) release energy from nutrients
(4) manufacture cell protein

18. Which cell organelles are most closely associated with energy changes in a plant?

(1) mitochondria and chromosomes
(2) chloroplasts and mitochondria
(3) chromosomes and nucleus
(4) chloroplasts and nucleus

19. Which is the most accurate statement concerning protein synthesis in cells?

(1) Proteins are synthesized by mitochondria in all living cells.
(2) Proteins are synthesized at the ribosomes in all living cells.
(3) Proteins are synthesized at the ribosomes in plant cells only.
(4) Proteins are synthesized by nuclei in animal cells only.

The Cell Membrane

The **cell membrane** is a thin structure that surrounds the cell. It is made mainly of fats (lipids), with some proteins embedded throughout. Some of the functions of the cell membrane include

- separating the contents of the cell from the outside environment
- controlling the transport of materials—including waste products—into and out of the cell
- recognizing and responding to chemical signals

Maintaining Separation Cells are organized internally. Without the cell membrane, this organization would be lost.

Unlike animals, plants and most bacteria and fungi have a cell wall outside the cell membrane. This wall of plant cells is made of nonliving material (a carbohydrate called cellulose) that surrounds the cell and gives it strength and rigidity. If the plant gains too much water, its membranes could burst. The cell wall helps prevent this.

Controlling Transport In and Out of the Cell If the cell is to survive, the membrane cannot totally separate the cell from its environment. Some materials, such as water, oxygen, and nutrients, must pass through the membrane and into the cell. Other materials, such as waste products, must pass out of the cell. Molecules can enter or leave a cell through either diffusion or active transport.

Diffusion Molecules are constantly in motion. As they jiggle, they bump into one another, then bounce away like bumper cars at an amusement park. In time, the molecules will have bumped and bounced until they are evenly distributed. The result is that the concentration of molecules in any container remains approximately the same everywhere in the container.

However, when the concentration of molecules is greater in one part of a substance, molecules will spread into areas where their concentration is lower. This movement of molecules from areas of high concentration to areas of low concentration is called **diffusion**. (See Figure 1-4.) Because diffusion results from the normal jiggling of molecules, it requires no outside energy. It is like sledding downhill.

Many molecules diffuse into and out of cells. One of the most important of these molecules is water. The diffusion of water into and out of cells is important to the maintenance of homeostasis. For example, plant cells maintain a stable balance of water and dissolved minerals. This is typically about 98% water and 2% dissolved materials. When salt is spread on roads and walkways, that balance changes. The runoff water from these salted roads may reach concentrations of 5% salt (which means only 95% water). Damage can occur when water in the plant cells diffuses from the higher (98%) concentration in the cell to the lower (95%) concentration outside the cell. Under these conditions, the loss of water places serious stress on the plant. In some cases the plant may die.

Active Transport Moving a molecule from an area of low concentration to an area of high concentration is like pulling a sled uphill. (See Figure 1-5.) It requires energy. Cells must use energy from ATP to transport molecules

Figure 1-3. The cell membrane

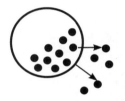

Figure 1-4. Diffusion: These molecules are moving from an area of high concentration to an area of low concentration.

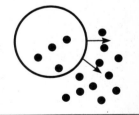

Figure 1-5. Active transport: These molecules are moving from an area of low concentration to an area of high concentration.

from areas of low concentration through the cell membrane to areas of high concentration. The process is called **active transport.**

Many desert plants use active transport to bring water (which is at low concentrations in the soil) into root cells where the water concentration is higher. Some pond organisms use active transport to "collect" calcium or other minerals that are in very low concentrations in the pond water.

Molecules in Cells Both organic and inorganic substances are dissolved in cells and are involved in the chemical reactions that maintain life. Some organic molecules, such as proteins and starches, are too large and complex to enter the cell. Large molecules must first be broken down into simpler molecules in the process known as **digestion.**

The digestion of proteins results in smaller molecules of **amino acids;** the digestion of starches results in **simple sugars.** Digestion is vital because only small molecules, such as amino acids and simple sugars, can enter blood vessels or cells.

When some nutrients from our food enter a cell, they become the building blocks of compounds necessary for life. This process, called cell synthesis, is like manufacturing. Simple molecules (such as amino acids and sugars) are assembled or reassembled into more complex molecules of proteins, starches, DNA, or other substances necessary for life.

Not all nutrients are used as building blocks. Some nutrients that enter a cell are broken down even more to release the energy stored in their chemical bonds. This is the process of cell respiration. All of these processes will be reviewed in detail in later topics.

Recognizing Signals Scientists have learned that certain protein molecules in the cell membrane can receive chemical messages from other cells. These molecules are called **receptor molecules.**

When cells are part of a larger organism, receptor molecules play an important role in the interactions between cells. As shown in Figures 1–6 and 1–7, chemicals produced in the endocrine glands—**hormones**—and chemicals produced by nerve cells are primarily responsible for communication between cells. If nerve or hormone signals are blocked, cellular communication is interrupted, and the organism's homeostasis may be affected.

Figure 1-6. Receptor molecules: Specific receptor molecules on the membranes of some cells detect hormones that stimulate the cell to respond. In this case, only cell B (not cell C) will respond to the hormone from cell A.

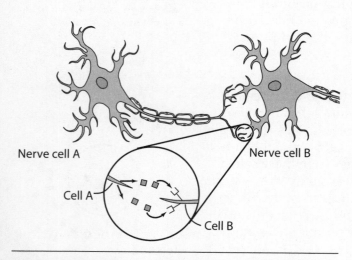

Figure 1-7. Receptor molecules: Nerve cells secrete chemicals that signal adjacent nerve, muscle, or gland cells. These secretions are detected by specific receptor molecules on cell membranes.

20. Defective receptor proteins on a cell membrane have the *least* effect on

(1) homeostasis
(2) muscle activity
(3) nerve signals
(4) diffusion

21. In the following diagram, nerve cell A is communicating with nerve cell B. Identify the structures present on the membranes of nerve cell B that enable it to detect a message from nerve cell A.

22. Which process accomplishes the movement of gases illustrated by the arrows in the diagram?

(1) excretion
(2) diffusion
(3) active transport
(4) chemical digestion

23. In both plant and animal cells, the cell membrane

(1) produces enzymes
(2) controls reproduction
(3) is composed of sugars
(4) regulates diffusion

24. Since the relative concentration of water in the pond in which a paramecium (a single-celled organism) lives is greater than the concentration of water in its cytoplasm, water molecules constantly move from the pond into the paramecium. The best long-term solution to the problem of maintaining a stable internal environment is for the paramecium to

(1) change the water into carbon dioxide and excrete it
(2) store water molecules
(3) incorporate water molecules into its structure
(4) actively transport water molecules out of its cell

25. A biologist diluted a blood sample with distilled water. While observing the sample with a microscope, she noted that the red blood cells had burst. This bursting is most likely the result of which process?

(1) staining
(2) diffusion
(3) digestion
(4) active transport

26. A student using a compound light microscope to study plant cells observed that most of the cells resembled the one shown in the following diagram.

Which diagram best illustrates how the plant cell will appear after being placed in a solution that has a lower water concentration than the cell?

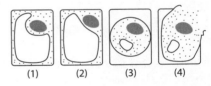

27. Amino acids tend to diffuse from a blood capillary to the adjacent cell because

(1) this is the only direction they can move
(2) the brain directs the movement into cells
(3) the cell needs the amino acids to make protein
(4) the concentration of amino acids is lower in the cell

28. In the following diagram of a plant cell, the small circles represent water molecules.

Which statement *best* describes the behavior of most of these water molecules?

(1) They move from region A to region B.
(2) They move from region B to region A.
(3) They do not move in either direction.
(4) Their overall movement is equal in both directions.

29. Nutrients that are not used as building blocks for the cell may be broken down to release the energy stored in their chemical bonds. This process, which provides cells with energy, is called

(1) chemical synthesis   (3) digestion
(2) cell respiration   (4) homeostasis

30. Cytoplasm in a plant cell will shrink if the cell is

(1) placed in a concentrated salt solution
(2) kept warm and moist and in medium light
(3) placed in distilled water
(4) exposed to a different concentration of nitrogen gas

31. The diagram below represents a cell in water. Formulas of molecules that can move freely across the membrane are shown. Some molecules are located inside the cell and others are in the water outside the cell.

Based on the distribution of molecules, what would most likely happen to these molecules after a few hours?

(1) The concentration of $C_6H_{12}O_6$ will increase inside the cell.
(2) The concentration of CO_2 will increase outside the cell.
(3) The concentration of NH_3 will increase inside the cell.
(4) The concentration of O_2 will increase outside the cell.

32. A cell containing 98% water in its cytoplasm is placed in a 2% salt solution. It should

(1) lose water
(2) gain water
(3) neither lose nor gain water
(4) gain salt because of the high rate of diffusion

33. A cell is placed in distilled water and then transferred to a 5% salt solution. As a result of this procedure, the cell would be likely to

(1) get larger
(2) get smaller
(3) get larger, then smaller
(4) get smaller, then larger

34. A high concentration of calcium salts is normally found within the cytoplasm of a certain protozoan, while the surrounding environment contains a lower concentration of the calcium salts. The higher concentration in the protozoan is most probably the result of

(1) diffusion   (3) active transport
(2) excretion   (4) cellular dehydration

35. A student prepared a normal wet mount slide of an *Elodea* leaf and observed it with a compound microscope. He then made drawing A from his observations. His second drawing, B, shows his observations of the same cell after it was mounted in a 5% salt solution.

The results are most fully explained by

(1) loss of water from the cell
(2) entrance of water into the cell
(3) shrinkage of the cell wall
(4) entrance of salt into the cell

Multicellular Organisms

Multicellular organisms can be highly complex. They require multiple organs and systems to complete their life processes. These systems must interact to maintain the life of the organism.

Human Body Systems

Humans are complex organisms. Their specialized cells must interact to maintain life. Humans require a variety of organs and organ systems to complete the life processes of digestion, respiration, circulation, excretion, movement, coordination, immunity, and reproduction.

Digestion The human digestive system, shown in Figure 1-8, is a one-way passage through the body. This passageway includes the mouth, stomach, and intestines as well as other organs.

Food enters the body through the mouth and is moved slowly through the system by muscular contractions. The food never actually enters the body tissue. Instead, it is broken down both mechanically (by chewing) and chemically. This produces molecules that are small enough to pass through cell membranes and that can be transported to wherever nutrients can be used by the body. Undigested food is eliminated from the body as solid waste.

Respiration The process of **respiration** uses oxygen to break down food molecules to release energy. The function of the respiratory system is the exchange of gases between the blood of the circulatory system and the environment. The system takes in oxygen for cell respiration and transfers it to the blood. It also removes carbon dioxide—a waste of cell respiration—from the bloodstream and releases it from the body. As shown in Figure 1-9, the lungs and nose are parts of the respiratory system.

Circulation **Circulation** involves the movement of materials inside the cell as well as the movement between parts of a multicellular organism. The function of the human circulatory system, shown in Figure 1-10, is to transport materials throughout the body.

The system carries digested food and oxygen to cells. It also carries wastes from the cells to the lungs, kidneys, and the skin for excretion. The blood vessels of the system also carry chemical messengers (hormones) and the proteins that attack foreign substances to give the body immunity (antibodies). The human circulatory system includes the heart, blood vessels, and blood.

Excretion Many people confuse the process of excretion with the removal of the waste products of digestion. **Excretion,** however, is actually the removal of all the waste produced by the cells of the body. The human excretory system, shown in Figure 1-11, includes the lungs and kidneys as well as the sweat glands in the skin.

Movement Movement of the body involves the interaction of muscles and bones. The <u>muscular</u> and <u>skeletal</u> systems, shown in Figure 1-12, work together to provide movement and support for the body. These body systems make it possible for the organism to avoid danger and to find food, mates, and shelter.

Coordination The nervous system and endocrine system, shown in Figure 1-13, control the coordination of many of the body's activities. Together these systems respond to and send messages to cells throughout the body.

The nervous system sends signals along nerves. The glands of the endocrine system produce chemical messengers (hormones) that travel in the bloodstream. The brain and nerves are part of the nervous system. The endocrine system includes several glands—such as the pancreas and ovaries or testes.

Immunity The immune system increases the body's **immunity**—its ability to resist disease. Some white blood cells of the immune system engulf and

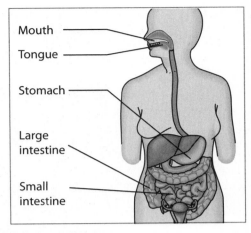

Figure 1-8. The human digestive system

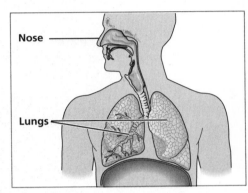

Figure 1-9. The human respiratory system

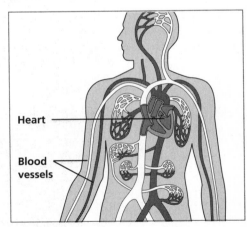

Figure 1-10. The human circulatory system

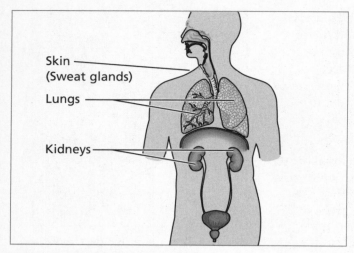

Figure 1-11. The human excretory system

Figure 1-12. The human muscular (A) and skeletal systems
(B): The bones provide support; the muscles allow movement.

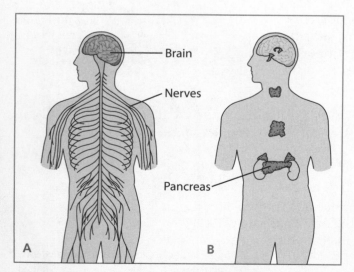

Figure 1-13. The human nervous (A) and endocrine
(B) systems

destroy invading bacteria and viruses by digesting them. Others protect the body against specific foreign invaders.

Reproduction The process by which organisms produce new organisms of the same kind is called **reproduction**. The reproductive system releases sex cells and hormones that are critical to the creation of offspring and the regulation of their development. The human reproductive system allows for sexual rather than asexual reproduction. Sexual reproduction makes it possible for two individuals to produce offspring that are of the same species but not exactly like either parent.

Interactions for Life Processes and Regulation

Like all organisms, the human body's systems continually interact to perform life processes. Examples of these interactions may involve several systems.

- Nutrients from the digestive system are transported to cells by the circulatory system.
- The functioning of the reproductive system is regulated by hormones from the endocrine system.
- Body systems also continuously interact to maintain a balanced internal environment (homeostasis). To successfully accomplish this, humans and other complex organisms have a variety of control mechanisms that constantly monitor and correct deviations that could throw the body's internal environment off balance. Examples of these control systems include the regulation of body temperature and blood sugar level.
- When body temperature drops, nerve impulses from the brain signal the muscles to shiver, which generates heat and warms the body.
- Blood sugar level is constantly monitored, and hormones are released as needed to keep it at acceptable levels.

If any organ or organ system does not function properly, the entire organism may fail to maintain homeostasis. The result may be disease or even death. For example, if the heart fails to beat regularly, the circulation of blood will be affected. This may result in a failure of certain materials (oxygen, for example) to flow throughout the body. Without oxygen, cells may stop functioning and death may result.

Comparing Single-celled and Multicellular Organisms

The organelles of single-celled organisms are far less complex than organ systems of multicellular organisms. However, organelles and organ systems are equally capable of completing metabolic activities. For example, the paramecium in Figure 1-15 has a specialized organelle—the food vacuole—that digests food. The human digestive system is more complex and also digests food. The organelle and organ system accomplish the same function: breaking down nutrients so that they can be used by the organism.

Table 1-1 shows examples of life functions that are handled by organelles in single cells and by organ systems in multicellular organisms.

Comparing Humans and Other Organisms

In most biological respects, humans are like other organisms.

- Humans have much the same chemical composition as other organisms. All organisms—from bacteria to tulips to humans—are made of mainly carbon, hydrogen, oxygen, and nitrogen. These elements combine in different ways and amounts to form carbohydrates, proteins, and other essential organic molecules.

- Humans are made up of different kinds of cells that are similar to those found in other animals. For example, human muscles, nerves, and blood cells are similar in structure and function to the muscles, nerves, and blood cells of other complex animals—from geese to gorillas.

- Humans have organ systems and physical characteristics similar to many other complex animals. For example, worms, frogs, and pigs have digestive systems that break down large food molecules. They also have systems that circulate blood. Pig hearts, in fact, are so similar to human hearts that they can be used for transplants.

- Humans reproduce in the same way as many other organisms. For example, fish, amphibians, reptiles, birds, and mammals reproduce sexually; the sperm and egg cell combine, each contributing half of the genetic information to the offspring.

- Humans use the same kind of genetic information as other organisms. Like nearly every living organism—from *E. coli* bacteria and fruit flies to roses and dogs—humans use DNA as their genetic material.

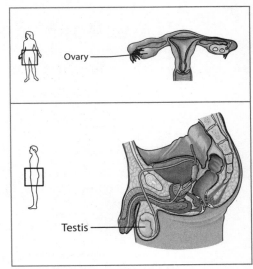

Figure 1-14. The reproductive systems of the human male and female

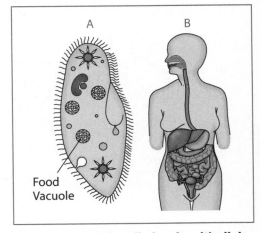

Figure 1-15. Single-celled and multicellular function: The food vacuoles in a one-celled organism (A) are much simpler than the human digestive system (B), but they still digest the organism's food.

Table 1-1. The Function of Organelles in Single Cells and Organ Systems in Multicellular Organisms		
Function	**Single Cell**	**Multicellular Organism**
Gas exchange	Cell membrane	Respiratory system
Transport of substances	Cytoplasm	Circulatory system
Nutrition	Specialized vacuoles	Digestive system
Excretion	Cell membrane	Excretory system

36. Organisms remove metabolic cellular wastes by the process of

(1) excretion
(2) absorption
(3) coordination
(4) digestion

37. A similarity between the nervous system and the hormone-secreting system in humans is that they both

(1) are composed of the same type of cells
(2) are composed of many glands
(3) help to maintain homeostasis
(4) secrete chemicals directly into the blood

38. The diagram below shows an air sac surrounded by the thin-walled blood vessels of a human lung.

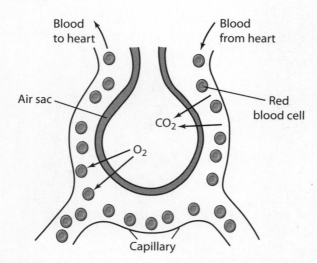

Which two body systems are interacting in the diagram?

(1) respiratory and coordination
(2) respiratory and circulatory
(3) digestive and circulatory
(4) reproductive and coordination

39. Finding shelter, avoiding predators, and obtaining food are most closely related to the ability of an animal to

(1) use structures adapted for movement
(2) increase the rate of mitosis
(3) transport carbon dioxide to cells
(4) excrete waste products of metabolism

40. Which letter in the diagram below indicates an organelle that functions primarily in the synthesis of protein?

(1) A   (2) B   (3) C   (4) D

41. Inhaling carbon monoxide reduces the ability of red blood cells to carry oxygen. This can lead to brain damage. Which three systems of the body interact in this situation?

(1) digestive, respiratory, and circulatory
(2) immune, circulatory, and digestive
(3) respiratory, circulatory, and nervous
(4) excretory, nervous, and respiratory

42. The activity of all human body systems is coordinated by

(1) the secretion of hormones and the nervous system
(2) the interaction of nerve impulses with the excretory system
(3) the movement of digested food by the circulatory system
(4) the secretion of hormones and the circulatory system

43. Before it can be used by individual cells, food must be broken down and distributed throughout the human body. Identify the two systems that must interact to accomplish this. [1]

44. Your finger brushes against a hot stove and you quickly pull away. Identify which two human body systems work together to respond to this painful stimulus and explain the specific interaction between them. [1]

45. Compare the chemical composition and genetic information of humans to the chemical composition and genetic information found in other organisms. [1]

Directions

Review the Test-Taking Strategies section of this book. Then answer the following questions. Read each question carefully and answer with a correct choice or response.

Part A

1 A few bacteria are placed in a nutrient solution. After several hours, thousands of bacteria are present. Which life activities are primarily responsible for this?
(1) digestion and movement
(2) digestion and reproduction
(3) circulation and respiration
(4) excretion and coordination

2 Mitochondria are organelles that
(1) are necessary for the process of diffusion to take place
(2) are found in the nucleus of some cells
(3) initiate cell division in living cells
(4) contain respiratory enzymes

3 Most of the enzymes found in the mitochondria are involved in the reactions associated with
(1) extracting energy from nutrients
(2) storing energy in nutrients
(3) DNA production
(4) protein synthesis

4 Which statement best describes a cell membrane?
(1) It is found only in animal cells.
(2) It is a nonliving structure.
(3) It controls reproduction in a cell.
(4) It controls the passage of materials into the cell.

5 The transfer of specific molecules through cell membranes is an important factor in the process of
(1) cytoplasmic flow   (3) homeostasis
(2) mitotic division   (4) nuclear transfer

6 After a cookie has been eaten and digested, sugar molecules enter the bloodstream by the process of
(1) active transport   (3) excretion
(2) diffusion   (4) cellular respiration

7 The concentration of nitrates is often higher in plant roots than it is in the soil around them. Plants maintain this difference in concentration through
(1) active transport   (3) excretion
(2) diffusion   (4) coordination

8 In the diagram of root cells below, in which direction would the net flow of water be the greatest as a result of diffusion?
(1) A to C
(2) A to B
(3) B to C
(4) C to B

Key
• = Water molecule

9 Diagrams A and B represent two slide preparations of *Elodea* leaves (an aquatic plant).

A   B

Elodea leaf mounted   Elodea leaf mounted
in tap water   in 6% salt solution

The tap water used contained 1 percent salt and 99 percent water, while the salt solution contained 6 percent salt and 94 percent water. *Elodea* cells normally contain 1 percent salt. Ten minutes after the slides were prepared, a microscopic examination of cells in leaves A and B would most likely show evidence that
(1) water had moved out of the cells of leaf B
(2) salt had moved out of the cells of leaf B
(3) water had moved into the cells of leaf A
(4) salt had moved into the cells of leaf A

10 One reason a fish that lives in the ocean may have trouble living in a freshwater lake is that
(1) there are more carnivores in freshwater habitats
(2) salt water holds more dissolved nitrogen than fresh water
(3) more photosynthesis occurs in fresh water than in salt water
(4) water concentration in the fish is affected by salt levels in its environment

11 Refer to the diagram below of a beaker with a membrane dividing it into two halves containing two kinds of molecules.

Which process explains the change in the positions of molecules after five hours?
(1) respiration
(2) photosynthesis
(3) diffusion
(4) excretion

12 Most of the reactions by which energy from sugars is released for use by the cell takes place within the
(1) vacuoles
(2) nuclei
(3) ribosomes
(4) mitochondria

13 The diagram below shows how an animal is organized.

Which label is needed to complete the diagram?
(1) atoms   (3) organelles
(2) molecules   (4) tissues

14 Two organs are considered to be a part of the same body system if the organs
(1) are located next to each other
(2) work independently of each other
(3) work together to carry out a life function
(4) are made up of cells with organelles

15 During exercise, the heart beats faster to
(1) carry digestive juices to the small intestine
(2) provide muscles with additional oxygen
(3) lower the blood pressure
(4) digest more food

16 The ability to avoid danger is possible because of the life process of
(1) excretion
(2) reproduction
(3) nutrition
(4) movement

17 The diagram below shows several organs of the human body.

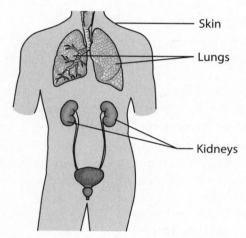

All of these organs interact to help carry out the
(1) removal of waste products
(2) digestion of food
(3) production of hormones
(4) coordination of body movements

18 The circulatory system helps to maintain homeostasis by interacting with the
(1) nervous system and transporting chemicals produced by nerve cells from one cell to another
(2) respiratory system and producing oxygen for gas exchange
(3) digestive system by removing undigested food from the stomach
(4) excretory system in helping to regulate body temperature through sweating

19 In the diagram of the ameba (a single-celled organism), the arrows show the direction of movement of various substances.

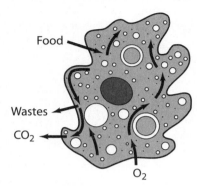

Which of the cell's life activities are represented by the arrows?
(1) digestion, reproduction, and respiration
(2) excretion, transport, and respiration
(3) immunity, digestion, and movement
(4) digestion, coordination, and reproduction

20 All cells are able to continue living because of their ability to
(1) produce food
(2) excrete wastes
(3) produce offspring
(4) produce hormones

21 Which structure in a cell corresponds with the function of the human lungs?
(1) nucleus
(2) vacuole
(3) cell membrane
(4) mitochondria

Part B

22 A scientist wanted to know whether the cells of a particular single-celled green algae could survive without any mitochondria. The scientist removed all of the mitochondria from hundreds of these cells. All of the cells died.

Explain the most likely reason the green algae could not survive without mitochondria. [1]

23 Explain why cell-to-cell communication is important to a multicellular organism, such as a human. [1]

Base your answers to questions 24 through 26 on the information and the graph below and on your knowledge of biology.

24 Four pieces of apple were cut so that all were the same mass and shape. The pieces were placed in four different concentrations of sugar water. After 24 hours, the pieces were removed and their masses determined. The graph indicates the change in the mass of each piece. What was the change in mass of the apple piece in the 10 percent sugar solution?
(1) a decrease of 0.45 grams
(2) an increase of 0.30 grams
(3) a decrease of 0.30 grams
(4) an increase of 0.10 grams

25 At approximately what sugar concentration should pieces neither lose nor gain weight?
(1) 6 percent
(2) 10 percent
(3) 3 percent
(4) 20 percent

26 The four points on the graph represent
(1) assumptions   (3) hypotheses
(2) data   (4) conclusions

Part C

27 A student claims that a dead cell can still carry out diffusion and active transport.

Explain why this claim is not entirely correct. In your answer be sure to explain why a dead cell can or cannot carry on

• diffusion [1]
• active transport [1]

28 Skin cells from a pond animal and skin cells from a land animal were placed in a solution with a 0.85% concentration of salt. When examined later, the cells of the pond animal had swollen and burst, while the cells of the land animal had shrunk.

Explain why the cells responded as they did. In your answer be sure to explain why

- the pond animal cells swelled and burst [1]
- the land animal cells got smaller [1]

29 People sometimes use large quantities of salt to preserve food. The salt kills bacteria that would otherwise cause the food to spoil. Based on your knowledge of diffusion, explain how the salt kills the bacteria. [1]

Base your answers to questions 30 through 33 on the information below and on your knowledge of biology.

The heart of an older person or of someone recovering from a heart attack may become severely weakened or damaged. This sometimes leads to a serious condition called congestive heart failure in which the heart muscle is too weak to pump enough blood throughout the body. As a result, the heart may become exhausted. Sometimes it completely stops.

In a recent study, 2647 patients were given medication called beta-blockers that lowered their risk of death by 34 percent over 15 months (compared to patients who did not take the drugs). Another study reached a similar conclusion.

Although beta-blockers have long been used for treating heart attacks and other medical problems, doctors thought them too dangerous for patients with congestive heart failure. Their reason was that beta-blockers counteract the body's response to adrenaline, a hormone that prepares the body for emergencies by attaching to receptors on heart muscle cells, stimulating the heart to beat faster. Since beta-blockers attach to these adrenaline receptors too, they keep the adrenaline molecules from making contact. This leads to a slowing of the heart, which would appear to cause a problem for a person whose heart is not pumping blood effectively anyway.

The opposite turns out to be the case. When the heart of a person with congestive heart failure is not pumping enough blood, the body responds by releasing more adrenaline to stimulate the heart. As a result, the heart is overstimulated and works even harder—making it more likely to fail. Since beta-blockers interrupt this destructive cycle, the heart stabilizes.

Doctors hope that once more studies are done, proper use of beta-blockers may eventually save many thousands of lives.

30 Describe how adrenaline is involved in the cell-to-cell communication of a person with congestive heart failure. [1]

31 Label the following parts of the illustration of the heart muscle cell below:
1—beta-blocker molecule [1]
2—adrenaline molecule [1]
3—heart cell receptor [1]

32 Explain how you could tell which objects represent the adrenaline and which represent the beta-blocker in the illustration in question 31. [1]

33 Many drugs have side effects that make them dangerous to some people. For this reason, individuals who take prescription medicine must watch for any unexpected changes in their health.

Based on the information provided in the passage and on your knowledge of biology, describe one possible side effect that might result when people *without* congestive heart failure use beta-blockers. [1]

Homeostasis in Organisms

What do YOU Think?

Respiration and Photosynthesis

Plants don't carry out respiration. They use photosynthesis instead.

At night, plants use oxygen for respiration just like animals, but not during the day.

I think that animals use oxygen and plants use carbon dioxide for the process of respiration.

I think both plants and animals use oxygen for respiration, and they do this day and night.

Homeostasis in Organisms

Vocabulary

AIDS	dynamic equilibrium	mitochondria
allergy	enzyme	pancreas
antibiotics	feedback mechanism	parasite
antibodies	fungi	pathogen
antigen	gas exchange	pH
ATP	glucose	photosynthesis
bacteria	guard cells	respiration
biochemical processes	homeostasis	stimuli
catalyst	immune system	synthesis
cellular respiration	insulin	vaccine
chloroplast	microbe	virus
disease		

Topic Overview

All living things—from the simplest single-celled bacteria to the most complex multicellular animals—are organized biological systems. To stay alive, all organisms must keep their biological systems stable even though they live in a changing, and sometimes life-threatening, environment. To maintain this stability, organisms continually monitor and respond to changes in the environment. The internal stability that organisms maintain is known as **homeostasis.**

Homeostasis is the maintenance of internal conditions within a narrow range that varies only slightly over time. For example, your body temperature must stay within a specific temperature range (approximately 98.6°F, or 37°C) for you to survive. If you become too hot or too cold, the biochemical processes that keep you alive will begin to fail.

Digging Deeper

Homeostasis sometimes appears with the words *dynamic equilibrium* or *steady state*. These terms all involve the idea of "a constant balance." To picture this concept, it may help to think of a child learning to balance a bicycle. There may be some wobbling back and forth, but generally the rider remains upright.

Basic Biochemical Processes of Living Organisms

Biochemical processes are the chemical processes that occur in living things. All organisms need both energy and raw materials (atoms and molecules) to carry on the internal biochemical processes that are essential for their survival. Two of these enzyme-controlled biochemical processes are photosynthesis and respiration. **Photosynthesis** is the process by which energy is stored in chemical bonds of organic molecules such as carbohydrates. Plants, algae, and many single-celled organisms carry out photosynthesis. Recall that **respiration** is the process by which chemical energy stored in nutrients is released for use in cells. All living organisms carry out respiration.

Storing Energy: Photosynthesis

The energy for life comes primarily from the sun. In Figure 2-1, notice that photosynthesis is the connection between the energy released by the sun and the energy available to living systems.

The cells of organisms that carry out photosynthesis contain light-capturing molecules. In plant cells, these molecules are located in the **chloroplasts,** which are green-colored organelles where photosynthesis occurs. In Figure 2-2, the chloroplasts are the oval structures. You may have seen these green structures on microscope slides of cells prepared from plant leaves.

All plants, algae, and many one-celled organisms use solar energy to convert inorganic molecules (carbon dioxide and water) into any one of several energy-rich organic compounds. One such organic compound is the sugar **glucose**—a simple carbohydrate.

In the chemical reaction shown in Figure 2-3, notice that water and carbon dioxide from the environment are combined to make glucose. Oxygen gas, which is also formed in the process, is released into the environment.

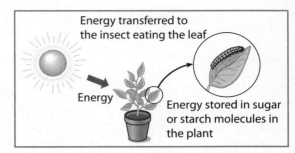

Figure 2-1. Energy transfer: The sun provides energy for most of the life on Earth.

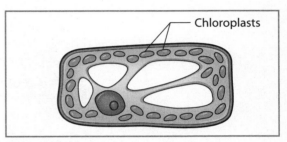

Figure 2-2. Chloroplasts in a typical plant cell: The chloroplasts capture light energy.

light energy + water + carbon dioxide $\longrightarrow$ glucose + oxygen
light energy + 6 H_2O + 6 CO_2 $\longrightarrow$ $C_6H_{12}O_6$ + 6 O_2

Figure 2-3. Photosynthesis

What Happens to the Sugar Produced by Photosynthesis? Plant cells use the organic compounds (such as glucose) from photosynthesis in two ways. Their primary use is to generate ATP molecules during **cellular respiration,** which is the process of releasing the energy in chemical bonds. Glucose is also used as a raw material for building more complex molecules, such as those listed in Table 2-1.

Using Glucose to Produce ATP Molecules One way plants (and animals) use glucose is to generate high energy molecules known as **ATP.** This process occurs during cellular respiration. Energy stored in the chemical bonds of ATP molecules is the energy source for almost all life processes from obtaining, transforming, and transporting materials to eliminating wastes. Because cell processes actually "run" on ATP (rather than glucose), the transfer of energy from glucose to ATP is essential to both plants and the

Table 2-1. Complex Molecules and Their Functions	
Molecule	**Function**
ATP	Supplies energy for cells to run on
DNA	Carries hereditary information
Carbohydrates	Acts as a food reserve molecule
Lipids (fats and oils)	Acts as a food reserve molecule
Protein	Makes up enzymes and many cell parts

organisms that consume them. All organisms—not just plants and animals—use organic food compounds to supply the ATP energy they need to live.

Using Glucose to Build Complex Molecules Cells also use glucose as the starting point for **synthesis** (chemical combining) that forms complex organic compounds. For example, plants store much of the glucose from photosynthesis as starch. Table 2-1 provides some examples of complex molecules and how they are used.

When animals eat plants or other animals, they digest the complex molecules into simpler molecules for their own cells to use. Some of these molecules provide energy for the organism. For example, starches from plants and fats from animals can both be digested and used right away for energy. If they are not all needed for energy, the molecules can be stored as fat to provide a food reserve for the animal.

Table 2-2. Summary of Photosynthesis	
Energy	The energy comes from sunlight as solar energy and ends up in glucose molecules as chemical bond energy.
Materials used	Carbon dioxide gas and water are used; both molecules come from the environment.
Materials produced	Molecules made from the carbon dioxide and water include molecules of the sugar glucose (a simple carbohydrate) and oxygen gas. Oxygen is actually released as a byproduct of photosynthesis.
Time frame	Photosynthesis occurs in plant cells when light is available, which is generally during the daytime.
Location	Photosynthesis occurs in the chloroplasts of plant cells, algae, and some one-celled organisms when they are exposed to light.
Importance of photosynthesis	Organisms either (1) use glucose to synthesize other molecules they need or (2) break down the glucose to release its stored energy.
Relationship to respiration	The energy originally stored in glucose during photosynthesis is transferred to the chemical bonds of ATP. All cells "run" on the energy released from ATP.

Review Questions

1. In a plant cell, the synthesis of sugar compounds from inorganic raw materials occurs in the

(1) cell membrane
(2) mitochondria
(3) nucleus
(4) chloroplasts

2. Which word equation represents the process of photosynthesis?

(1) glucose → alcohol + carbon dioxide
(2) carbon dioxide + water → glucose + oxygen
(3) chlorophyll + water → glucose + alcohol
(4) glucose + oxygen → carbon dioxide + water

3. Which factor *least* influences the rate of photosynthesis?

(1) atmospheric concentration of carbon dioxide
(2) time of day
(3) number of chloroplasts
(4) concentration of nitrogen in the air

4. The basic raw materials of photosynthesis are

(1) sugar and carbon dioxide
(2) oxygen and water
(3) water and carbon dioxide
(4) oxygen and sugar

5. Which compound is formed as a common product of the process of photosynthesis?
   (1) DNA
   (2) sugar
   (3) chlorophyll
   (4) carbon dioxide

6. In the test tube shown, what is produced by the snail that is used by the plant?
   (1) oxygen
   (2) carbon dioxide
   (3) food
   (4) egg cells

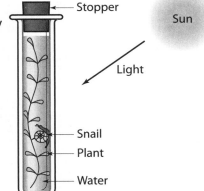

Stopper

Sun

Light

Snail

Plant

Water

7. Which activity occurs during the process of photosynthesis?
   (1) Chemical energy from organic molecules is converted into light energy
   (2) Organic molecules are absorbed from the environment.
   (3) Organic molecules are converted into inorganic food molecules.
   (4) Light energy is stored as chemical energy in organic molecules.

8. Photosynthesis in plants requires chloroplasts and light energy.
   • Identify two raw materials plants also use in this process [1]
   • Explain why these two substances are needed [1]

Releasing Energy: Cell Respiration

All living things need energy to stay alive. Before the energy in the bonds of complex carbohydrates, such as starch, can be used, the molecules must be broken down (digested) into simpler ones, such as glucose.

Then, the glucose (or other simple molecules) must be broken down further. This process involves a series of chemical reactions controlled by **enzymes,** which are special proteins that affect the rate of chemical reactions.

In the final step, the chemical bonds of the glucose molecule are broken, and the energy in those bonds is released. This process of releasing the energy in chemical bonds is called cellular respiration.

In many organisms, cellular respiration requires oxygen, which must be brought into the organism from the environment. Obtaining oxygen from the environment and releasing carbon dioxide is called **gas exchange.**

During cellular respiration, cells capture much of the energy that is released from the glucose bonds. The captured energy is then used to form new bonds in high-energy molecules known as ATP. Figure 2-4 shows how ATP temporarily stores energy. Most of the energy that the cell fails to capture to make ATP is lost to the environment as heat.

Memory Jogger

Sometimes people use the term *respiration* when they really mean *breathing*. *Respiration* is the process that involves oxygen and breaks down food molecules to release energy. *Cellular respiration* refers specifically to the transfer of energy from simple organic molecules like glucose to ATP molecules within cells.

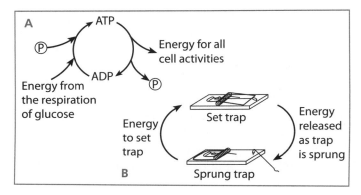

Figure 2-4. Energy storage in ATP molecules: (A) Chemical energy from the breakdown of glucose molecules is used to attach a phosphate (P) to a molecule of ADP. The result is called ATP. When the cell needs energy, the ATP is broken down into ADP. During that process, the phosphate (P), along with the energy that was stored in its chemical bond, is released. (B) A similar form of temporary energy storage occurs when a mousetrap is set. The mechanical energy that is put into the act of setting the trap is stored in the spring. When the trap is sprung, that energy is released.

Figure 2-5. **Cellular respiration in a mitochondrion:** Partially broken down glucose molecules and oxygen (O_2) enter the organelle and are rearranged, with the help of enzymes. Water (H_2O) and carbon dioxide (CO_2) are released as waste products. The energy that was stored in the glucose is transferred to ATP molecules.

Cellular respiration in many organisms is completed in organelles called **mitochondria.** (See Figure 2-5.) Mitochondria are common in animal cells. Cells that require more energy contain more mitochondria. For example, muscles require more energy to complete their functions than skin cells do. Muscle cells usually contain mitochondria, which corresponds with their increased energy needs.

As they generate ATP, mitochondria release carbon dioxide and water molecules that come from fragments of molecules that were involved in the reactions. Most cellular processes use ATP as a direct source of energy. Basically, cells "run" on ATP.

Table 2-3. Summary of Cellular Respiration	
Energy	Comes from the chemical bond energy of glucose molecules; ends up in the bonds of ATP where it can be utilized for cell activities
Materials used	Sugar or other energy-rich organic food compounds and oxygen gas from the environment • Food is obtained through photosynthesis in producers and by feeding in consumers. • Oxygen is obtained through gas exchange.
Materials produced	ATP molecules and two waste products— carbon dioxide gas and water. The release of carbon dioxide into the environment is part of the process of gas exchange.
Time frame	Cellular respiration occurs in all cells (including plant cells) 24 hours a day.
Location	Respiration occurs in the cells of all living things. In most organisms, cellular respiration is concluded in mitochondria.
Importance of respiration	All cells "run" on the energy released from ATP. Organisms can use the ATP they make as the source of energy to help them obtain raw materials and nutrients, to transform materials in chemical reactions, to transport materials (for example, active transport), and to eliminate wastes. ATP is essential for metabolic processes. The energy is also used to allow the organism to grow and to move from one place to another.

Digging Deeper

The D in ADP is for **Di**phosphate, or two phosphates. The T in ATP is for **Tri**phosphate, or three phosphates. ADP and ATP are converted back and forth as a phosphate is added or removed.

$$ADP + P = ATP$$
$$ATP - P = ADP$$

Review Questions

9. Energy for use in cells is stored in the form of

(1) chemical bond energy
(2) physical energy
(3) heat energy
(4) mechanical energy

10. In which process do organisms transfer the chemical bond energy in organic molecules to ATP molecules?

(1) excretion
(2) cellular respiration
(3) autotrophic nutrition
(4) photosynthesis

11. Energy released from the cellular respiration of glucose is

(1) first stored within ATP
(2) stored in the liver as fat
(3) turned into fat
(4) used directly for body activity

12. The process during which energy is released from digested foods is called

(1) cellular respiration
(2) chemical digestion
(3) photosynthesis
(4) excretion

13. As a direct result of the life process called cellular respiration in humans,

   (1) liquid wastes are eliminated from the body
   (2) food is digested and absorbed into the blood
   (3) energy is released from digested food within the cells
   (4) nutrients are transported within the cells

14. Which process involves the transfer of energy from carbohydrates to ATP molecules?

   (1) photosynthesis   (3) digestion
   (2) respiration   (4) circulation

15. During respiration, the energy within the bonds of a glucose molecule is released in small amounts in a step-by-step, enzyme-controlled reaction. In this process, the energy released is used to

   (1) synthesize ATP
   (2) control the process of diffusion
   (3) synthesize more glucose
   (4) produce oxygen molecules

16. Which statement best describes one of the events taking place in the chemical reaction represented below?

$$H_2O + ATP \xrightarrow{\text{enzymes}} ADP + P + \text{energy}$$

   (1) Energy is being stored as a result of cellular respiration.
   (2) Energy is being released for metabolic processes.
   (3) Decomposition is taking place, resulting in the synthesis of ATP.
   (4) Photosynthesis is taking place, resulting in the storage of energy.

17. Compare photosynthesis and respiration with regard to each of the following:

   • source of energy [1]
   • materials used by each process [1]
   • location of each process in the cell [1]
   • when each process occurs in plants and animals [1]

18. Which statement most accurately describes the process of respiration?

   (1) It occurs only in plants during the daylight hours and usually involves the exchange of gases.
   (2) It occurs only in plants during the daylight hours and involves the taking in of preformed organic molecules.
   (3) It occurs continuously in the cells of all organisms and involves the synthesis of carbohydrate molecules.
   (4) It occurs continuously in the cells of all organisms and often involves an exchange of gases.

19. During daylight hours green plants carry out photosynthesis. Do they also carry out respiration at this time? Support your answer. [1]

Base your answers to questions 20 through 22 on the diagram of a mitochondrion below and on your knowledge of biology.

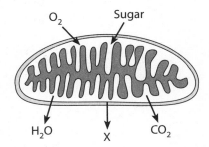

20. The process represented in this diagram is

   (1) respiration   (3) photosynthesis
   (2) coordination   (4) immunity

21. What term would most appropriately be represented by the "X"?

   (1) ATP   (3) antibodies
   (2) chlorophyll (4) glucose

22. What is present within the mitochondrion that allows the reaction to occur?

   (1) enzymes   (3) bacteria
   (2) chlorophyll (4) carbon dioxide

Enzymes

A **catalyst** is any substance that can affect the rate of a chemical reaction without itself being changed or used up during the reaction. Because it is neither changed nor used up, the catalyst is capable of carrying out the same function again and again. Protein catalysts known as enzymes affect the chemical reactions in living things.

The Function of Enzymes Biochemical processes, such as digestion (breakdown), synthesis (building up), cellular respiration (energy release),

Figure 2-6. Enzymes interact with specific molecules: Enzyme interactions are determined by molecular shape. After the two molecules W and X collide with enzyme Y (A), the enzyme forms a temporary physical connection with them (B) and then separates after a reaction has occurred (C). As a result, the molecules W and X have chemically bonded for the synthesis of the new molecule Z. If the arrows in the illustration were reversed, the reaction would involve splitting molecule Z into two smaller molecules, W and X. This reverse process is digestion.

and photosynthesis (energy capture), are made possible in living things by enzymes.

All living organisms contain enzymes. Enzymes interact with other molecules when they collide. Chemical reactions in living organisms are regulated by many different enzymes that function best at whatever the normal "body" temperature is for the organism.

Importance of Molecular Shape Enzymes and several other molecules, such as hormones, antibodies, and receptor molecules on cell membranes, have specific shapes that influence both how they function and how they interact with other molecules. Many enzymes will interact with some substances, but not others. The enzyme salivary amylase, for example, acts on starches but not proteins. In Figure 2-6, notice how the shapes of W, X, and Y fit together precisely. If the shape of an enzyme is altered, it will not interact with other molecules the way it must to catalyze a reaction, and its function will be impaired.

Enzyme Reaction Rates

Several conditions, such as shape, temperature, and pH, can either speed up or slow down the rate of enzyme action.

Shape Enzymes are chain-like protein molecules that are folded into precise shapes. Each enzyme must have a specific shape to work correctly, and anything that alters that shape will affect the enzyme's ability to function properly. High temperatures and strong <u>acids</u> or <u>bases</u> can change the enzyme's shape either temporarily or permanently. When this happens, the enzyme cannot function, and the reaction rate will decrease in proportion to the number of enzyme molecules that are altered.

Temperature Most enzymes have an <u>optimum</u> temperature at which they function most efficiently and produce the highest reaction rate. For human enzymes, this temperature is typically 98.6°F (37°C). As the temperature of a cell or organism reaches its optimum level, enzymes and the molecules they are interacting with will move faster and collide more often, causing the reaction rate to increase. Beyond the optimum temperature, the rate falls rapidly because the fragile enzyme molecules begin to change shape or break apart. Trace the rise and fall of an enzyme reaction rate in Figure 2-7.

pH The **pH** of a substance is a measure of whether a substance is <u>acidic</u>, <u>neutral</u>, or <u>basic</u>. Placing enzymes in solutions of varying pH values affects their activity. Many enzymes work best in an optimum pH of about 7, which is neutral. This makes sense, since most body fluids and cells maintain a pH of near 7. However, some parts of organisms have typical pH values that are far from neutral. For example, the human stomach is acidic and has a pH of 2 or 3. The small intestine has a pH around 8. Enzymes in these locations typically have optimum rates that correspond to the pH of their environment, as shown in Figure 2-8.

A pH of about 7 is neutral, the same as pure water. A low pH, such as 1 or 2, indicates a strong acid. A high pH, such as 13 or 14, indicates a strong base. In a typical high school biology laboratory, pH is measured with pH paper treated with various indicator dyes.

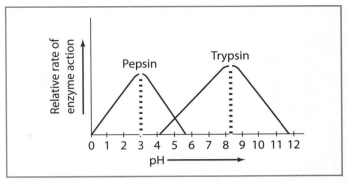

Figure 2-7. Enzymes and temperature: Note that the rate of enzyme action is fastest at about 37°C, which is typical of a human enzyme. The reason the rate declines so quickly beyond the optimum is that the higher temperature alters the shape of the enzyme. In this example, by the time the temperature reaches 55°C, all the enzyme molecules have been altered, and as a result, they no longer function.

Figure 2-8. Enzymes and pH: Pepsin is found in the human stomach and has a pH that matches the acid environment found there. Trypsin is an enzyme located in the small intestine where the pH is close to 8. Notice that each enzyme is less effective if the pH is either raised or lowered from its optimum point.

Review Questions

23. Only small amounts of enzymes are required for reactions within cells because enzymes are

(1) fragile
(2) reused
(3) small molecules
(4) constantly synthesized

24. Which cell organelle indicated in the diagram below controls the synthesis of enzymes?

(1) A
(2) B
(3) C
(4) D

25. In order to survive, all organisms must carry out

(1) autotrophic nutrition
(2) heterotrophic nutrition
(3) enzyme-controlled reactions
(4) the process of reproduction

26. Which group of organic compounds includes the enzymes?

(1) proteins
(2) carbohydrates
(3) sugars
(4) fats

27. Luciferin is a molecule that, when broken down in fireflies, produces heat and light. The rate at which luciferin is broken down in cells is controlled by

(1) a carbohydrate
(2) a simple sugar
(3) an enzyme
(4) a complex fat

28. At which point on the graph below can the rate of enzyme activity be increased by increasing the concentration of sugar molecules?

(1) 1   (3) 3
(2) 2   (4) either 2, 3, or 4

29. Which statement best describes the relationship between enzyme action and temperature shown in the graph below?

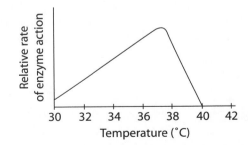

(1) Enzyme synthesis begins at 30°C.
(2) Enzyme activity constantly increases with increasing temperature.
(3) The pH has a greater effect on this enzyme than temperature does.
(4) Enzyme activity increases as the temperature increases from 32°C to 34°C.

30. The enzyme salivary amylase will act on starch but not on protein. This action illustrates that salivary amylase

(1) contains starch
(2) is chemically specific
(3) is not reusable
(4) lacks protein

31. The graph below shows the effect of temperature on the relative rate of action of enzyme X on a protein.

Which change would not affect the relative rate of action of enzyme X?

(1) the addition of cold water when the reaction is at 50°C
(2) an increase in temperature from 70°C to 80°C
(3) the removal of the protein when the reaction is at 30°C
(4) a decrease in temperature from 40°C to 10°C

32. Enzymes influence chemical reactions in living systems by

(1) becoming part of the product after the reactions occur
(2) combining with atmospheric gases to form waste products
(3) affecting the rate at which reactions occur
(4) absorbing water during synthesis and digestion

33. The diagram below represents three steps in the digestion of the sugar sucrose. In this diagram, structure X is most likely

(1) a molecule of oxygen
(2) the end product
(3) an enzyme molecule
(4) the sugar

Base your answers to questions 34 through 36 on the diagram of an enzyme-controlled reaction and on your knowledge of biology.

34. Explain what is happening during Steps 1-3 in the following diagram. Use the labels—A, B, C, D, and E—to help you with your explanation. As part of your answer, indicate which molecules represent the enzyme and the product.

35. Is this reaction an illustration of synthesis or digestion? Support your answer. [1]

36. Explain why heating these molecules might *slow* the rate at which this reaction occurs? [1]

Base your answers to questions 37 through 41 on the diagram and data table below and on your knowledge of biology.

A student is studying the effect of temperature on the action of a protein-digesting enzyme that is contained in stomach fluid. An investigation is set up using five identical test tubes. Each test tube contains 40 milliliters of stomach fluid as well as a 20-millimeter glass tube filled with cooked egg white, as shown in the diagram. After 48 hours, the amount of egg white digested in each tube was measured. The data collected are shown in the following table.

Digestion at Different Temperatures		
Tube	Temperature (°C)	Amount of Digestion After 48 Hours
1	4	0.0 mm
2	8	2.5 mm
3	21	4.0 mm
4	37	7.5 mm
5	100	0.0 mm

37. Identify the independent variable in this investigation.

(1) gastric fluid
(2) length of glass tubing
(3) temperature
(4) time

38. State the amount of digestion (in mm) that might be expected after 48 hours in a test tube that is identical to the other 5 test tubes, but at a temperature of 15°C.

(1) less than 2.5 mm
(2) between 2.5 and 4 mm
(3) between 4.0 and 7.5 mm
(4) more than 7.5 mm

39. The best graph of the results of this investigation would be made by plotting the data on which set of axes?

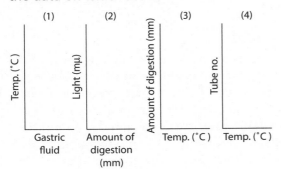

40. The student repeated this same experiment using a glass tube containing potato instead of egg white. After 48 hours, he found no evidence of any digestion.

Explain why no digestion occurred. [1]

41. During the winter, many fish eat very little. Some students thought this might be because less oxygen is dissolved in the cold winter water than in the same water during the warm summer months. The students tested the water and found that cold water holds more dissolved oxygen than warm water. They also discovered that the fish have nearly as much food available during the winter as in the summer.

Explain why the fish eat very little during the winter. [1]

Feedback and Homeostasis

Because an organism's external and internal environment is constantly changing, its homeostasis is constantly threatened. As a result, living things must monitor and respond to changes in the environment. Stability (homeostasis) results when the organism detects <u>deviations</u> (changes) in the environment and responds with an appropriate corrective action that returns the organism's systems to normal. If an organism's monitoring systems or control mechanisms fail, disease or even death can result.

As you go about your daily tasks, your body temperature readjusts, your heart and breathing rates alter slightly, and your blood flow increases or decreases. If your monitoring were to fail, these small adjustments would not be made. Soon, your body's homeostasis would begin to deteriorate. Under extreme conditions, you could become quite ill or even die. However, simple corrective actions usually take care of problems with your homeostasis and life goes on. Some examples of responses organisms have to changes they encounter are shown in Table 2-4.

Dynamic Equilibrium

Organisms have a variety of mechanisms that maintain the physical and chemical aspects of the internal environment within the narrow limits that are favorable for cell activities. The stability that results from these responses is called homeostasis or a "steady state." To many biologists, the phrase *steady state* suggests an

Table 2-4. Responses to Environmental Change

Organism	Change (stimulus)	Response
Species of bacterium	Temperature falls below a certain point.	Bacterium produces a chemical that acts as an antifreeze.
Many plants	Air is hot and dry.	Leaf pores close to conserve water.
Monarch butterflies	Seasons change.	Butterflies migrate.
Human	Person hears a loud noise.	The person becomes alert; heart rate increases for "fight or flight."

Figure 2-9. Dynamic equilibrium: (A) Temperature: Our body temperature shows a regular pattern of slight changes around a "normal" temperature of about 98.6°F (37°C). The graph represents the slight differences in temperature that are part of a daily cycle. Mechanisms such as shivering and sweating help maintain this range. **(B)** Blood sugar: Normal blood sugar levels show a rise in blood sugar after a meal, but blood sugar level is quickly restored to equilibrium as the hormone insulin prompts glucose to move from the blood to body cells.

unchanging condition. They prefer to use the term **dynamic equilibrium** to describe the constant small corrections that normally keep the internal environment within the limits needed for survival.

In Figure 2-9, notice that these small corrections include a normal range of variations. Certain microorganisms or diseases can interfere with dynamic equilibrium, and therefore with homeostasis. Organisms, including humans, have mechanisms to deal with such interference and restore the normal state. Homeostatic adjustments have their limits. They can operate only within certain set ranges.

Feedback Mechanisms

A **feedback mechanism** involves a cycle in which the output of a system "feeds back" to either modify or reinforce the action taken by the system. A variety of feedback mechanisms have evolved for helping organisms detect and respond to **stimuli** (changes in the environment). Multi-celled organisms detect and respond to change both at the cellular level and at the organism level. Their systems detect deviations from the normal state and take corrective actions to restore homeostasis.

Feedback responses can be simple or complex. A simple feedback response might involve a hormone that regulates a particular chemical process in a cell. A complex feedback response might be an elaborate behavior, such as bird migration.

Positive Feedback Feedback mechanisms can be either positive or negative. In positive feedback systems, a change prompts a response, which leads to a greater change and a greater response. Childbirth is an example of a positive feedback system. The first contractions push the baby's head against the base of the uterus, which causes stronger contractions in the muscles surrounding the uterus. This increases the pressure of the baby's head against the base of the uterus, which causes stronger contractions and so on. Eventually the baby is born, and the feedback cycle ends.

Figure 2-10. Negative feedback systems: (A) The furnace and thermostat in most houses are part of a negative feedback system. **(B)** Like the household heating system, the regulation of body temperature is a negative feedback system.

Negative Feedback Negative feedback systems are the most common. In this case, a change in the environment can prompt system 1 to send a message (often a hormone) to system 2, which responds by attempting to restore homeostasis. When system 1 detects that system 2 has acted, it stops signaling for further action.

A typical house heating system is an example of negative feedback. The furnace has a thermostat that is set to a specific temperature called the set point. When the room cools below the set point, the thermostat sends a message to turn on the furnace. When the room temperature rises above the set point, the thermostat stops sending the message, and the furnace shuts down. (See Figure 2-10.)

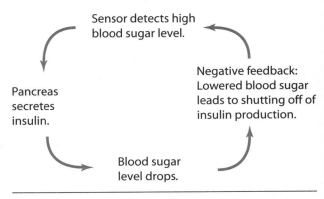

Figure 2-11. **Negative feedback involving blood sugar level**

Regulating human body temperature uses a similar system. A structure in the brain detects that the temperature of the blood is too low. This brain structure then sends a signal to muscles, causing them to contract and relax in rapid cycles. The result is shivering, which generates body heat. When shivering has sufficiently warmed the body and blood, <u>sensors</u> in the brain detect the change, and the signal to shiver stops.

Negative Feedback and Cell/Organ System Interaction

Maintaining dynamic equilibrium often involves interactions between cells and body organs or systems. For example, certain cells in the body monitor the level of glucose in the blood. When the glucose level is above normal limits, an endocrine organ called the **pancreas** secretes insulin. **Insulin** is a hormone that prompts glucose to move from the blood into body cells, resulting in a lower glucose level in the blood. Another hormone secreted by the pancreas works in the opposite way. When the glucose level in the blood is too low, this hormone prompts the release of glucose stored in the liver. The negative feedback process involving insulin is shown in Figure 2-11.

Other examples of cell/organ feedback interactions include:

- Increased muscle activity is often accompanied by an increase in heart rate and breathing rate. If this did not occur, the muscles would not receive the increase in blood flow and oxygen they need to continue working.
- When plant leaves detect a shortage of water, **guard cells**—specialized cells that surround pores on the surface of the leaf—change shape to close the pores and reduce evaporation. The process is shown in Figure 2-12.

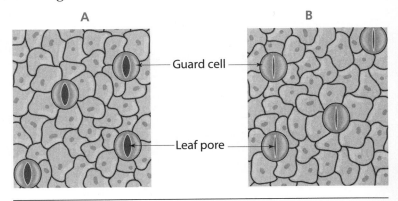

Figure 2-12. **Guard cell activity on the surface of a leaf:** (A) The guard cells have opened the pores in the leaf, allowing gas exchange between the leaf and the environment. Water can exit from the leaf, and CO_2 can enter. This situation commonly exists when the sun is shining, the air is warm, and water is available from the soil. (B) The guard cells have nearly closed the pores in the leaf, thus protecting the leaf from drying out. Under these conditions, gas exchange is limited. Photosynthesis slows down because little CO_2 is available. This situation commonly exists when the sun is shining, the air is hot and dry, and little water is available from the soil.

42. Some plants respond to light with a sudden enlargement of their leaf pores. This response is important because it enables the plant to increase its intake of

(1) carbon dioxide (3) oxygen
(2) soil (4) nitrogen

43. An increase in the blood's level of a thyroid gland hormone decreases the release of thyroid-stimulating hormone. This mechanism illustrates

(1) negative feedback
(2) enzyme action
(3) immune response
(4) positive feedback

44. Maintenance of the pH of human blood within a certain range is an example of

(1) chemical digestion
(2) synthesis
(3) respiration
(4) dynamic equilibrium

45. Homeostasis is illustrated in the human body by the effects of insulin on the amount of

(1) proteins digested
(2) amino acids absorbed into the blood
(3) oxygen transport to the lungs
(4) glucose in the blood

46. The chart below shows the amount of oxygen and carbon dioxide exchanged through the skin and lungs of a frog for a period of one year.

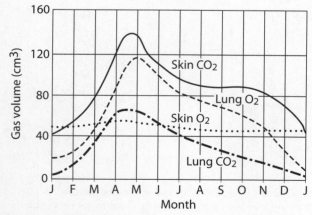

The lowest rate of gas exchange is most likely the result of

(1) increased mating activity
(2) elevated body temperature
(3) environmental conditions
(4) competition with other species

47. A student is frightened by a loud noise, which results in a hormone being released into the blood. The hormone causes the student's heart to beat rapidly. The two systems that work together to cause this reaction are the endocrine system that secretes the hormone and the

(1) nervous system (3) excretory system
(2) reproductive system (4) digestive system

48. Which important human process is represented in the diagram below?

(1) coordination (3) excretion
(2) digestion (4) cell respiration

49. Describe what normally happens to a person's blood sugar level soon after he or she eats a meal that contains carbohydrates. [1]

50. Describe the role of insulin in regulating blood sugar levels. [1]

51. On a sheet of graph paper, mark an X and a Y-axis, then draw a line representing the relative blood sugar levels for two individuals (Person A and Person B) over a 5-hour period after a meal. Both people ate the same foods. Person A produces a normal amount of insulin, and Person B does not.

Explain any differences in the lines representing Persons A and B. [1]

52. During hot weather and vigorous exercise, people sweat. As the water on their skin evaporates, the water molecules absorb heat energy.

Explain why this process is important to the individual. [1]

53. Many different feedback mechanisms have evolved over time. These mechanisms allow an organism to respond to changes in both its internal and external environment.

Select an organism from those you have learned about and describe how a specific feedback process works within that organism. Include how the feedback specifically helps the organism maintain homeostasis. [1]

Disease as a Failure of Homeostasis

Disease is any condition that prevents the body from working as it should. As a result, the body may fail to maintain homeostasis. Diseases in humans may result from foreign invader organisms, called **pathogens,** or from abnormal cells in the body that lead to cancer. Disease may also result from toxic substances, poor nutrition, organ malfunction, an inherited disorder, or risky personal behavior. All can lead to a disruption of the body's ability to function normally—that is, to maintain homeostasis.

Sometimes the onset of a disease becomes apparent right away, as in the case of some birth defects or poisoning. Sometimes, however, the disease may not show up for many years, as is the case with lung cancer caused by exposure to tobacco smoke. Some examples of these kinds of diseases are noted in Table 2-5.

Pathogens There are many potentially dangerous disease-causing organisms in the air, water, and food we take in every day. A variety of pathogens—viruses, bacteria, fungi, and other parasites—can interfere with our normal functioning and make us seriously ill. Plants and other animals can also be infected by these and similar organisms. Some examples of pathogens and the diseases they cause are shown in Table 2-6.

Cancer Certain genetic mutations in a cell can result in uncontrolled cell division called cancer. Exposing cells to certain chemicals and radiation increases mutations and thus increases the chance of cancer. In this disease, genes that control and coordinate a cell's normal cycle of growth and division are altered by mutation. As a result, the cell begins to divide abnormally and uncontrollably. The result is a mass of abnormal cells referred to as a tumor.

Table 2-5. Causes of Disease

Cause of Disease	Examples
Inherited disorders	Down syndrome, cystic fibrosis, sickle cell disease
Exposure to toxins	Lead poisoning, radiation poisoning
Poor nutrition	Scurvy (vitamin C deficiency), goiter (iodine deficiency)
Organ malfunction	Heart attack, diabetes
High-risk behaviors	Lung cancer, drug addiction, skin cancer

Table 2-6. Pathogens and Disease

Pathogen	Description of Pathogen	Examples of Disease
Virus	**Viruses** are particles composed of nucleic acid and protein. They reproduce when they invade living cells.	Examples include the common cold, influenza, AIDS, and chicken pox. Immunizations have been developed to combat many viral diseases.
Bacterium	**Bacteria** are one-celled organisms.	Bacterial illnesses include strep throat, syphilis, and food poisoning. **Antibiotics**, drugs like penicillin that we get from microorganisms, are used to treat many bacterial diseases.
Fungus	**Fungi** are organisms made of either one or many cells. They include yeasts and molds. They eat by absorbing organic substances.	Examples include athlete's foot and ringworm. Fungicides and antibiotics are used to fight fungal diseases.
Parasites	Some animals and one-celled organisms are **parasites** that survive by living and feeding on other organisms.	Parasites include leeches and tapeworms. Malaria is a disease caused by a one-celled organism. It is transmitted to humans by mosquitoes. Heartworm is a parasitic worm that lives in dogs and cats. Medicines are available to treat some parasitic diseases. Avoiding exposure to the parasite is also effective.

Once they are identified, often by abnormal proteins on their surfaces, cancer cells may be attacked by the immune system and destroyed. If the immune system is unable to destroy the cancer cells, the disease may become life-threatening.

The Immune System

Humans have many ways of protecting themselves from danger and disease. For example:

- Our eyes, ears, and sense of smell help us detect danger.
- We release hormones that stimulate emergency responses to danger.
- Our muscles allow us to fight off some threats and to flee from others.
- Our skin—when unbroken—keeps out many foreign organisms that could be harmful.
- Our tears, saliva, and other body secretions trap and/or destroy invaders that come into contact with them.
- Our nervous system provides rapid coordination of many of our responses to danger.

Once invaded, however, the body needs an effective way to combat invaders or body cells that malfunction. The **immune system** is the body's primary defense against disease-causing pathogens.

Pathogens, foreign substances, or cancer cells that threaten our homeostasis can usually be identified by molecules on their outer surfaces or membranes. These molecules, called **antigens,** trigger a response from the immune system. Toxins, the poisonous wastes of certain pathogens, can also act as antigens.

All cells have potential antigens on their surfaces. However, the immune system can usually tell the difference between the molecules of "self" cells, which belong to the body, and "non-self" (foreign) cells, which come from outside the body. When cells of our immune system recognize foreign antigens, specialized white blood cells and antibodies attack them and the cells that display them.

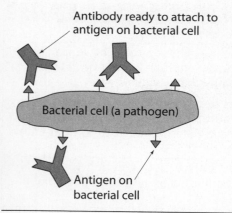

Antibody ready to attach to antigen on bacterial cell

Bacterial cell (a pathogen)

Antigen on bacterial cell

Figure 2-13. Certain white blood cells produce Y-shaped antibodies: The antibodies match the shape of certain antigens on pathogens or abnormal proteins on cancer cells. Note that the antibodies and antigens are not drawn to scale. They would be MUCH smaller than the pathogen cell.

White Blood Cells and Antibodies Some white blood cells are specialized to surround and engulf invading pathogens that are recognized as a threat. Others produce **antibodies**—proteins that either attack the invaders or mark them for killing. The marked invaders may then be destroyed by other white blood cells. In Figure 2-13, notice the Y-shaped antibodies that match the shape of antigens.

Most of the antibodies and white blood cells that attack an invader break down soon after they have defended the body. However, some specialized white blood cells will remain. These cells are capable of quickly dividing and producing more antibodies of the same kind to fight off later invasions of the same **microbes** (microscopic organisms). Antibodies are effective even against microbes that appear years later.

Vaccinations Scientists have discovered that weakened microbes (pathogens) or even parts of microbes can stimulate the immune system to react. The antigens found on the live pathogens are usually present on the weakened or killed ones, too. As shown in Figure 2-14, **vaccines** are made using these weakened, killed, or parts of microbes (pathogens). When vaccines are injected into the body, the immune system responds just as if it had been invaded by a live pathogen. It produces antibodies. These antibodies can attack and destroy any of that pathogen that is still present in the body.

After a vaccination, the immune system "remembers" specific pathogens by leaving behind white blood cells that protect the body for years. The vaccinated body reacts as if it has already defeated the specific pathogen and responds faster in the future than it did when attacked the first time. The second response is so rapid that in most cases the disease will not even have time to develop before the immune system wipes it out.

Damage to the Immune System A person's immune system may weaken with age or other factors. Stress and fatigue, for example, can lower our resistance and make us more vulnerable to disease. Some viral diseases, such as **AIDS,** result from an attack on the immune system. Damage from the disease may leave the person with AIDS unable to deal with infections and cancerous cells. Their weakened immune system is one reason people with AIDS often die of infections that a healthy immune system would easily destroy.

Problems Associated with the Immune Response Although our immune system is essential for our survival, it creates problems for some people. These people have an **allergy**—a rapid immune system reaction to environmental substances that are normally harmless. Examples of such substances include certain foods, pollen, and chemicals from insect bites.

In people with allergies, the immune system reacts by releasing <u>histamines</u>. This leads to anything from a runny nose and sneezing to a rash and swelling. It is the swelling that makes some allergies dangerous: Occasionally, the throat swells, interfering with the victim's ability to breathe. People with allergies often use <u>antihistamines</u> to reduce the effects of the histamines and the symptoms they cause.

Sometimes the immune system fails to recognize the "self" molecules and attacks the body's own cells. For example, in some cases, the immune system attacks and destroys the pancreas cells that produce insulin. The result is one type of diabetes.

Since transplanted organs come from another person, they have foreign antigens on their cells. As a result, the immune system recognizes transplants as "invaders" and attacks them. To avoid "rejection" of their new organ, transplant patients receive injections of special drugs to reduce the effectiveness of their immune system. Of course, because the immune system's ability to protect the transplant patient from normal pathogens is reduced, the patient may become ill from a pathogen that normally would be no threat.

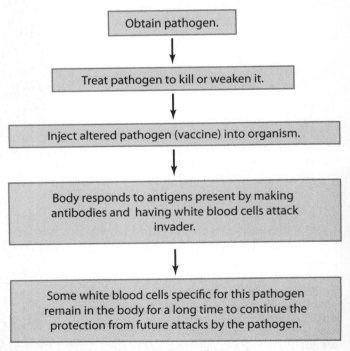

Obtain pathogen.

↓

Treat pathogen to kill or weaken it.

↓

Inject altered pathogen (vaccine) into organism.

↓

Body responds to antigens present by making antibodies and having white blood cells attack invader.

↓

Some white blood cells specific for this pathogen remain in the body for a long time to continue the protection from future attacks by the pathogen.

Figure 2-14. Preparation and use of a vaccine

Research and Progress Against Disease Biological research of diseases and their causes has generated a vast amount of knowledge that is used to find ways of diagnosing, preventing, controlling, or curing diseases of plants and animals. Some examples of how medical knowledge has developed are shown in Table 2-7.

Table 2-7. Biological Research of Diseases

Category of Research	Methods Developed
Diagnosing disease	• Culturing (growing) bacteria from the infected person to determine what specific pathogen is responsible for the illness • Using X-rays, CAT scans, ultrasound, blood pressure monitoring devices, and other methods to determine the cause or extent of the illness • Detecting genetic abnormalities that may be present in cells
Preventing and controlling disease	• Promoting improved sanitation measures, including frequent hand washing, safe garbage disposal, and sewage treatment • Sterilizing surgical instruments and treating wounds with antiseptics and other chemicals • Controlling populations of rats, flies, mosquitoes, and other disease-carrying organisms with pesticides or sanitation measures • Treating water, milk, and other foods to reduce the presence of pathogens • Vaccinating to promote the body's immune response to pathogens • Identifying the dangers of risky behaviors such as tobacco use
Treating and curing disease	• Developing antibiotics and other drugs to kill pathogens • Developing medical procedures, including surgical operations and laser techniques, to remove damaged or diseased tissue from the body

Review Questions

54. When a person is suffering from an infection, such as strep throat or chicken pox, his blood usually shows a significant increase in the number of

    (1) enzymes   (3) hormones
    (2) antibodies   (4) sugars

55. When microscope slides are stained to show blood cells, the small red blood cells that appear on the slides are much more numerous than the large white blood cells. This supports the concept that

    (1) the body's need for white blood cells is less than its need for red blood cells
    (2) red cells are more numerous because they are smaller than white blood cells
    (3) the nuclei of the white blood cells help them work more efficiently than the red blood cells, which lack nuclei
    (4) each kind of cell is present in the numbers best suited to meet the needs of the body

56. Which response usually occurs after an individual receives a vaccination for the influenza virus?

    (1) Hormones in the blood stop reproduction of the virus.
    (2) Pathogens from the vaccine deactivate the virus.
    (3) Enzymes released from antigens digest the virus.
    (4) Antibodies against the virus are found in the blood.

57. A patient has just received an organ transplant. Which treatment would be most effective in preventing the patient's body from rejecting the organ?

    (1) Treat the patient with medications that decrease the immune system's response.
    (2) Treat the patient with antibiotics to fight off a possible viral infection.
    (3) Restrict the patient's salt intake.
    (4) Give the patient blood transfusions.

58. The body makes chemicals that can help to destroy harmful viruses and bacteria. These chemicals are called

(1) antibodies
(2) vaccines
(3) hormones
(4) antibiotics

59. A vaccine can protect you against a disease because it

(1) destroys toxic substances from bacteria before they can make you sick
(2) stimulates your immune system against the pathogen
(3) kills any pathogenic bacteria in your body
(4) changes pathogenic bacteria into harmless bacteria

60. The body is protected against harmful flu viruses by

(1) red blood cells and hormones
(2) white blood cells and antibodies
(3) white blood cells and enzymes
(4) red blood cells and antibodies

61. A scientist wishes to determine how effective a vaccine is in protecting rats against a contagious disease. Which experimental procedure should the scientist use to determine the vaccine's effectiveness?

(1) Expose 100 rats to the disease and then vaccinate them all.
(2) Give vaccinations to 50 of the 100 rats and then expose all 100 to the disease.
(3) Give vaccinations to 100 of the rats and expose them all to the disease.
(4) Vaccinate 50 of the 100 rats and then expose only the 50 vaccinated rats to the disease.

62. Parasitic strains of *E. coli* may produce poisonous chemicals that attack living tissue and cause disease in humans. These chemicals are called

(1) antibodies
(2) toxins
(3) viruses
(4) antibiotics

63. Uncontrolled cell division is known as

(1) meiosis
(2) cancer
(3) antibody production
(4) sexual reproduction

64. The resistance of the body to a pathogen is called

(1) immunity
(2) antigen
(3) cancer
(4) infection

65. Diseases can be caused by inherited disorders, exposure to toxic substances, organ malfunction and certain personal behaviors.

Choose *two* of the above causes and *for each one* give a specific example of an associated disease. [1]

66. Our immune system normally helps us resist infection and disease. Sometimes, however, it may actually work against us by attacking certain tissues or organs in the body.

State one example of the immune system attacking the body and explain how we try to counteract the problem. [1]

67. Vaccinations play a major role in medicine today. Explain the role of vaccines in the prevention of disease. Your answer must include at least:

• a description of the contents of a vaccine [1]
• a description of how a vaccine protects the body from disease [1]
• one specific reason certain vaccinations are required for students to attend public schools. [1]

68. Biological research has generated much knowledge about diagnosing and preventing disease.

Give one specific example of how research has helped us *diagnose* a disease and one specific example of how research has helped us *prevent* a disease. [1]

69. Various kinds of pathogens cause illness or interfere with body functioning. For each pathogen type listed below, identify one specific organism or disease associated with that type of pathogen.

Pathogen Types:

(a) virus
(b) bacteria
(c) fungus
(d) other parasites

Directions

Review the Test-Taking Strategies section of this book. Then answer the following questions. Read each question carefully and answer with a correct choice or response.

Part A

1 Most of the oxygen in our atmosphere comes from processes carried out
- (1) in the soil
- (2) by animals
- (3) in factories
- (4) by plants

2 Which organism releases oxygen into the atmosphere?
- (1) mold
- (2) bird
- (3) fish
- (4) tree

3 Plants provide food for animals through the process of
- (1) respiration
- (2) digestion
- (3) photosynthesis
- (4) excretion

4 Which word equation represents the process of photosynthesis?
- (1) starch → many glucose molecules
- (2) glucose + oxygen → carbon dioxide + water + energy
- (3) carbon dioxide + water → glucose + oxygen
- (4) fats → sugar molecules

5 Which statement correctly relates the two organisms in the illustration below?

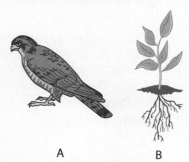

A   B

- (1) A carries out cell division, but B does not.
- (2) B transports needed organic materials, but A does not.
- (3) Both A and B carry out cellular respiration to release energy from organic molecules.
- (4) Neither A nor B is able to use energy to combine carbon dioxide and water to make organic compounds.

6 A plant cell that lacks chloroplasts will not
- (1) give off oxygen
- (2) take in food
- (3) give off carbon dioxide
- (4) take in water

7 Which process removes carbon dioxide from the atmosphere rather than adding it?
- (1) cellular respiration
- (2) combustion of gasoline
- (3) photosynthesis
- (4) deforestation

8 Which process in plants produces carbon dioxide?
- (1) respiration
- (2) photosynthesis
- (3) coordination
- (4) digestion

9 The size of the openings in a leaf through which gases move in and out is controlled by the
- (1) root cells
- (2) chloroplasts
- (3) chromosomes
- (4) guard cells

10 What process does the word equation below represent?

$$\text{glucose} + \text{oxygen} \xrightarrow{\text{enzymes}} \text{carbon dioxide} + \text{water} + \text{energy}$$

- (1) photosynthesis
- (2) breathing
- (3) transport
- (4) respiration

11 The major source of weight gain in a growing plant is
- (1) sunlight
- (2) carbon dioxide
- (3) oxygen
- (4) soil

12 Green plants do not release large amounts of CO_2 all the time because they use CO_2 in the process of
- (1) photosynthesis
- (2) respiration
- (3) reproduction
- (4) evolution

13 The diagram below represents some events that take place in a plant cell. With which organelle would these events be most closely associated?

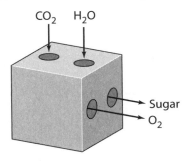

(1) mitochondrion
(2) chloroplast
(3) ribosome
(4) vacuole

14 An enzyme that digests starch will not act upon the sugar sucrose. This fact is an indication that enzymes are
(1) specific
(2) synthetic
(3) starches
(4) generalized

15 Which statement best describes the enzyme represented in the graphs below?

(1) This enzyme works best at a temperature of 37°C and a pH of 8.
(2) This enzyme works best at a temperature of 55°C and a pH of 12.
(3) Temperature and pH have no effect on the action of this enzyme.
(4) This enzyme works best at a temperature near freezing and a pH above 4.

16 The body usually responds to foreign material by forming
(1) hormones   (3) vaccines
(2) antibodies   (4) antigens

17 A sudden increase in the number of white blood cells in a human may be an indication of
(1) growth
(2) color blindness
(3) mental retardation
(4) an infection

Part B

Base your answers to questions 18 and 19 on the equation below and on your knowledge of biology.

$$C_6H_{12}O_6 + 6\,O_2 \rightarrow H_2O + 6\,CO_2 + 36\,ATP$$

(glucose) + (oxygen) → (water) + (carbon dioxide) + ATP

18 The equation represents the process of
(1) excretion   (3) respiration
(2) photosynthesis   (4) coordination

19 Explain the energy connection between the glucose and the formation of ATP in this process. [1]

Base your answers to questions 20 through 24 on the following selection from the work of an early scientist and on your knowledge of biology.

A sprig (stem with leaves) of a nettle plant was put in a jar full of air fouled by breathing so as to extinguish a candle; it was placed in a room and left overnight; the next morning the air was found to be as bad as before. At 9 o'clock in the morning, the jar was put in the sunshine and, in the space of two hours, the air was so much corrected that it was found to be nearly as good as common air.

20 The "jar full of air fouled by breathing" probably contained an excess of what gas? [1]

21 The fact that "the air was found to be as bad as before" was due to a process taking place in the plant. Name that process. [1]

22 What process did the plant perform to produce air nearly as good as "common air"? [1]

23 Identify the gas produced by the plant in the process that improved the air in the jar. [1]

24 Identify the gas that was produced by the plant in the dark. [1]

Base your answers to questions 25 through 29 on the information and data table below and on your knowledge of biology.

An investigation was designed to determine the effect of temperature on respiration in germinating seeds. Two sets of test tubes were prepared. In each set of two test tubes, one tube contained a number of germinating peas, and the other tube contained an equal number of glass beads. An equal amount of chemical was placed in each tube to absorb the carbon dioxide produced so that the volume of oxygen consumed could be measured. One set of tubes was placed in a controlled-temperature water bath at 10°C. The other set of test tubes was placed in a controlled-temperature water bath at 26°C. Total oxygen consumption was measured every 5 minutes for a period of 20 minutes. The data are summarized in the data table.

Use the information in the data table at the right and follow the directions in questions 25 through 27 to construct a line graph on the grid provided.

25 Label each axis and mark an appropriate scale on each axis, without any breaks. [1]

26 Plot the data for oxygen consumption by peas at 10°C on the grid. Surround each point with a small circle and connect the points. [1]

Example:

27 Plot the data for oxygen consumption by peas at 26°C on the grid. Surround each point with a small triangle and connect the points. [1]

Example:

28 State one conclusion that relates the rate of respiration in germinating peas to temperature. [1]

29 State one reason for including the tube containing the glass beads in each set. [1]

Total Oxygen Consumption (mL)				
Time (in minutes)	Temperature			
	10°C		26°C	
	Beads	Peas	Beads	Peas
0 (Start)	0	0.0	0	0.0
5	0	0.3	0	0.5
10	0	0.6	0	1.0
15	0	0.9	0	1.5
20	0	1.2	0	2.0

30 The greenhouse effect leads to global warming by trapping heat in our atmosphere. Carbon dioxide produced through the burning of coal and oil for industrial processes, power generation, and transportation is one of the main atmospheric gases that contributes to the problem.

Some people have suggested that planting many long-lived trees along the interstate highways in New York and other states could help counteract the greenhouse effect. Explain how this could help. [1]

Base your answers to questions 31 through 34 on the passage below and on your knowledge of biology.

Lyme Disease

Since 1980, the number of reported cases of Lyme disease in New York State has been increasing. The vector (carrier) of Lyme disease is the black-legged tick, *Ixodes scapularis*. The disease is spread from infected animals to ticks that bite these animals. Humans bitten by these ticks may then become infected.

The symptoms of Lyme disease do not always occur immediately after a tick bite. An individual may develop a skin rash several days to weeks after being bitten by a tick. Flu-like symptoms, such as headaches, muscle aches, joint pain, and fever, may also develop. Generally, these symptoms clear up even if the individual does not seek medical help. In some cases, there may be no symptoms other than a sudden onset of arthritis. However, in a small number of cases, if the infection is not treated, it may lead to chronic arthritis, disorders of the heart and nervous system, or in a few cases, death. A blood test can help to confirm a diagnosis, and antibiotics are effective in treating the infection.

People may take preventive action by frequently checking themselves and their pets for ticks, tucking their pant legs into socks when walking through woods or high grass, wearing light-colored clothing to aid in spotting a tick, and using insect repellent.

31 Describe how Lyme disease is transmitted. [1]

32 State one way people might protect themselves from Lyme disease. [1]

33 State two symptoms that may occur if a person has Lyme disease. [2]

34 State one danger of ignoring any symptoms that may develop after a tick bite. [1]

Base your answers to questions 35 through 37 on the information and data table below and on your knowledge of biology.

Twenty-five geranium plants were placed in each of four closed containers and then exposed to the light conditions shown in the data table. All other environmental conditions were held constant for a period of two days. At the beginning of the investigation, the quantity of carbon dioxide (CO_2) present in each container was 250 cm^3 (cubic centimeters). The data table shows the amount of CO_2 remaining in each container at the end of two days.

Changes in CO_2 Levels			
Container	Color of Light	CO_2 (cm^3) at Start	CO_2 (cm^3) After 2 Days
1	blue	250	50
2	red	250	75
3	green	250	200
4	orange	250	150

35 The independent variable in this investigation was the
(1) type of plant
(2) color of light
(3) amount of CO_2 in each container at the beginning of the investigation
(4) number of days needed to complete the investigation

36 State the problem being investigated in this experiment. [1]

37 Identify the source of the carbon used in photosynthesis. [1]

Part C

Base your answers to questions 38 through 40 on the information below and on your knowledge of biology.

An investigation was performed to determine the effects of enzyme X on three different disaccharides (double sugars) at 37°C. Three test tubes were set up as shown in the diagram below.

At the end of 5 minutes, the solution in each test tube was tested for the presence of disaccharides (double sugars) and monosaccharides (simple sugars). The results of these tests are shown in the table below.

Result of Sugar Test			
	Test Tube 1	Test Tube 2	Test Tube 3
Monosaccharide	not present	not present	present
Disaccharide	present	present	not present

38 What can be concluded about the activity of enzyme X from the data table? [1]

39 With only the materials list supplied below and common laboratory equipment, design an investigation that would show how a change in pH would affect the activity of enzyme X. Your design must include a *detailed procedure* and a *data table*. [3]

          Materials
        Enzyme X
        Sugar C Solution
        Indicators
        Substances of various pH values —
            vinegar (acidic)
            water (neutral)
            baking soda (basic)

40 State one safety precaution that should be used during the investigation. [1]

41 Enzyme molecules are affected by changes in conditions within organisms. Explain how a prolonged, excessively high body temperature during an illness could be fatal to humans. your answer must include:
- the role of enzymes in a human [1]
- the effect of this high body temperature on enzyme activity [1]
- the reason this high body temperature can result in death [1]

Base your answers to questions 42 and 43 on the statement below and on your knowledge of biology.

Some internal environmental factors may interfere with the ability of an enzyme to function efficiently.

42 Identify two internal environmental factors that directly influence the rate of enzyme action. [2]

43 Explain why changing the shape of an enzyme could affect the ability of the enzyme to function. [1]

Base your answer to question 44 on the information below and on your knowledge of biology.

Immunization protects the human body from disease. The success of vaccinations can be seen in the fact that smallpox has been eliminated worldwide from the list of common infectious diseases. The only remaining smallpox viruses on Earth are thought to be those kept in certain research laboratories.

The United States is now committed to the goal of immunizing all children against common childhood diseases. However, many parents are choosing not to immunize their children against childhood diseases such as diphtheria, whooping cough, and polio.

For example, the mother of a newborn baby is concerned about having her child receive the DPT (diphtheria, whooping cough, and tetanus) vaccine. Since these diseases are caused by bacteria, she believes antibiotic therapy is a safe alternative to vaccination.

44 Discuss the use of antibiotics and vaccines in the treatment and prevention of bacterial diseases. In your answer be sure to include:
- what is in a vaccine [1]
- how a vaccine promotes immunity [1]
- one advantage of the use of vaccinations to fight bacterial diseases [1]
- one disadvantage of the use of antibiotics to fight bacterial diseases [1]

Genetic Continuity

What do **You** Think?

Genes in Cells

The genes in my brain cells are different from the genes in my liver cells.

The genes in all of my cells are the same and all of them are turned on and making proteins.

The genes that are turned on in my brain are not the same genes as the ones turned on in my liver.

TOPIC 3: Genetic Continuity

Vocabulary

asexual reproduction	egg	replicate
biotechnology	expressed	selective breeding
body cell	genes	sexual reproduction
bond	genetic engineering	sperm
chromosome	genetic recombination	subunit
clone	heredity	template
DNA	mutation	traits

Topic Overview

When two organisms reproduce, their offspring receive genetic instructions, called **genes**, from each parent. The genes determine which traits—or characteristics—each offspring will have. All organisms—whether they are animals, plants, or members of one of the other kingdoms—pass their genetic characteristics along in this manner. Because of this transfer of genetic information, offspring tend to resemble their parents.

Heredity and Genes

Heredity is the passing of genetic information from one generation to the next through reproduction. The hereditary information (**DNA**) is organized in the form of genes located in the **chromosomes** of each cell. Recall that chromosomes, which are found in the cell nuclei, contain the DNA molecules. (See Figure 3-1.) It is the DNA molecules that carry the genetic information of the cell.

A human cell contains many thousands of genes in its nucleus, and each gene carries a separate piece of coded information. The traits inherited by an individual can be determined by one pair of genes or by several pairs of genes. It is also true that a single gene pair can sometimes influence more than one trait. Table 3-1 shows several examples of these variations.

Some traits that an organism inherits are readily observable. These include traits such as hair color, leaf shape, flower scent, and wing structure. The overall structure of the body is also an observable trait that is inherited from the parents. Some children, for example, inherit long, slender toes or large ear lobes.

Other traits are not so obvious. Less obvious traits may involve a defective heart, a single kidney, or

Chromosome

Unwinding

DNA

Figure 3-1. Chromosomes contain DNA: Notice that the chromosome contains one very long double strand of DNA.

Table 3-1. Human Traits Inherited with Different Numbers of Genes

Trait	Number of Gene Pairs Needed to Affect Trait
Cystic fibrosis	Single gene pair
Skin color	Multiple gene pairs
Sickle cell disease	Single gene pair affecting multiple traits

how some of the body's chemicals function. Examples include the ability to produce insulin, the types of receptors present on a cell membrane, and whether an individual can make a particular respiratory enzyme.

Methods of Reproduction

There are two common methods of reproduction: asexual and sexual. The major difference between these two methods is whether one or two parents are involved in producing the offspring. **Asexual reproduction** involves one parent or individual (often a single-celled organism); **sexual reproduction** involves two parents.

Asexual Reproduction In organisms that reproduce asexually, all the genetic instructions (genes) come from one individual or parent. Since the genes are all from one parent, offspring are usually identical to the parent.

Because the coded instructions in their cells are the same as the instructions in their parent's cells, asexually produced offspring are genetically identical to their parents. Identical genetic copies are known as **clones.** Because they are asexually produced, entire populations of bacteria—perhaps millions of cells—may be genetically identical clones.

Sexual Reproduction In organisms that reproduce sexually, two parents are required to produce offspring. Each parent produces sex cells. **Sperm** are the sex cells produced by the male; the **egg** is the sex cell produced by the female. Recall that genes in **body cells**—cells other than sex cells—occur in pairs, but each sex cell contains only one gene from each pair. The offspring that results from sexual reproduction therefore receives half of its genetic information from the female parent (via the egg) and half from the male parent (via the sperm).

Genetic Recombination When a sperm and egg combine to form a new cell with a complete set of genetic instructions, a unique combination of genes results. The term for this is **genetic recombination.** This unique combination of thousands of genes produces an offspring that may resemble either or both parents in many ways but will not be identical to either of them.

Digging Deeper

Sometimes people use the word *gene* when they really mean *allele*. A gene is actually an area or part of a chromosome with coded information about some trait or characteristic of the organism. In many cases, there are two or more ways for this trait to appear. The alternate forms of the genes are the alleles—the actual information contained in the gene.

In pea plants, for example, genes carry information about the color of their seeds. However, the seeds can be either green or yellow. The actual color of the seeds will be determined by the alleles. If the plant has two alleles with genetic instructions for yellow seeds, the seeds will be yellow. If they both have genetic instructions for green, the seeds will be green. However, if there is one allele for yellow and one for green, the seeds will be . . . yellow. In this case, the yellow allele is referred to as the dominant allele.

Review Questions

1. A cell is represented in the diagram below.

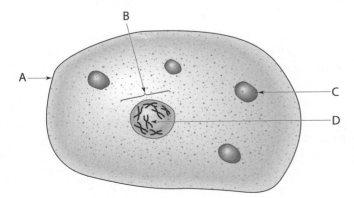

Which statement about the cell is correct?
(1) Structure A synthesizes and secretes cellular products.
(2) Structure B contains chromosomes involved in transmitting genetic information.
(3) Structure C utilizes DNA in the process of photosynthesis.
(4) Structure D is the site of protein synthesis.

2. Which materials are composed of DNA?

(1) proteins
(2) genes
(3) nerve secretions
(4) fluid in vacuoles

3. In an animal cell, DNA is found in the greatest concentration in the

(1) vacuole   (3) nucleus
(2) ribosome   (4) cytoplasm

4. Cystic fibrosis is a genetic disease. Examine the illustration below.

Father with cystic fibrosis
Father has two abnormal genes for the trait

Mother who does not have cystic fibrosis
Mother has ???

Child with cystic fibrosis
Child has two abnormal genes for the trait

The mother's cells most likely contained

(1) a disease-causing virus
(2) one normal gene and one abnormal gene
(3) two normal genes
(4) an abnormal number of chromosomes

5. Bacteria in culture A produce slime capsules around their cell walls. A biologist removed the DNA from some of the bacteria in culture A. He then injected it into bacteria in culture B, which normally do not produce slime capsules. After the injection, bacteria with slime capsules began to appear in culture B. What conclusion could best be drawn from this investigation?

(1) The bacteria in culture A are mutations.
(2) Bacteria reproduce faster when they have slime capsules.
(3) The slime capsules of bacteria in culture B contain DNA.
(4) DNA is most likely involved in the production of slime capsules.

6. The letters in the diagram below represent genes on a particular chromosome.

Gene *B* contains the code for an enzyme that cannot be synthesized unless gene *A* is also active. Which statement best explains why this can occur?

(1) A hereditary trait can be determined by more than one gene.
(2) Genes are made up of double-stranded segments of DNA.
(3) All the genes on a chromosome act to produce a single trait.
(4) The first gene on each chromosome controls all the other genes on the chromosome.

7. Which cell structure includes all of the others?

(1) nucleus   (3) DNA
(2) gene   (4) chromosome

The Genetic Code

The inherited instructions (genes) that are passed from parent to offspring exist in the form of a chemical code. This genetic code, as the chemical code is called, is contained in the DNA molecules of all organisms. DNA molecules resemble a flexible, twisted ladder formed from many smaller repeating units, as shown in Figure 3-2.

DNA Structure

Like other large molecules of life, the DNA molecule is made of thousands of smaller sections called **subunits.** Each subunit has three chemical parts: a sugar, a phosphate, and a base. The subunits vary from one another according to the kind of bases they contain. The bases are represented by the letters A, G, C, and T. The four subunits of DNA molecules are

Figure 3-2. Model of a section of a DNA molecule

arranged in pairs, each subunit forming one side and half of one rung of the "twisted ladder." Base A of one subunit always pairs with the base T of another subunit. In a similar way, base G always pairs with base C. Figure 3-3 shows the details of the structure in an untwisted molecule.

Once the chemical and structural properties of DNA were discovered by scientists, it became clear how this molecule could contain a kind of message that functions as a code. Notice in Figure 3-3 that the sequence of bases on this molecule's left strand, reading from top to bottom, is ACAG. A different molecule might have a sequence in the same position reading GCAG or AACG. The specific sequence of bases in a DNA molecule forms a coded message. The message of a single gene is often a sequence of hundreds of bases. The code for an entire human is estimated to be around 3 billion base pairs!

DNA Replication

The ability to copy the coded instructions in the DNA molecule is critical to its function. Knowing the chemical makeup and structure of DNA molecules gave scientists an immediate clue to how the molecule could be copied, or **replicated**. When scientists realized that the bases used weak chemical bonds to pair with each other, they also realized that the DNA could separate at that weak **bond** to form two single strands. Each single strand became a **template**, or pattern, for a new molecule.

The new molecule was built by attaching new subunits to each template strand, always following the base pairing rules of linking A with T and C with G. The result is the formation of two new molecules whose base pair sequences are exactly alike. See Figure 3-4.

When the structure of DNA was determined, scientists finally understood how cells could copy and transfer information to new cells each time they divide and to new offspring during reproduction. Replication produces two identical copies of the cell's genetic information, each ready to be passed from the parent cell to two offspring cells during cell division. Offspring cells are commonly called daughter cells.

Proteins and Cell Functioning

The work of the cell is carried out by the many types of molecules the cell assembles (synthesizes). Many of these molecules are proteins. Protein molecules are long chains. They are formed from various combinations of 20 kinds of amino acids arranged in a specific sequence.

The sequence of amino acids in a particular protein influences the shape of the molecule. This is because some of the amino acid parts are attracted to (and may bond with) other amino-acid parts of the chain. The connections that form between different parts of the chain cause it to fold and bend in a specific way. The final folded shape

Figure 3-3. Portion of a DNA molecule: A single subunit is shown in black. The bases of the DNA molecule are arranged in pairs, represented here by letters. The base pairs form the rungs of the twisted DNA ladder. The sugar and phosphate of each subunit form the sides of the ladder and are connected by strong chemical bonds. The two sides are held together by weak chemical bonds between the paired bases. (Bonds are the links between atoms that hold molecules together.)

Figure 3-4. The replication of a DNA molecule: This is how cells copy their genetic information to be passed on to two offspring cells when cell division occurs. Both strands are replicated at the same time.

of the protein enables it to carry out its function in the cell. Many proteins made by a cell become enzymes that regulate chemical reactions. Remember that an enzyme can interact with a specific molecule because their shapes correspond.

Some of the proteins made in cells become parts of organelles, such as the cell membrane. Other proteins include the hormone insulin or the many antibodies that bind to antigen molecules on pathogens. The color of your eyes and skin are also the result of proteins synthesized by your body.

The DNA-Protein Connection

Cells store vast amounts of coded information in their genes. Much of this coded information is used to make the thousands of proteins that each cell requires for its functions and the structures it contains. The proteins for these structures and functions are made at the ribosomes according to the directions stored in the cell's DNA code.

Because offspring inherit genetic information from their parents, their cells make many of the same proteins. This is what causes the resemblance between some children and their parents. Making many of the same proteins causes both parent and offspring to form similar structures that give them similar features. One example of a protein-dependent trait includes hair texture (curly, straight, or kinky).

If a parent's DNA carries a code for a protein that does not function correctly, the children may also make that defective protein. For example, an albino does not produce the usual amount of eye, hair, or skin color pigment. The condition is caused by a defect in the gene that codes for the protein that produces color pigment. If albino parents pass this gene to their offspring, they, too, may not produce the normal color pigment.

Protein Synthesis The process of synthesizing a protein from DNA begins in the nucleus. There, the DNA code of a particular gene is "read" by a special enzyme and used to produce a "messenger" molecule. This messenger molecule then travels to the ribosomes in the cell's cytoplasm. With the aid of specialized transfer molecules, amino acids are moved to the ribosomes for assembly into protein. They are bonded in the order specified by the messenger molecule. In this way, the sequence of amino acids of any protein, and therefore its overall structure, is determined by the gene's DNA sequence in the nucleus. The process is shown in Figure 3-5.

Figure 3-5. Protein synthesis: Notice that the DNA in the nucleus supplies the instructions for how to assemble the protein to the messenger molecule. The transfer molecules help assemble amino acids. The assembly process occurs at a ribosome.

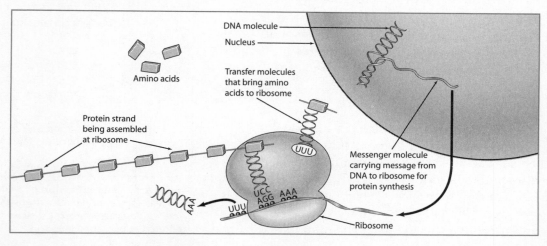

8. In a DNA molecule, the letters A, T, C, and G represent

(1) bases
(2) sugars
(3) starches
(4) proteins

9. The individuality of an organism is determined by the organism's

(1) amino acids
(2) nitrogen bases
(3) DNA base sequence
(4) order of ribosomes

10. What would most likely happen if the ribosomes in a cell were not functioning?

(1) The cell would undergo uncontrolled mitotic cell division.
(2) The synthesis of enzymes would stop.
(3) The cell would produce antibodies.
(4) The rate of glucose transport in the cytoplasm would increase.

11. The diagram below represents a portion of a DNA molecule.

The letter X represents two bases that are

(1) identical and joined by weak bonds
(2) identical and joined by strong bonds
(3) a part of the genetic code of the organism
(4) amino acids used to build folded protein molecules

12. The kinds of genes an organism possesses are dependent on the

(1) type of proteins in the organism's nuclei
(2) sequence of bases in the organism's DNA
(3) number of ribosomes in the organism's cytoplasm
(4) size of the mitochondria in the organism's cells

13. What is the role of DNA molecules in the synthesis of proteins?

(1) They catalyze the formation of bonds between amino acids.
(2) They determine the sequence of amino acids in a protein.
(3) They transfer amino acids from the cytoplasm to the nucleus.
(4) They supply energy for protein synthesis.

14. The diagram at the right represents a molecule of

(1) ATP
(2) protein
(3) carbohydrate
(4) DNA

15. During replication, the strands of a double-stranded DNA molecule separate when the bonds are broken between their paired bases.

Explain why, in terms of the genetic code, it is important that the molecule separate between the bases and not at some other point. [1]

Base your answers to questions 16 and 17 on the diagram below and on your knowledge of biology.

16. Within which organelle does process A occur?

(1) ribosome   (3) vacuole
(2) nucleus   (4) cell membrane

17. Within a living cell, which organelles are directly necessary for process B to occur?

(1) ribosomes   (3) vacuoles
(2) mitochondria   (4) cell membranes

18. In all living cells, DNA controls cellular activities by

(1) determining the order of amino acids in protein molecules
(2) regulating the concentration of molecules on both sides of the cell membrane
(3) varying the rates of starch synthesis
(4) coordinating active and passive transport

19. Which cell organelle indicated in the diagram controls the synthesis of enzymes?

(1) A
(2) B
(3) C
(4) D

20. The sequence of amino acids that makes up a protein molecule is determined by the sequence of

(1) bases in DNA
(2) glucose in DNA
(3) ribosomes in the cytoplasm
(4) chloroplasts in the vacuoles

21. In DNA, the base represented by an A always pairs with the base represented by

(1) A   (2) T   (3) C   (4) G

22. The presence of DNA is important for cellular metabolic activities because DNA

(1) directs the production of enzymes
(2) is a structural component of cell membranes
(3) directly increases the solubility of nutrients
(4) is a major component of the cytoplasm

Mutations

Genes are actually segments of DNA molecules. Any alteration of the DNA sequence is a **mutation**, which changes the normal message carried by the gene. Many mutations involve the substitution of one base for another. This often causes a different amino acid to be placed in a particular position in the growing protein chain. Some mutations involve the insertion of an additional base into an existing DNA sequence. This affects all of the code past the change, just as skipping a blank on the answer sheet for a test can cause all of the remaining answers to be shifted to the next blank, making almost all of them wrong. The deletion of a base from the normal gene sequence would also alter all the code past the change.

Some mutations occur when the bases within a gene are accidentally rearranged. This, too, alters the genetic code. Figure 3-6 shows several ways that DNA can mutate.

All of these alterations are totally random and can occur anywhere along the molecule, making the result of the change almost impossible to predict. However, when a DNA sequence is changed, it is quite likely that the protein it codes for may be assembled incorrectly. If some amino acids are replaced by others, or if their sequence is different, the folding of the protein may be different. Incorrect folding means that the protein's shape would not be normal. This could cause the protein to malfunction. One mutation caused by a substitution is sickle cell disease. (See Figure 3-7.)

Mutations can cause such serious changes that the cell may die. However, if a mutated cell does survive and can replicate its DNA, its changed instructions will be copied and passed on to every cell that develops from it. In sexually reproducing organisms, only mutations found in sex cells can be inherited by the offspring.

Original DNA template strand coding for part of "Protein X"

Mutated strands carrying altered code for "Protein X"

Figure 3-6. Mutation of DNA: The DNA on the left is part of the original template strand that codes for protein X. The four strands on the right show the DNA that would result from several types of mutations.

DNA and Individuality Although an individual's body cells all originally come from a single cell, the body is made up of many types of cells. Each body cell's nucleus—whether it is a nerve cell, skin cell, or bone cell—has a complete set of identical genetic instructions for that individual.

Figure 3-7. **Effects of a substitution mutation:** Normal red blood cells are round. The abnormal cell shapes are due to a substitution mutation that forms a defective protein which changes the cell's shape.

For years, scientists wondered how cells with identical genetic instructions could be so different. The answer is that each kind of cell uses only some of the genetic information it contains. It uses only the instructions it needs to operate its own kind of cell. For instance, information for building all of a person's enzymes is coded in the chromosomes of each cell, but a muscle cell uses only the specific enzymes that are needed by a muscle cell.

Both the internal and external environment of the cell can influence which genes are activated in that cell. Some of this influence may occur during development, leading to the many different types of cells that an organism needs.

The selective activation of genes in a cell may continue as conditions change throughout life. For instance, chemical signals from within the cell or from other cells may activate a particular gene. Hormones are one kind of molecule that can activate parts of a cell's DNA code, leading to the production of a particular protein.

Although genes are inherited, an organism's environment can affect the way some genes are revealed, or **expressed,** in the organism. For example, in some animals, such as the Himalayan rabbit, the outside temperature can cause the activation or inactivation of the genes for fur color. When the rabbit's body area is cold, black fur grows. If the same body area becomes warm, white fur grows instead. (See Figure 3-8.) The environment can also influence human genes. Studies of identical twins (those with identical genetic information) who were raised in different environments show that they have differences that can only be explained by the influence of the environment on gene expression.

Figure 3-8. **Body temperature and fur color in the Himalayan rabbit:** From what you know about the activation and inactivation of the genes for fur color in this animal, why do you think the ears, feet, nose, and tail are black?

Review Questions

23. A dog breeder can determine that the sudden appearance of hairlessness in one of the puppies is a mutation if the dog

(1) is still hairless after 5 years
(2) shows no change in the hairless condition after its diet is changed
(3) develops other conspicuous differences from the parent
(4) is bred and the trait is capable of being inherited

24. Explain how a change in the sequence of nitrogen bases in a DNA molecule could result in a gene mutation. [1]

25. Which mutation could be passed on to future generations?

(1) a gene change in a liver cell
(2) cancer caused by excessive exposure to the sun
(3) a chromosomal alteration during gamete formation
(4) random breakage of a chromosome in a leaf cell of a maple tree

26. Mutations can be transmitted to the next generation if they are present in

(1) brain cells
(2) sex cells
(3) body cells
(4) muscle cells

27. Overexposure of animals to X-rays is dangerous because X-rays are known to damage DNA. A direct result of this damage is cells with

(1) unusually thick cell walls
(2) no organelles located in the cytoplasm
(3) abnormally large chloroplasts
(4) changes in chromosome structure

28. The diagram below shows a portion of a DNA molecule. The base sequence of the unlabeled strand shown in the diagram is *most* likely

(1) G-A-G-T
(2) C-U-C-A
(3) T-C-T-G
(4) G-A-G-U

29. The individuality of an organism is determined by the

(1) sequence of bases in DNA
(2) number of amino acids in a cell
(3) position of ribosomes in the cytoplasm
(4) number of bases in the mitochondria

30. In which situation could a mutation be passed on to the offspring of one of the organisms listed in the data table below?

Data Table	
Name of Organism	Number of Chromosomes in a Body Cell
Human	46
Fruit fly	8

(1) Ultraviolet radiation causes fruit-fly wing cells to undergo uncontrolled division, resulting in cells with 9 chromosomes.
(2) A cell in the wall of the human uterus undergoes a change, resulting in cells with 47 chromosomes.
(3) A primary sex cell in a human forms a sperm that contains 23 chromosomes.
(4) A cell in the ovary of the fruit fly undergoes a chromosomal change that results in 5 chromosomes per egg cell.

31. A change in the sequence of bases in a DNA molecule is most accurately referred to as

(1) an insertion, deletion, or substitution
(2) a chromosomal replication
(3) carbohydrate molecule synthesis
(4) selective breeding

Genetic Engineering

Genetic engineering is a new technology that humans use to alter the genetic instructions in organisms. The idea of altering organisms to have more desirable traits, however, is not new. In fact, **biotechnology**—the application of technology to biological science—has been producing useful products for thousands of years. Cheese and bread are just two examples of "biotech" products made with the use of microbes.

Throughout recorded history, humans have also used **selective breeding**—a process that produces domestic animals and new varieties of plants with traits that are particularly desirable. Many meat products, for example, come from animals that have been bred to contain less fat. In addition, many of the fruits and vegetables we consume have been selectively bred to be larger, sweeter, hardier, or even juicier.

To breed a better plant, farmers might select a bean plant that produces many pods and then crossbreed it with a bean plant that resists fungus infections. The farmers would expect to get seeds that would grow into bean plants with both features.

Gene Manipulation

In recent years, plants and animals have been genetically engineered by manipulating their DNA instructions. The result of this genetic manipulation is new characteristics and new varieties of organisms. Consequently, we have been able to produce plants with many beneficial traits. In one instance, plants can now contain genes with the instructions for making chemicals that kill the insects that feed on them. Scientists have also engineered bacteria that can be used to clean up oil spills or that produce human growth hormone.

The basic method that alters genes in organisms uses special enzymes. These enzymes cut DNA segments in a way that allows the segments to be spliced, or moved and attached, to the DNA of a new organism. Once in the new organism, the transferred genes direct the new organism's cells to make the same protein product as the original organism. For example, when we move a human insulin-producing gene into a bacterial cell, the bacterium—and all its offspring—will produce human insulin. This provides a way to produce large quantities of a hormone at low cost. Genes for other human proteins have also been inserted into bacterial cells, as illustrated in Figure 3-9.

Other enzymes have been found that can be used to make many copies of segments of DNA. These can be used to increase the amount of DNA available from a tiny sample. This procedure is helpful even when only a drop of blood or saliva is found at a crime scene. By copying and re-copying the DNA in the sample, criminal investigators can produce a sample that is large enough to test. The test results may identify or clear suspects.

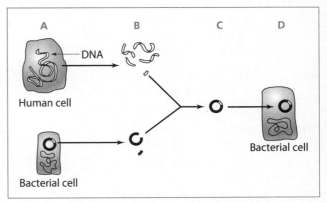

Figure 3-9. Genetic engineering using bacteria: On the left (area A), a special enzyme is used to cut a segment of DNA from a human cell and to also cut open a circular piece of DNA from a bacterial cell. When the piece of human DNA is mixed with the open loop of bacterial DNA (area B), they join to form a closed loop (area C). That loop is then taken up by another bacterial cell (area D). The transformed bacterial cell will produce the protein product of the human DNA segment and that DNA loop will be duplicated and passed to all future offspring.

Applications of Biotechnology

The health care field has much to gain through our increasing knowledge of genetics and biotechnology. New methods enable us to locate and decode genes that cause diseases. Once we have a better understanding of the gene's specific defect, we may be able to develop ways to treat the disease. In some cases, we may be able to alter the DNA in affected cells and cure the person.

Due to mutations in their genes, people with genetic diseases are sometimes unable to produce certain hormones, enzymes, or other body chemicals. At times, we can extract these chemicals from animals, such as sheep and cattle. These extractions, however, can be expensive, and the chemicals may contain contaminants that cause side effects. If scientists can produce the chemicals using genetically engineered organisms, we may be able to economically provide the missing chemicals in a pure enough form to avoid the side effects associated with chemicals obtained from animal sources.

32. Genetic engineering is used in the biotechnology industry to

(1) eliminate all infections in livestock
(2) synthesize hormones such as insulin and human growth hormone
(3) increase the frequency of fertilization
(4) eliminate asexual reproduction

33. Describe two examples of how an understanding of genetics is making new fields of health care (treatment or diagnosis) possible. [1]

34. The insertion of a human DNA fragment into a bacterial cell might make it possible

(1) for the bacterial cell to produce a human protein
(2) to clone the human that donated that DNA fragment
(3) for humans to become immune to an infection by this type of bacteria
(4) to clone this type of bacteria

35. Assume that a section of double-stranded DNA contains 100 base pairs. If 40 of the pairs contain base C, how many of the pairs would contain base A?

Base your answers to questions 36 through 40 on the passage below and on your knowledge of biology.

Advances with Cells and Genes

Recent advances in cell technology and gene transplanting have allowed scientists to perform some interesting experiments, including splicing human DNA into the chromosomes of bacteria. The altered bacteria express the added genes.

Bacteria reproduce rapidly under certain conditions. This means that bacteria with the gene for human insulin could multiply rapidly, resulting in a huge bacterial population capable of producing large quantities of human insulin.

The traditional source of insulin has been the pancreases of slaughtered animals. Continued use of this insulin can trigger allergic reactions in some humans. The new bacteria-produced insulin is actually human insulin. As a result, it does not produce many side effects.

The bacteria used for these experiments are *E. coli*, which are found in the digestive system of humans and many other animals. Some scientists question these experiments and are concerned that the altered *E. coli* may accidentally get into water supplies.

For each of the statements below, write the number 1 if the statement is true according to the passage, the number 2 if the statement is false according to the passage, or the number 3 if not enough information is given in the passage.

36. Transplanting genetic material into bacteria is a simple task. [1]

37. Under certain conditions, bacteria reproduce at a rapid rate. [1]

38. The continued use of insulin from animals may cause harmful side effects in some people. [1]

39. The bacteria used in these experiments are normally found only in the nerve tissue of humans. [1]

40. Bacteria other than *E. coli* are unable to produce insulin. [1]

---

41. A product of genetic engineering technology is represented below.

Bacterial DNA

Human insulin gene

Which substance was needed to join the insulin gene to the bacterial DNA as shown?

(1) a specific carbohydrate
(2) a specific enzyme
(3) hormones
(4) antibodies

42. Explain the following: An individual has a nutrient deficiency due to a poor diet and is missing a specific amino acid. How would this affect the ability of

- the individual's DNA code to replicate itself? [1]
- the cell to synthesize particular proteins? [1]

43. In recent research, the DNA that codes for a different key enzyme was removed from each of three different species of soil bacteria. A new bacterium, containing DNA for all three key enzymes, could be produced by

(1) selection breeding
(2) screening for mutations
(3) genetic engineering
(4) random alteration

Directions

Review the Test-Taking Strategies section of this book. Then answer the following questions. Read each question carefully and answer with a correct choice or response.

Part A

1 Hereditary information for most traits is generally located in
   (1) genes found on chromosomes
   (2) chromosomes found on genes
   (3) the ribosomes of sperm cells
   (4) the mitochondria in the cytoplasm

2 An analysis of chromosomes in a culture containing mutated cells may show the loss of one or more bases making up the chromosome. This type of chromosomal change is known as
   (1) an addition
   (2) an insertion
   (3) a deletion
   (4) a substitution

3 What is the genetic engineering technique in which DNA is transferred from the cells of one organism to the cells of another organism?
   (1) gene splicing   (3) electrophoresis
   (2) chromatography   (4) selective deleting

4 A change that alters the base sequence in an organism's DNA is a
   (1) mutation   (3) clone
   (2) replication   (4) zygote

5 The technique illustrated in the diagram is known as

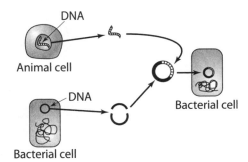

   (1) genetic engineering
   (2) protein synthesis
   (3) internal fertilization
   (4) external fertilization

6 The diagram represents a portion of DNA.

Which DNA strand could correctly pair with the one illustrated?

(1)	(2)	(3)	(4)
G	T	A	C
C	A	T	A
A	G	G	T
T	C	C	G
C	A	T	A
G	T	A	C

7 The diagram illustrates what happens to the fur color of a Himalayan rabbit after prolonged exposure to a low temperature.

The change in fur color is most likely due to
   (1) the effect of heredity on gene expression
   (2) the arrangement of genes on chromosomes
   (3) environmental influences on gene action
   (4) mutations resulting from a change in the environment

Part B

Base your answers to questions 8 and 9 on the diagram below and on your knowledge of biology. The diagram represents part of a double-stranded DNA molecule.

Strand I   Strand II

8 The base sequence of Strand II is most likely
   (1) C–G–G–A   (3) G–T–C–A
   (2) G–A–G–T   (4) T–G–A–C

9 Which event must occur if a nucleus containing this molecule is to undergo mitotic cell division?
   (1) The bonds at point 3 break, and the molecule replicates.
   (2) The molecule separates at point 2, and new bases attach.
   (3) The bonds at point 3 break, and the molecule deletes bases.
   (4) The bonds at points 1, 2, and 4 break, and new sequences of bases form.

10 The technology of genetic engineering has allowed humans to alter the genetic makeup of organisms. Describe one example of such an alteration. [1]

Base your answers to questions 11 and 12 on the information below and on your knowledge of biology.

Some geneticists are suggesting the possibility of transferring some of the genes that influence photosynthesis from an efficient variety of crop plant to a less efficient crop plant. The goal is to produce a new variety with improved productivity.

11 To produce this new variety, the project would most likely involve
   (1) genetic engineering
   (2) a gene mutation
   (3) chromatography
   (4) vaccinations

12 Which technique would most likely be used to produce large numbers of genetically identical offspring from this new variety of plant?
   (1) cloning
   (2) sexual reproduction
   (3) electrophoresis
   (4) selective breeding

Base your answers to questions 13 through 17 on the information and data table below and on your knowledge of biology.

Certain chemicals cause mutations in cells by breaking chromosomes into pieces. Cells containing such broken chromosomes are known as mutated cells. Certain nutrients, such as beta carotene (a form of vitamin A), have the ability to prevent chromosome breakage by such mutagenic chemicals.

The results of an investigation of the effect of beta carotene in preventing chromosome damage are presented in the following data table. In the investigation, varying amounts of beta carotene per kilogram of body weight were added to the diets of hamsters. A mutagenic chemical at a constant dose rate was also added to the diets of the hamsters.

The Effect of Beta Carotene Added to Hamster Diet on Cell Mutation	
Amount of Beta Carotene per Kilogram of Hamster's Body Weight	Percentage of Mutated Cells
0 mg	11.5
20 mg	11.0
30 mg	8.0
40 mg	7.0
50 mg	4.5
75 mg	3.5
100 mg	2.0
150 mg	1.2

Using the information in the data table, construct a line graph on the grid provided. Follow the directions given.

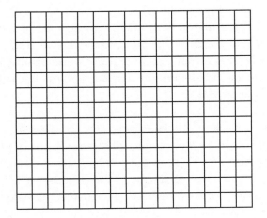

13 Mark an appropriate scale, without any breaks, on each of the axes. [1]

14 Label the axes. [1]

15 Plot the data from the table. Surround each point with a small circle and connect the points. [1]

Example:

16 State an appropriate conclusion for the above experiment regarding the use of beta carotene for the prevention of chromosome damage. Use experimental data to support your conclusion. [1]

17 Vitamins A and E are essential vitamins that can dissolve in oil. A student, knowing this and seeing the above results with beta carotene, suggested that vitamin E will increase the percentage of mutations in the cells of hamsters. State whether or not this is a valid conclusion. Support your statement with an explanation. [1]

Part C

Base your answers to questions 18 through 22 on the passage below and on your knowledge of biology.

Genetic Engineering

Genetic engineering is a technique used by scientists to combine or splice genetic material from different organisms. Gene splicing involves changing the normal base sequences of DNA by removing a section of DNA and introducing another gene. The technique may involve the use of the bacterium *E. coli*. The bacterium has one large chromosome and several small plasmids, which are ring-shaped pieces of DNA found in the cytoplasm.

Genetic engineers have been able to extract plasmids from *E. coli*. Restriction enzymes are used to cut the DNA of the plasmid at designated places in the base sequence. The same enzymes are used to cut a section of human DNA. This section of human DNA is then placed into the space in the cut DNA of the bacterial plasmid. The human DNA codes for the synthesis of a product such as human growth hormone.

The spliced bacterial DNA, which now contains a piece of human DNA, is referred to as a hybrid. This hybridized plasmid is then taken in by *E. coli* cells. When the bacterium reproduces, the hybrid DNA will replicate. The offspring will possess the ability to synthesize the human growth hormone.

18 Describe a bacterial plasmid. [1]

19 Describe a hybrid plasmid. [1]

20 Explain how genetic engineers remove sections from human DNA for splicing into bacterial DNA. [1]

21 State one benefit of gene splicing. [1]

22 Explain why it is not necessary to continue splicing the gene for human growth hormone into *E. coli* once cultures of the bacteria with the spliced gene are established. [1]

Base your answers to questions 23 through 25 on the reading passage below and on your knowledge of biology.

The Plight of the Monarch

Along with producing most of the corn consumed by humans and livestock, the U.S. Corn Belt also produces about half of the monarch butterflies that migrate between Canada and Mexico. During migration, the butterflies mate and lay their eggs. The caterpillars that hatch from these eggs immediately begin to feed on milkweed leaves. This is what monarch butterflies have done successfully for decades. Now it seems that this behavior could be the cause of their extinction.

Cornell University scientists have discovered that the increased use of genetically engineered corn is the problem. Caterpillars feeding on milkweed dusted with pollen from this corn die. The new strain of corn has had the bacterial gene that codes for the production of a toxin referred to as Bt inserted. Bt functions as a natural pesticide and kills European corn borer caterpillars, which are responsible for the destruction of millions of ears of corn every year. The use of Bt corn saves crop growers from having to purchase and apply toxic chemical pesticides.

Originally everyone thought that Bt corn was the answer to many financial, environmental, and health issues associated with pesticide use. However, nearly half of the monarch butterfly caterpillars fed milkweed dusted with Bt corn pollen died within four days during the Cornell University study. None of the caterpillars in the control group died.

23 Corn plants that contain the Bt gene in their cells make the toxin that kills corn borer caterpillars. Explain how the gene enables the plants to make the toxin. [1]

24 Explain why more research is needed to know for sure if corn containing the Bt gene is responsible for the death of monarch butterflies on a large scale. [1]

25 Pollen is the male sex cell. It performs the same role in plants as sperm does in animals. Explain why it is reasonable to expect pollen produced by the genetically engineered corn plants to carry the Bt gene. [1]

---

26 One variety of wheat is resistant to disease. Another variety contains more nutrients of benefit to humans. Explain how a new variety of wheat with disease resistance and high nutrient value could be developed. In your answer, be sure to:
- identify one technique that could be used to combine disease resistance and high nutrient value in a new variety of wheat [1]
- describe how this technique would be carried out to produce a wheat plant with the desired characteristics [1]
- describe one specific difficulty (other than stating that it does not always work) in developing a new variety using this technique [1]

27 Animal cells utilize many different proteins. Discuss the synthesis of proteins in an animal cell. Your answer must include at least:
- the identity of the building blocks required to synthesize these proteins [1]
- the identity of the sites in the cell where the proteins are assembled [1]
- an explanation of the role of DNA in the process of making proteins in the cell [1]

Reproduction and Development

What do **You** *Think?*

Genes and Reproduction

One parent gives you the genes for some traits while the genes for your other traits come from the other parent.

Boys get most of their genes from their dad and girls get most of their genes from their mom.

Both parents contribute genes for each of the traits you have.

TOPIC 4

Reproduction and Development

Vocabulary

asexual reproduction	fetus	sex cell
cloning	gamete	sexual reproduction
development	gene expression	species
differentiation	meiosis	sperm
egg	mitosis	testes
embryo	ovaries	testosterone
estrogen	placenta	uterus
expressed	progesterone	zygote
fertilization	recombination	

Topic Overview

A **species** is a group of closely related organisms that share certain characteristics and can produce new individuals through reproduction. For any species to survive past a single generation, reproduction is essential. All individuals eventually die, but the species continues because individuals reproduce. When individuals reproduce, their offspring begin a period of **development** that ends in adulthood. Once an individual reaches adulthood, it is usually able to reproduce and continue the species for another generation.

Types of Reproduction

Two methods of reproduction are associated with living organisms: asexual and sexual. **Asexual reproduction** involves just one parent and results in one or more offspring that are genetically identical to that parent. **Sexual reproduction** involves two parents and results in offspring that have some genetic material (DNA) from each parent. The result is an organism that may be similar to one or both parents, but is not identical to either.

Asexual Reproduction Organisms that reproduce asexually produce their offspring in a variety of ways. In some cases they merely divide in two, producing two new individuals. (The parent in this case *becomes* the offspring!) Other organisms produce special cells that have a complete set of genetic information, and these individual cells can develop into new members of the species. Still others produce an outgrowth of the body that later detaches to become a separate individual. Many plants can develop from parts that are either broken off intentionally by humans or separated naturally from the parent plant. In every case, organisms produced by asexual reproduction have only one parent, and they have the same genetic information (in the form of DNA) as the parent. Figure 4-1 shows some examples of asexual reproduction.

Figure 4-1. Examples of asexual reproduction: (A) An ameba divides to form two new amebas. (B) A yeast cell divides into two cells that are different sizes but genetically alike. (C) Mold spore cells reproduce the mold. (D, E, and F) Some offspring develop attached to the parent, but later separate to become independent individuals.

Sexual Reproduction In sexual reproduction, offspring receive half of their genes from one parent and half from the other. The genes are carried on chromosomes in **sex cells** (also known as **gametes** or egg or sperm cells), which join in **fertilization.** Each parent supplies half of the genetic information needed to form a complete individual. The **sperm,** which is the sex cell from the father, provides half of the information; the **egg,** which is the sex cell from the mother, provides the other half.

Offspring produced by sexual reproduction combine genes inherited from each parent's gametes. Since an offspring gets only half of its DNA from each parent, it will not be identical to either of its parents. Also, since each offspring gets a unique combination of genes from its parents, it will differ from its <u>siblings</u> (brothers and sisters).

Cloning **Cloning** is a technique that accomplishes the same end result as asexual reproduction. It is a way of making identical genetic copies. For example, if you cut a piece of stem from a plant and it grows roots and develops into a new plant, you have produced a genetically identical copy of the original plant. This could be called a clone of the plant.

Recently, however, it has also been possible to produce clones of animals that ordinarily only reproduce sexually. This is done by inserting a nucleus from a "parent" organism's cell (one that has a complete set of genetic information from that individual) into an egg cell from which the nucleus has been removed. The result is an egg that now contains not 50%, but 100% of the genetic information from a single parent. If this new egg cell with all of its genes can be made to develop normally, the resulting offspring is a clone of the individual that donated the original cell nucleus. (In mammals, the egg would be implanted and develop inside the body of the female.) Cloning has been accomplished with animals as complex as sheep and pigs.

Review Questions

1. Which statement best describes the process of asexual reproduction?
   (1) It involves two parents.
   (2) It requires the combination of sperm and egg.
   (3) It results in variation in the offspring.
   (4) It involves the production of genetic copies.

2. Which statement concerning an organism produced by cloning is correct?
   (1) The clone is genetically identical to its parent.
   (2) The clone has the combined genes of both of its parents.
   (3) The genetic makeup of the clone will be somewhat different from each of its parents.
   (4) The appearance of the clone will be entirely different from that of its parents.

3. A student using a compound light microscope to observe a cell saw a number of threadlike nuclear structures resembling those shown below.

These threadlike structures are composed primarily of
   (1) fat
   (2) glucose
   (3) DNA
   (4) ATP

4. Plants with desirable qualities can be rapidly produced from the cells of a single plant by
   (1) cloning
   (2) gamete fusion
   (3) meiosis
   (4) immune response

5. Asexual reproduction differs from sexual reproduction in that, in asexual reproduction
   (1) new organisms are usually genetically identical to the parent
   (2) the reproductive cycle involves the production of gametes
   (3) nuclei of sex cells fuse to form a zygote
   (4) offspring show much genetic variation

6. Orchid plants reproduce slowly and take many years to produce flowers when grown from seeds. One technique that can be used in genetic research to reproduce rare orchid plants more rapidly is
   (1) sexual reproduction   (3) selective breeding
   (2) fertilization   (4) cloning

7. Some bacteria produce an enzyme known as penicillinase, which prevents their destruction by penicillin. Since these same organisms reproduce asexually, they normally produce offspring that
   (1) can be killed by penicillin
   (2) have an abnormally high rate of mutation
   (3) have variable numbers of chromosomes
   (4) are resistant to penicillin

8. In plants, one way sexual reproduction differs from asexual reproduction is that in sexual reproduction
   (1) more offspring are produced
   (2) more genetic variation is seen in the offspring
   (3) the offspring and the parents are identical
   (4) more offspring survive to maturity

9. A man cuts some stems from several plants that are growing in his garden. He places the stems in wet sand until they grow roots, and then he transplants them to new pots. This method of reproducing plants is most like
   (1) sexual reproduction
   (2) cloning
   (3) natural selection
   (4) fertilization

10. Compared to the offspring of sexual reproduction in animals, the offspring of asexual reproduction will
    (1) show greater variety
    (2) be more resistant to disease
    (3) be genetically identical to the parent
    (4) grow larger

Cell Division

Cell division is the orderly separation of one cell into two. Before a cell divides, the genetic information in the DNA of the cells is duplicated exactly.

The process, by which a cell's genetic material divides, creating two complete sets of the cell's genetic material, is known as **mitosis.** Mitosis produces two cells that each have a full set of identical genes and chromosomes (unless a mutation occurs somewhere along the way).

During mitosis, one copy of the genetic information is distributed to each new cell. As a result, each new cell has all the information it needs to function properly. One-celled organisms make use of mitosis for asexual reproduction. Multicellular organisms mainly use mitosis for growth and for cell replacement and repair.

A second type of cell division is **meiosis.** This process divides the genetic material in a way that results in the production of the sex cells required by organisms that reproduce sexually. Each sex cell has only half the genetic material needed for a cell to function properly.

Mitotic Division/Mitosis

During the process of mitotic cell division, the double-stranded chromosomes that are visible during mitosis split into two identical single strands and move apart to opposite ends of the cell. This process is shown in Figure 4-3.

The process concludes when the cytoplasm divides, resulting in two smaller, but genetically identical, cells. Mitotic cell division in plants is illustrated in Figure 4-4.

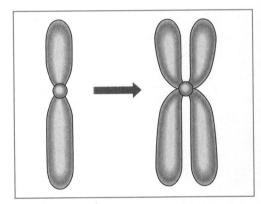

Memory Jogger

Recall that DNA replication makes an identical copy of all the genetic information in the molecule. The replicated strand carries the instructions for the same proteins as in the original strand. When the DNA replicates, it is actually turning a single-stranded chromosome into a double-stranded one. The double-stranded chromosome then has a duplicate set of instructions to pass on to each of two cells, as shown in Figure 4-2.

Figure 4-2. Chromosome duplication resulting from DNA replication: As a result of DNA replication, chromosomes become double-stranded.

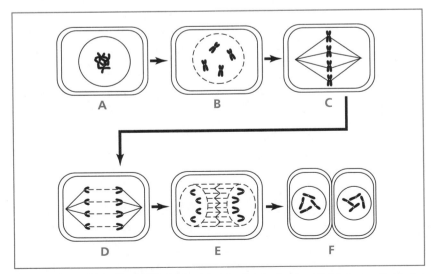

Figure 4-4. Mitotic cell division: The chromosomes in cell A have replicated, forming the double-stranded chromosomes that are finally visible in the cell at stage B. The four chromosomes line up single-file (C). Then the strands separate and move apart (D and E). The final result is two cells (F), each with four single-stranded chromosomes containing identical genetic information in their nuclei.

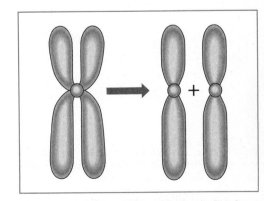

Figure 4-3. Chromosome during mitosis: When cells divide, each double-stranded chromosome separates into two identical single strands.

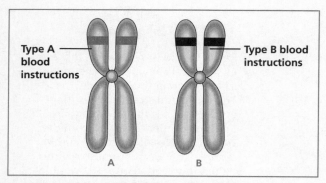

Figure 4-5. Two chromosomes with different information: The two chromosomes of each pair differ in the specific information they carry. For example, chromosome A may have coded gene instructions for type A blood, while the coded gene information on chromosome B may be for type B blood. Information for many other traits coded in the genes of these two chromosomes will be different, too, while some will be the same.

Meiotic Division/Meiosis

The gametes (sperm and eggs) formed during meiotic cell division each have only one half of the organism's genetic information—only one chromosome of each pair that is present in the body cells of that organism. However, a full set of genetic information is needed to produce a complete individual. When sperm and egg combine during **fertilization,** all of the newly paired chromosomes and all of the required genetic information are present in the fertilized egg.

Meiotic division begins with a body cell that has the full number of chromosomes typical of the species. Depending on the species, the cell contains one or more pairs of chromosomes that determine the traits of the organism. Figure 4-5 shows an example.

During the first phase of meiotic division, the double-stranded chromosomes line up in pairs in the center of the cell. The two chromosomes of each pair (still double-stranded) then separate, moving to opposite ends of the cell. Following this separation, the cell divides physically to form two cells.

The second phase involves the division of each of these two new cells. This time, however, the chromosomes line up in single file in the center of each cell. Each chromosome still consists of two strands. The strands separate and move to opposite ends of each of the dividing cells. When the process is complete, four cells have been formed, each having half the number of chromosomes of the organism's body cells. Each contains only one member of each original chromosome pair. Meiotic cell division is illustrated in Figures 4-6 and 4-7.

Figure 4-6. Meiotic cell division in the testes of males: Note the *four double-stranded chromosomes* (two pairs) present in the original cell. The pairs separate from each other during the first division—resulting in *two double-stranded chromosomes* in each of two cells. In the next division, the double-stranded chromosomes separate, leaving each final cell with *two single-stranded chromosomes*. These four cells can develop further into sperm cells in the testes of male individuals.

Egg cell   Nonfunctioning cells

Figure 4-7. Meiotic cell division in the ovaries of females: This process is different from sperm cell formation because the cytoplasm divides unequally in each division, resulting in one large egg cell and three smaller cells that do not function. The egg cell is the one with the most cytoplasm.

Notice that the formation of cells during meiotic division, in which each cell has half the usual number of chromosomes, is very different from the duplication and distribution of a full set of chromosomes that occurs in mitotic division.

Meiotic division in females involves the same number of divisions and chromosome changes as in males. The division of the cytoplasm is where the two differ. The cytoplasm in a cell destined to become an egg cell divides unequally, resulting in one large egg cell and three small nonfunctioning cells. Meiotic division in females is shown in Figure 4-7.

Meiosis as a Source of Variation The events that occur during meiosis do more than simply divide chromosomes into smaller sets and form smaller cells. Meiosis is responsible for much of the genetic variation among the sex cells of each individual. For example, the two members of each pair of chromosomes carry different ways of expressing many of the organism's traits, so the way the different pairs randomly line up *in relation to other pairs* leads to many possible combinations in the sex cells that result. Two combinations are shown in Figure 4-8.

Another way variation can arise is by the exchange of parts of chromosomes, which occurs as they pair up during the first division. The process is sometimes called crossing-over. The result is shown in Figure 4-9. After separation, each set is unique. This means that there are no two sperm or egg cells, even from the same parent, that are alike. Each time a sperm and egg combine, a unique combination of genetic information results.

Figure 4-8. Two equally likely combinations of chromosomes lined up for meiotic division: A pair of chromosomes can be arranged in two ways when they pair up at the start of meiosis. This helps increase genetic variation. How many combinations do you see in the gametes? How would more pairs of chromosomes affect the number of possible arrangements?

Figure 4-9. Result of exchanging parts between chromosomes: When chromosomes line up in pairs during meiosis (Step 1), their strands may connect or cross over (Step 2) and then separate in a way that parts are exchanged. All four strands now carry different combinations of information (Step 3).

Table 4-1. Summary of Mitotic and Meiotic Cell Division		
Points of Comparison	**Mitotic Division**	**Meiotic Division**
Number of cell divisions	One	Two
Exchange of genetic material between chromosomes	No	Yes
Number of functioning cells produced from original	Two	Four sperm (in males) or one egg (in females)
Genetic makeup of final cells produced	Same as original	Highly variable gametes produced, each containing half of the genetic information of the original
Function of cells produced in multicellular organisms	Growth or replacement of body cells	Combine to form the zygote for reproduction

11. When complex plants are produced by cloning, which process is most directly involved?

(1) mitotic cell division
(2) meiotic cell division
(3) gamete production
(4) sperm cell fertilization

12. If a lobster loses a claw, it is capable of growing a new one. What process makes this possible?

(1) meiosis   (3) sexual reproduction
(2) fertilization   (4) mitosis

13. Organisms that reproduce asexually usually do so by a form of cell division called

(1) meiosis   (3) gamete formation
(2) mitosis   (4) sperm formation

14. A normal body cell of a fruit fly contains eight chromosomes. Each normal gamete of this organism contains

(1) four chromosomes as a result of meiosis
(2) four chromosomes as a result of mitosis
(3) eight chromosomes as a result of meiosis
(4) eight chromosomes as a result of mitosis

15. The process of mitotic cell division normally results in the production of

(1) four cells with half the number of chromosomes as the parent
(2) two cells with the same number of chromosomes as the parent
(3) two cells with only one chromosome from each parent
(4) one cell with a replicated set of matched chromosomes

16. Each of the two daughter (or offspring) cells that result from the normal mitotic division of the original parent cell contains

(1) the same number of chromosomes but different genes than the parent cell
(2) the same number of chromosomes and genes identical to those of the parent cell
(3) one half of the number of chromosomes but different genes than those of the parent cell
(4) one half of the number of chromosomes and genes identical to those of the parent cell

17. All types of asexual reproduction involve the process known as

(1) mitosis   (3) meiotic division
(2) fertilization   (4) aging

18. The diagrams below represent the sequence of events in a cell undergoing normal meiotic cell division.

- How many cells will finally be produced? [1]
- How many chromosomes will be in each cell? [1]
- Sketch one of the final cells, showing its chromosomes. [1]

19. The species chromosome number of orangutans is 48. Which diagram represents normal fertilization in orangutans?

20. Which process is represented in the following photographs?

(1) mitotic cell division   (3) fertilization
(2) zygote formation   (4) recombination

21. If the sperm cells of a fish have 12 chromosomes, how many chromosomes would be found in the cells forming the scales of the fish?

(1) 6   (3) 24
(2) 12   (4) 48

Zygote Formation During fertilization, the gametes unite to form a **zygote**—a cell that contains all of the genetic information needed by the offspring. This process is known as **recombination,** since the genes from both parents recombine when fertilization occurs. Since a sex cell contains a unique combination of genetic material, the result of the random combination of any sperm and egg explains the variation found in offspring produced by sexual reproduction. This variation plays a key role in evolutionary change and species survival.

The zygote contains all the information necessary for growth, development, and eventual reproduction of the organism. The zygote divides by mitosis to form a multicellular organism. Fertilization, zygote formation, and some early mitotic divisions that occur in development are shown in Figure 4-10.

Early Development During the early stages of development, the cells that are formed by mitotic division begin to undergo **differentiation,** which simply means that they become different from one another. This leads to the formation of specialized cells, which form the tissues, and then the organs, of multicellular organisms.

In an **embryo,** an organism in an early stage of development, all the genetic information in each cell starts out the same. However, different genes are activated or deactivated in certain cells, causing them to make only some of the many proteins they are capable of synthesizing. As a result, these cells become different from others, and may develop into skin cells, muscle cells, or any of the other specialized cells of the organism. The activation or inactivation of genes can be due to environmental influences from within the cell, from surrounding cells, or from outside the organism.

When a gene is actively producing its protein, scientists say that the gene is **expressed.** There is much evidence that **gene expression,** which is the result of activated genes, can be modified through interaction with the environment. For example, fruit flies that have genes to develop curly wings will develop straight wings instead, if they are raised in a cooler than normal environment. Another example of an environmentally produced gene modification is a plant grown without light. Such a plant is white instead of green, because sunlight is needed to stimulate the gene that produces chlorophyll.

Figure 4-10. Fertilization, zygote formation, and early development: Note that all cell divisions here are by MITOTIC division.

Review Questions

22. An exact duplication of the complete set of chromosomes of a cell, followed by the separation of these duplicate sets into two new cells, is known as

    (1) mitotic cell division   (3) meiotic cell division
    (2) zygote formation   (4) fertilization

23. New cells are produced within the uterus as a direct result of

    (1) gamete formation
    (2) meiotic cell division
    (3) mitotic cell division
    (4) ecological succession

24. The data table below summarizes the results of an experiment using primrose plants grown under different temperature conditions.

Data Table: Primrose Color Under Two Growing Conditions		
Flower Color	Temperature of 20°C	Temperature of 31°C
Color coded in DNA	Red White	Red White
Actual color expressed	Red White	White White

Which conclusion can be drawn from this data table?

(1) Color in primroses is determined only by gene action.
(2) Many traits are not inherited.
(3) Gene exchanges only occur when the plants are grown at lower temperatures.
(4) There is an interaction between environment and heredity.

---

25. When organisms reproduce sexually, the species number of chromosomes is maintained. This can be demonstrated with a diagram like the one below. Complete the diagram by filling in the blanks with the appropriate information.

Organism with 10 chromosomes in each body cell

Process A

Name of process A: _____

Gamete cell

Number of chromosomes in gamete cell: _____

Process B

Name of process B: _____

Zygote

Number of chromosomes in zygote: _____

Process C

Name of process C: _____

New multicellular organism

Number of chromosomes in new multicellular organism: _____

Base your answers to questions 26 through 29 on the diagrams below and on your knowledge of biology.

Diagram A represents the chromosomes in the nucleus of the body cell of a worm. Diagrams B through G represent chromosomal arrangements that may occur in other cells produced by this worm.

26. If meiosis failed to occur in both male and female worms, the zygote nucleus would resemble diagram

(1) E   (2) G   (3) C   (4) D

27. If genes were exchanged between a single pair of chromosomes during gamete formation, the gamete nucleus would most closely resemble diagram

(1) F   (2) B   (3) C   (4) G

28. The nucleus of a normal zygote formed when fertilization occurs in this species would most likely resemble diagram

(1) E   (2) F   (3) C   (4) D

29. The nucleus of a mature gamete from a female worm would most likely resemble diagram

(1) E   (2) B   (3) C   (4) D

---

30. In human females, gametes are produced in the

(1) uterus   (3) ovaries
(2) testes   (4) estrogen

31. Complex organisms produce sex cells that unite during fertilization forming a single cell known as

(1) an embryo   (3) a clone
(2) a gamete   (4) a zygote

Human Reproduction and Development

Human reproduction and development are carried out by specialized organs. The function of these organs is regulated by hormones from the endocrine system. In humans, as in nearly all mammals, fertilization and development occur internally—within the mother's body. Reproductive organs in other mammals are similar in appearance and function.

Female Reproductive System The human female reproductive system is organized to produce gametes, to support internal fertilization and development, to exchange materials through the placenta, and to provide milk to the offspring.

In human females, the **ovaries** produce egg cells (female gametes) and the hormones **estrogen** and **progesterone.** These hormones are associated with sexual development and the reproductive process. The ovaries are located near the open ends of tubes called <u>oviducts</u> (egg ducts). The egg cell can be fertilized in the oviduct if sperm are present. The oviducts lead to the **uterus,** where the embryo develops into a fetus. The main parts of the female reproductive system are illustrated in Figure 4-11.

After the fertilized egg sinks into the thickened wall of the uterus, a placenta begins to form. The **placenta** is the organ responsible for the passage (by diffusion) of nutrients and oxygen from the mother's blood to the fetus. Wastes from the fetus also diffuse to the mother's blood through the placenta. During birth, the muscular uterus undergoes a series of contractions that eventually push the baby out of the mother's body. The early events of pregnancy are shown in Figure 4-12.

Male Reproductive System The **testes** of the male reproductive system are the organs that produce sperm cells. The testes also produce the hormone **testosterone,** which is associated with male sexual development and reproduction. Other structures associated with the male reproductive system produce the fluids and nutrients that are needed for the proper function and delivery of the male gametes to the female reproductive system. The essential parts of the human male reproductive system are shown in Figure 4-13.

Figure 4-12. **Early events of pregnancy:** The egg released by the ovary travels down the oviduct where fertilization occurs. Mitotic divisions of the zygote begin as it continues to the uterus, where the developing embryo sinks into the uterine wall, and the placenta forms. The placenta will supply essential materials and remove wastes throughout the rest of the pregnancy.

Table 4-2. The Functions of the Parts of the Human Female Reproductive System	
Structure	**Function**
Ovary	Produces egg cells; releases the hormones estrogen and progesterone
Oviduct	Site of fertilization; carries egg to uterus
Uterus	Site where embryo and fetus develop in association with placenta
Birth canal (vagina)	Site where sperm enter and swim to egg in oviduct; passageway for the birth of baby

Figure 4-13. Two views of the essential parts of the human male reproductive system and other structures: View A is from the side; View B is from the front.

A
- Urinary bladder
- Reproductive glands
- Penis
- Testes

B
- Urinary bladder
- Reproductive glands
- Testes
- Penis

Hormonal Regulation The male reproductive system and other male characteristics, such as facial hair and a deep voice, that develop as sexual maturity is reached are influenced by several hormones, including testosterone from the testes. The development of the female reproductive system and female features, such as breast development and widening of the hips, also involves several important hormones, such as estrogen and progesterone.

Once sexual maturity is reached, females begin a regular cycle of about 28 days, during which an egg is released on about day 14. The timing of the events of this cycle is regulated by two hormones from the ovaries, along with several others from an endocrine gland in the brain. Figure 4-14 illustrates the changes in the level of several hormones associated with regulating this monthly cycle. The cycle varies slightly from individual to individual.

Although the interactions of the hormones are quite complex, estrogen and progesterone play important roles in the female reproductive cycle. Estrogen from the ovaries influences the sexual development of females. Together, estrogen and progesterone influence the preparation of the lining of the uterus so that a fertilized egg that embeds itself there can develop normally. Progesterone also maintains the uterine lining throughout pregnancy. For this reason, progesterone is often called the hormone of pregnancy. At the end of the cycle, if an egg is not fertilized, the levels of estrogen and progesterone decrease, and the lining of the uterus breaks down. Then the cycle begins again.

Figure 4-14. Hormones and events associated with the monthly reproductive cycle in human females: Notice the rise and fall in hormone levels at various times. These changes influence such events as the release of the egg from the ovary, the preparation of the uterus for a possible pregnancy, and the breakdown of the uterine lining if no pregnancy occurs. Remember that the timing of this cycle is NOT the same for everyone.

Human Development As with most other mammals, embryonic development continues in the uterus. Figure 4-15 shows some of the features of the uterus during pregnancy.

During the first part of pregnancy, cells continue to divide by mitotic division and begin to differentiate, forming tissues and organs. The placenta and a fluid-filled sac that cushions and protects the developing embryo both form at this time, too. After about two months, when all the major organs have begun to form, the embryo is called a **fetus.**

During the first few months, when essential organs are forming in the embryo, things can go wrong. Problems associated with either the embryo's inherited genes or the mother's exposure to various harmful environmental factors can affect the embryo. Harmful environmental factors that a woman should avoid at any time during pregnancy include alcohol, drugs, and tobacco. Use of these can lead to the birth of a baby with brain damage, drug addiction, and/or low birth weight and the problems associated with it. An embryo or fetus may also be harmed if the mother has a poor diet, is exposed to certain toxic substances, or gets certain infections, such as German measles or AIDS.

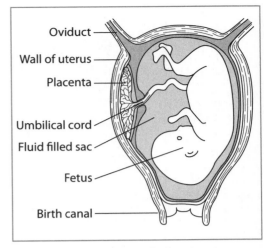

Figure 4-15. **The uterus during pregnancy**

After birth, cell differentiation and body growth continue until adulthood. During adulthood, the structures of the body slowly begin to age. Eventually, the organism weakens and dies. This process of birth, growth, development, aging, and death is a predictable pattern that applies not just to humans, but to all organisms.

Applications of Reproductive Technology

Recent discoveries by scientists have greatly changed the way we can deal with many problems involving the reproduction of humans as well as plants and other organisms. The knowledge we have gained has a variety of agricultural, ecological, and medical applications.

In the field of agriculture, scientists have produced plants that are resistant to insects, weed killers, and even frost. Such altered plants can then be cloned to produce thousands of genetically identical offspring. Using artificial insemination, scientists can generate hundreds of offspring from one farm animal. They can also freeze the sperm or fertilized eggs of an animal and transport them to animals thousands of miles away, at far less cost than transporting the animals themselves.

In the field of ecology, reproductive technology is being used to help build up populations of endangered species. Embryos from the endangered species have been transplanted into related species, who later give birth to offspring that are no different than they would be if they developed in the bodies of the endangered animals themselves. Also, hormones of insects that regulate their reproduction and development have been studied in an attempt to find ways to control insects without using poisonous chemicals.

In the field of medicine, recent scientific discoveries have led to new ways of dealing with reproductive problems in humans, other animals, and plants. Some women cannot become pregnant because of problems with their hormones, ovaries, or other parts of their reproductive systems. Reproductive technologies have enabled doctors to help infertile women become pregnant by using hormone therapy to adjust their hormones to normal levels. Sometimes doctors can extract several eggs from a woman's ovaries and fertilize them with sperm in a laboratory dish. When these

Figure 4-16. **Obtaining fetal cells and fluids during pregnancy:** Biochemical studies and chromosome analysis of the fetus can be done with cells and fluids removed during pregnancy.

fertilized eggs are implanted in the woman's uterus, a successful pregnancy may result.

Ultrasound and miniature video cameras allow doctors to view ovaries, oviducts, and other reproductive structures, or even a developing fetus, to determine if or where problems exist. Methods have also been developed to retrieve fetal cells that are present in the fluids around the developing fetus. (See Figure 4-16.) Doctors can then analyze the cells for chromosome abnormalities and the fluids for biochemical deficiencies that may threaten the health or development of the fetus.

Review Questions

32. What substances are involved in controlling the production of sperm and eggs in humans?

(1) vitamins   (3) starches
(2) hormones   (4) minerals

33. Which practice is essential to good prenatal care?

(1) increased egg production
(2) frequent dieting
(3) avoidance of drugs
(4) intake of antibiotics

34. Which part of the human male reproductive system produces hormones that influence the development of male sex characteristics?

(1) penis   (3) gametes
(2) testes   (4) ovaries

35. The diagram below represents a sequence of events in a human ovary.

The process that occurs between stage A and stage B is known as

(1) egg formation   (3) mitotic cell division
(2) sperm formation   (4) cell recombination

36. The diagram below represents a series of events that takes place in the life cycle of humans.

Which term best describes the event taking place in the box labeled X?

(1) fertilization   (3) meiosis
(2) immune response   (4) protein synthesis

Base your answers to questions 37 through 41 on the diagram below and on your knowledge of biology. The diagram represents the human female reproductive system.

37. Fertilization usually occurs within structure

(1) A   (2) B   (3) C   (4) D

38. A placenta normally develops in structure

(1) A   (2) B   (3) C   (4) D

39. The structure that produces estrogen and progesterone is

(1) A   (2) B   (3) C   (4) D

40. The structure that produces egg cells is

    (1) A   (2) B   (3) C   (4) D

41. Shortly after implantation, tissue from the embryo normally grows into the wall of

    (1) A   (2) B   (3) C   (4) D

Base your answers to questions 42 through 44 on the diagram below and on your knowledge of biology. The diagram represents the human male and female reproductive systems.

42. Gametes are produced in

  (1) A, only   (3) both A and B
  (2) B, only   (4) neither A nor B

43. Estrogen and progesterone are produced in

  (1) A, only   (3) both A and B
  (2) B, only   (4) neither A nor B

44. A substance is produced that influences both the reproductive cycle and the development of sex characteristics in

  (1) A, only   (3) both A and B
  (2) B, only   (4) neither A nor B

---

45. In humans and other mammals, nutrients are transferred from the mother's bloodstream to the embryo's bloodstream across the

  (1) placenta   (3) ovary
  (2) uterus   (4) intestine

46. Which substance is a waste that would normally diffuse across the placenta from the embryo to the mother?

  (1) glucose   (3) amino acid
  (2) oxygen   (4) carbon dioxide

47. The egg of a mammal is smaller than that of a bird because the embryo of the mammal obtains its nutrients from the

  (1) placenta through the process of diffusion
  (2) mammary glands of the mother
  (3) blood of the mother when it mixes with the blood of the embryo
  (4) yolk stored in the uterus of the mother

Base your answers to questions 48 and 49 on the diagram below, which represents an experiment, and on your knowledge of biology.

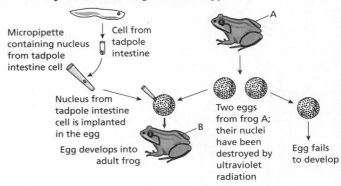

48. An inference that can be made from this experiment is that

  (1) adult frog B will have the same genetic traits as the tadpole
  (2) adult frog A can develop only from an egg and a sperm
  (3) fertilization must occur in order for frog eggs to develop into adult frogs
  (4) the nucleus of a body cell fails to function when transferred to other cell types

49. Other scientists substituted a nucleus from a frog sperm cell and no adult frog developed. Explain why a sperm cell nucleus would not work in this procedure. [1]

Base your answers to questions 50 through 52 on the information below and on your knowledge of biology.

Some women have a blockage in that portion of their reproductive tract where fertilization of the egg cell would normally occur. *In vitro* fertilization is a technique that has been developed to make it possible for such women to bear their own children. This technique involves fertilizing an egg in a sterile petri dish and then implanting the developing embryo into the mother.

50. To ensure that the mother will have mature egg cells available for *in vitro* fertilization, she must be treated with chemicals that regulate her reproductive cycle. Identify these chemicals that regulate the female reproductive cycle. [1]

51. Egg cells for *in vitro* fertilization must be surgically removed from the mother. Identify the structure in the body of the mother that is the source for these egg cells. [1]

52. An embryo that developed from *in vitro* fertilization would be implanted in the mother's

  (1) ovary   (2) uterus   (3) stomach   (4) placenta

Practice Questions
for the New York Regents Exam

Directions

Review the Test-Taking Strategies section of this book. Then answer the following questions. Read each question carefully and answer with a correct choice or response.

Part A

1 Compared to the number of chromosomes in a normal human body cell, the number of chromosomes in a normal sperm cell is
   (1) the same   (3) half as great
   (2) twice as great   (4) four times as great

2 Children born to the same parents are usually very different from each other. These differences result primarily from the process of
   (1) mitotic division
   (2) meiosis
   (3) asexual reproduction
   (4) cloning

3 Human growth and sexual development are controlled by
   (1) nerves   (3) the digestive system
   (2) hormones   (4) the excretory system

4 The diagram below represents the human male reproductive system.

If structure X were cut and tied off at the line, which change would occur immediately?
   (1) Hormones would no longer be produced.
   (2) Sperm would no longer be produced.
   (3) Sperm would be produced but no longer released from the body.
   (4) Urine would be produced but no longer released from the bladder

Base your answers to question 5 through 7 on the diagram below, which represents a stage in human development.

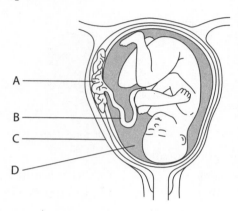

5 The exchange of oxygen, food, and wastes between mother and fetus occurs at
   (1) A   (3) C
   (2) B   (4) D

6 What is the function of the fluid labeled D?
   (1) nourishment
   (2) protection
   (3) excretion
   (4) respiration

7 The structure labeled C, within which development occurs, is known as the
   (1) birth canal   (3) ovary
   (2) uterus   (4) placenta

---

8 Which is arranged in the correct sequence?
   (1) fertilization → embryo development → meiosis → birth
   (2) embryo development → meiosis → fertilization → birth
   (3) meiosis → fertilization → embryo development → birth
   (4) fertilization → meiosis → embryo development → birth

74 Topic 4: Reproduction and Development

9 The diagram at the right represents a cell that will undergo mitosis.

Which of the diagrams best illustrates the daughter cells that result from a normal mitotic cell division of the parent cell shown?

(1)

(2)

(3)

(4)

Part B

Base your answers to questions 10 through 14 on the diagram below, which shows some events in the human female reproductive cycle, and on your knowledge of biology.

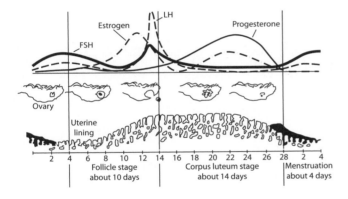

10 During which part of this cycle does the breakdown of the thickened uterine lining occur?
(1) ovulation
(2) corpus luteum stage
(3) menstruation
(4) follicle stage

11 On or about which day is the egg released from the ovary?
(1) day 8
(2) day 14
(3) day 20
(4) day 28

12 What is the average length of this reproductive cycle?
(1) 32 days   (3) 14 days
(2) 28 days   (4) 4 days

13 The hormone FSH stimulates the development of a follicle in the ovary of a human female. As the follicle develops, it secretes estrogen. A high level of estrogen decreases the secretion of FSH. This mechanism is an example of
(1) gamete development
(2) cell differentiation
(3) positive feedback
(4) negative feedback

14 Which hormones are secreted by the ovaries?
(1) progesterone and estrogen
(2) FSH and progesterone
(3) FSH and LH
(4) LH and estrogen

15 Compare the number of chromosomes present in the offspring with the number of chromosomes present in the parent organism in the process of cloning. [1]

Base your answers to questions 16 through 19 on the passage below and on your knowledge of biology.

Some researchers state that the level of a particular hormone present in the bloodstream of a pregnant woman may be used to predict whether birth will occur prematurely, on time, or late. During a study involving 485 pregnant women, the level of corticotropin-releasing hormone (CRH) was measured during weeks 16 through 20 of the usual 40-week gestation (development) period. A comparison of these hormone levels to times of birth indicated that women who delivered prematurely (less than 37 weeks) had an average of 3.6 times more CRH than those who gave birth on time.

CRH, a hormone produced by a hormone-secreting section of the brain called the hypothalamus, aids in regulating the secretion of hormones produced by the adrenal glands. CRH is also secreted by the placenta. Secretion of CRH by the placenta usually begins early in the second trimester of pregnancy. The level continues to increase dramatically as the delivery date approaches. For most of the pregnancy, another protein molecule binds to CRH, blocking its action. Researchers suggest that when CRH levels rise high enough to counteract the blocking protein, labor begins.

The placenta has a regulatory role over activities in the body of the mother during pregnancy. Secretions of placental estrogen and progesterone begin after the first few weeks. From the third to the ninth month, the placenta supplies these hormones at levels necessary to maintain pregnancy. Progesterone inhibits the uterine contractions necessary for delivery. It has been suggested that cortisol, an adrenal hormone released by the fetus, overcomes the inhibiting effects of progesterone as the level of progesterone drops toward the end of gestation. Also, at this time, oxytocin, a hormone synthesized by the hypothalamus of the mother, is released, stimulating uterine contractions and the onset of labor.

Although it is still not known whether CRH determines the length of pregnancy, researchers expect that experiments to lower CRH levels to prevent premature labor are not far off.

16 According to the passage, which structures play a role in initiating the birth process at the end of the gestation period?
   (1) adrenal glands and ovaries
   (2) uterus and ovaries
   (3) hypothalamus and placenta
   (4) placenta and zygote

17 In humans, the length of the period of gestation is usually
   (1) 120 days
   (2) 140 days
   (3) 250 days
   (4) 280 days

18 According to the passage, the release of cortisol by the adrenal gland of the fetus causes
   (1) a decrease in CRH levels in the blood of the mother
   (2) a decrease in the inhibiting effects of progesterone
   (3) contractions of the ovaries
   (4) the secretion of progesterone

19 Explain how the placenta controls certain activities that occur during pregnancy. [1]

20 An incomplete diagram of meiosis in the ovary of an animal is shown below.

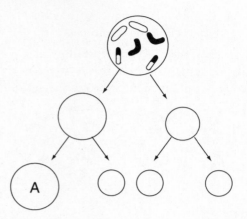

On the diagram below, draw in the chromosomes of cell A. Your drawing should show the usual result of the process of meiosis. [1]

Base your answers to questions 21 and 22 on the diagram below and on your knowledge of biology.

21 State why Process 2 is necessary in sexual reproduction. [1]

22 State *one* difference between the cells produced by Process 1 and the cells produced by Process 3. [1]

Directions (23–25): The diagrams below represent organs of two individuals. The diagrams are followed by a list of sentences. For each phrase in questions 23 through 25, select the sentence from the list below that best applies to that phrase and record its number.

Individual A　　　　**Individual B**

Sentences

1. The phrase is correct for both Individual *A* and Individual *B*.
2. The phrase is not correct for either Individual *A* or Individual *B*.
3. The phrase is correct for Individual *A*, only.
4. The phrase is correct for Individual *B*, only.

23 Contains organs that produce gametes [1]

24 Contains organs involved in internal fertilization [1]

25 Contains a structure in which a zygote divides by mitosis [1]

---

26 Which activity most directly involves the process represented in the diagram below?

(1) a gamete reproducing sexually
(2) a white blood cell engulfing bacteria
(3) a zygote being produced in an ovary
(4) an animal repairing damaged tissue

Part C

27 Early in the 1960s, many pregnant women took the drug thalidomide. Women who took thalidomide during their first three months of pregnancy gave birth to babies with severe birth defects. The babies typically had deformities of their arms and legs. Women who took thalidomide later in their pregnancies gave birth to normal babies.

Explain why the babies born to mothers taking thalidomide during their first few months of pregnancy suffered from birth defects while the others did not. [1]

28 Describe how the human fetus obtains food and oxygen during its development. In your explanation be sure to include:
- a description of how the food and oxygen move from the mother to the fetus [1]
- an explanation of the role of the placenta in this process [1]

29 The production of a normal baby involves protecting the developing embryo from harmful environmental factors. State three ways in which the pregnant woman could avoid exposing the developing embryo to environmental risks. [3]

30 The diagram below shows some steps involved in preparing tissue cultures in plants.

Compare the genetic makeup of the offspring plants that are transferred to the soil to that of the parent plant that provided the stem pieces. [1]

31 The process of meiosis followed by fertilization is necessary to maintain the species chromosome number of a sexually reproducing species. For instance, a species with 24 chromosomes in each body cell normally has offspring that also have 24 chromosomes in their body cells.

Explain the specific way that meiotic cell division and fertilization interact to help maintain the species chromosome number. [1]

Base your answers to questions 32 and 33 on the information below and on your knowledge of biology.

It is possible to collect human sperm and to use this sperm later to fertilize eggs in a process called artificial insemination. The collected sperm samples are frozen and stored in a sperm bank until needed. When a woman makes use of a sperm bank, she requests sperm from a donor with the physical features she wants. The name of the donor is not revealed. The artificial insemination process involves placing the sperm in the woman's body and allowing fertilization to occur in the normal manner.

32 A woman whose husband cannot produce sperm becomes pregnant through artificial insemination. Describe how the DNA of the baby will compare with the DNA of the woman and her husband. [1]

33 If the woman were given sperm from the same donor for three different pregnancies and she had three daughters, would the three girls look alike or would they be different? Support your answer with a biological explanation. [1]

34 Scientists have successfully cloned sheep and cattle for several years. A farmer is considering the advantages and disadvantages of having a flock of sheep cloned from a single individual. Discuss the issues the farmer should take into account before making a decision. Your response should include:
- how a cloned flock would be different from a noncloned flock [1]
- one advantage of having a cloned flock [1]
- one disadvantage of having a cloned flock [1]

- one reason that the farmer could not mate these cloned sheep with each other to increase the size of his flock [1]
- one reason that the offspring resulting from breeding these sheep with an unrelated sheep would not all be the same [1]

35 Compare asexual reproduction to sexual reproduction. In your comparison, be sure to include:
- which type of reproduction results in offspring that are usually genetically identical to the previous generation and explain why this occurs [1]
- one other way these methods of reproduction differ [1]

36 A human is a complex organism that develops from a zygote. Briefly explain some of the steps in this developmental process. In your answer be sure to:
- explain how a zygote is formed [1]
- compare the genetic content of the zygote to that of a body cell of the parents [1]
- identify one developmental process involved in the change from a zygote into an embryo [1]
- identify the structure in which fetal development usually occurs [1]
- identify two factors that can affect fetal development and explain how each factor affects fetal development [1]

37 Define fertilization and describe the resulting development of a human embryo. In your answer, be sure to include a definition of fertilization and the functions of the ovary, uterus, and placenta. Circle the terms *fertilization, ovary, uterus,* and *placenta* in your description. [4]

Base your answers to questions 38 and 39 on the information below and on your knowledge of biology. The reproductive cycle in a human female is not functioning properly. An imbalance of hormones is diagnosed as the cause.

38 Identify one hormone directly involved in the human female reproductive system that could cause this problem. [1]

39 Explain why some cells in a female's body respond to reproductive hormones while other cells do not. [1]

Evolution

What do **You** *Think?*

Evolution

Natural selection is a process that allows the best adapted of the species to survive and reproduce.

Evolution is based on natural selection, which is very, very slow.

Natural selection is a process that gives organisms what they need when they need it to survive and reproduce.

Evolution explains how life originated on Earth millions of years ago.

5 Evolution

Vocabulary

adaptive value	genetic variation	natural selection
evolution	geologic time	overproduction
extinction	mutation	theory
fossil record		

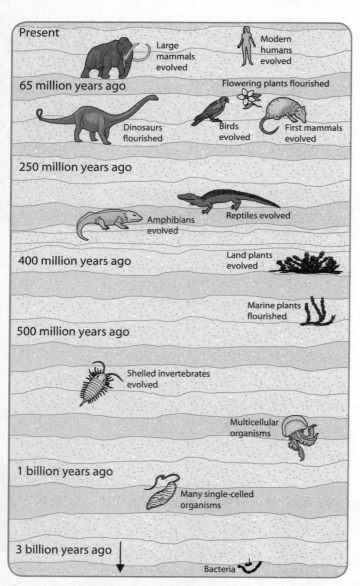

Figure 5-1. Examples from the fossil record

*(Labels within figure, from top to bottom:)*
Present
Large mammals evolved
Modern humans evolved
65 million years ago
Flowering plants flourished
Dinosaurs flourished
Birds evolved
First mammals evolved
250 million years ago
Amphibians evolved
Reptiles evolved
400 million years ago
Land plants evolved
Marine plants flourished
500 million years ago
Shelled invertebrates evolved
Multicellular organisms
1 billion years ago
Many single-celled organisms
3 billion years ago
Bacteria

Topic Overview

Extensive evidence indicates that life on Earth began more than three billion years ago. Fossils found in ancient rocks have given us many clues to the kinds of life that existed long ago. The first living organisms were simple, single-celled organisms. Over time, more complex single-celled creatures developed. Then, about a billion years ago, increasingly complex, multicellular organisms began to appear. The idea that explains how this change in species has occurred over time is known as **evolution.**

The Theory of Evolution

The theory of evolution is accepted as the central theme of modern biology. It helps biologists understand how the variations among individuals can lead to changes in an entire species of organism. Since it was first suggested by Charles Darwin, the concept of evolution has been refined by massive amounts of evidence offered by thousands of scientists. So much evidence has been collected that evolution now has the stature of a **theory,** which is a concept that has been tested and confirmed in many different ways and can be used by scientists to make predictions about the natural world.

The theory of evolution helps biologists understand the similarities (such as bone structure and biochemistry) among different organisms. It also helps to explain the history of life that is revealed by the **fossil record,** which is a collection of fossils that provides clues to the history of Earth's organisms.

The fossil record spans much of **geologic time**—the billions of years of Earth's history—revealing many changes in environments as well as species. Figure 5-1 shows examples from the fossil record through geologic time.

Evolution does NOT necessarily produce long-term progress in any set direction. Instead, evolutionary change appears to be more like the growth of a bush. Notice in Figure 5-2 that some branches survive from the beginning with little or no change. Some die out altogether. Others branch repeatedly, with each new branch representing a new species.

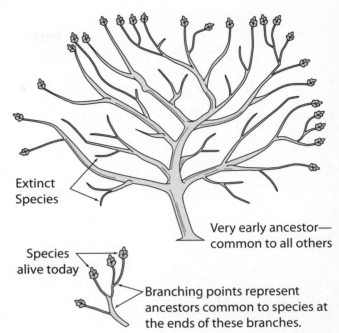

Figure 5-2. Evolution modeled as the growth of a bush: Evolutionary changes in species are like the growth of a bush in which some twigs grow and branch, while others die. The tips of the living twigs represent species that are alive now.

Review Questions

1. Evolution is the process of
   (1) development of one-celled organisms from mammals
   (2) change in species over long periods of time
   (3) embryonic development of modern humans
   (4) changing energy flow in food webs

2. Which phrase best defines evolution?
   (1) an adaptation of an organism to its environment
   (2) a sudden replacement of one community by another
   (3) the isolation of organisms from each other for many years
   (4) a process of change in species over a period of time

3. The study of fossils has allowed scientists to
   (1) describe past environments and the history of life
   (2) study present ocean temperatures at different depths
   (3) analyze the chemical composition of sedimentary rocks and minerals
   (4) describe the details of the process by which life first began on Earth

4. The evolution of species is often represented as a branching tree similar to the one shown in the diagram below. The names shown represent different groups of organisms alive today; the lines represent their evolutionary histories.

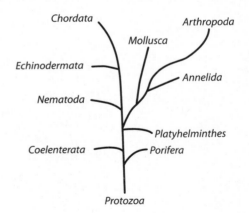

The statement that is best supported by the diagram is that
   (1) *Annelida* and *Arthropoda* have an ancestor in common
   (2) *Echinodermata* are more closely related to *Mollusca* than they are to *Chordata*
   (3) *Mollusca* and *Arthropoda* evolved before *Porifera*
   (4) *Annelida* and *Arthropoda* evolved from *Echinodermata*

5. The diagram below represents possible lines of the evolution of primates.

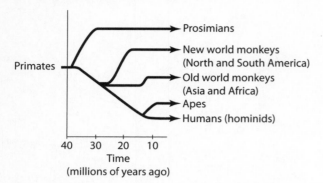

Primates

40 30 20 10
Time
(millions of years ago)

Prosimians

New world monkeys
(North and South America)

Old world monkeys
(Asia and Africa)

Apes

Humans (hominids)

Which inference can best be made based on the diagram?

(1) Adaptations for living in trees are inherited by all primates.
(2) Humans and apes have a common ancestor.
(3) The embryos of monkeys and apes are identical.
(4) The period of development is similar in most primates.

The Mechanics of Evolution

Darwin did not only suggest that species evolved. He also suggested how that evolution might have occurred. Darwin thought that the mechanism of evolution was like the process of <u>artificial selection</u> practiced by breeders of plants and animals. (See Figure 5-3.) He used the term **natural selection** to indicate that the process of evolution was controlled by "nature" rather than by people. In the process of natural selection, individuals that survive are able to breed and pass their genetic information to the next generation. Those that are not as successful in the environment often die without leaving any offspring.

Figure 5-3. Racehorses are bred for speed and stamina: When humans breed plants or animals, they select specific traits, such as speed, flower color, or resistance to insects. In a similar way, "nature" selects any trait that increases an organism's ability to survive and reproduce.

Overview of Evolution

Darwin's ideas are easy to understand: In any environment, an individual may be born with a characteristic that makes it stronger, faster—any sort of advantage that will help it survive and reproduce. The individuals that prove to be the best adapted to their environment will be more likely to survive. If they do survive, their favorable characteristics will be passed on to many of their offspring. As a result, these useful adaptations, which first appeared randomly, are likely to become more and more common with each generation. Similarly, characteristics that reduce an individual's chance of surviving and reproducing will tend to decrease over time.

The long-term result of natural selection is a change in the frequency of certain traits in a population. Beneficial traits tend to become more common; harmful traits tend to become less common. As the frequency of a trait in a population increases or decreases over time, it can be said that the species is evolving. Note that the population—not the individual—changes as a result of evolution. An individual does not evolve; each is born with genetic information that may or may not help it survive and reproduce. As natural selection leads to changes in the composition of a population, that population may have more individuals with a certain favorable characteristic than it did earlier.

Interactions and Evolution

The driving force behind evolution is the interaction between individual organisms and their environment. Conditions that are vital to the process of evolution include

- the potential for a species to increase its numbers, known as **overproduction**
- the <u>finite</u> (limited) supply of resources needed for life
- the genetic variation of offspring due to mutation and genetic "shuffling"
- the selection by the environment of those offspring better able to survive and reproduce

All of these conditions, which are explained below, are involved in the process of evolutionary change.

Overproduction In each generation, a species has the potential to produce more offspring than can possibly survive. Species with high reproductive potential include bacteria, insects, dandelions, and rabbits. (See Figure 5-4.) If all the offspring of these organisms survived, they would overrun Earth. However, that does not happen.

Scientists have learned that, in stable environments, the population of a species remains about the same from one year to the next. For example, no matter how many deer are born in one year, at the same time the next year, there will be about the same number of deer as there was the year before. Similarly, some fish species lay millions of eggs, but by the next year, the population of that species is the same as it was the previous year. This happens because not all of the new individuals that are born or hatched will survive to adulthood.

The Struggle for Survival Overproduction leads to competition among the members of a species. Not all offspring survive long enough to reproduce. In many cases, chance determines which offspring survive. For example, wind may blow a dandelion seed to a patch of fertile soil or into a lake. A deer may be born in a wildlife preserve or in the path of a forest fire.

But chance is not the only factor that determines which offspring will survive and which will die. The offspring all have to cope with environmental conditions, such as temperature, disease, parasites, and predators. They also need resources, such as oxygen, water, food, and shelter. However, the supply of these resources is finite. If they are to survive, organisms of the same species must compete for limited resources. Depending on their success as competitors, individuals will get the resources they need to survive, or they will not. Those that are the best suited to their environment are more likely to survive. Many of the losers in this struggle for resources will die before they have a chance to reproduce.

Variation The new traits that can lead to evolution come from normal variation within species. As shown in Figure 5-5, organisms within a species are never exactly alike. For example, some adult grasshoppers have longer legs than others; some have a lighter body color. In any group of gray squirrels, some have sharper or longer claws,

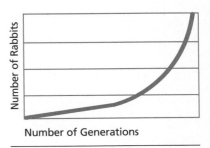

Rabbit Population Group	
Number of Generations	Number of Rabbits
1	100
72	3,354
100	13,150

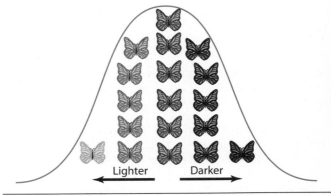

Figure 5-4. Overproduction: Rabbits are known for their high reproductive potential.

Figure 5-5. Genetic variation: In this example, a species of green butterflies might have individuals that vary in color from very dark green to very light green.

lighter or darker fur, bigger or smaller ears, and so on. The differences among offspring are due to **genetic variation**—the unique combination of traits each organism inherits from its parents.

Some variations give individuals an advantage over others in their struggle for resources. Any trait that helps an organism survive and reproduce under a given set of environmental conditions is said to have **adaptive value.** For example, a rabbit's ability to blend in with its surroundings may allow it to escape capture by a fox. The coloration it inherited has adaptive value for the rabbit, allowing it to escape predators and survive. When the fox population is high, this adaptation may be especially valuable to rabbits that inherited it.

Selection by the Environment As Darwin proposed with his idea of natural selection, traits with an adaptive value in a specific environment give individuals in that environment a competitive advantage. If the beneficial trait is passed to the offspring, they, too, are more likely to survive and reproduce. The proportion of individuals with these advantageous characteristics will increase because they are better able to compete than individuals without the beneficial trait. Eventually, nearly all the individuals in the population will have the beneficial trait. This change in the characteristics present in population over time is evolution.

Although some evolution may occur without much change in the environment, it is usually the adaptation of a species to changes in its environment that brings about evolution. Therefore, a changing environment is often the driving force for evolutionary change.

Review Questions

6. The process of natural selection is based on the assumption that

(1) environmental changes will cause changes in body structure in individuals
(2) most changes from generation to generation are the result of mutations
(3) part of the population of organisms always remains stable
(4) different traits inherited by offspring have different survival value.

Base your answers to questions 7 and 8 on the information below and on your knowledge of biology.

A study of beetles on an isolated oceanic island formed by volcanic action and far from any other land shows that all of the beetles that are presently on the island are incapable of flying. A study of fossils from different rock layers of the island shows that the island was once populated with flying beetles. The graph shows the probable change over the last 5,000 years.

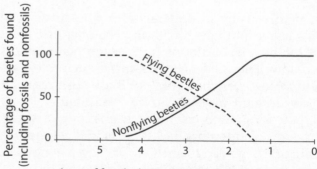

Ages of fossils discovered (in thousands of years)

7. The loss of flying ability by the beetle is most probably the result of

(1) predators eating the beetles' wings
(2) beetles not using their wings
(3) genetic changes in the beetles
(4) lack of vegetation for the beetle to feed on

8. The graph indicates that the non-flying beetles probably
   (1) were better adapted to the environment
   (2) arrived from other islands 5000 years ago
   (3) mutated and produced flying beetles
   (4) became extinct about 1.5 thousand years ago

9. When lions prey on a herd of antelope, some of the antelope are eliminated. Which part of the theory of evolution can be used to describe this situation?
   (1) asexual reproduction of the fittest
   (2) isolation of the species
   (3) survival of the best adapted
   (4) new species development due to mutation

10. Every spring, each mature female fish of a particular species produces several million eggs. However, the total population of this species remains at around 10,000 from one year to the next.

    State two reasons why the fish population remains approximately the same from one generation to the next. [1]

Base your answers to questions 11 and 12 on the diagram below and on your knowledge of biology.

The diagram represents a small island divided by a mountain range. The mountain range prevents populations A and B from making contact with each other. At one time in the past, however, lowlands existed in the area indicated, and the ancestors of population A and population B were members of the same population.

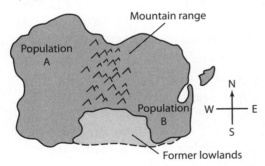

11. Over many years, the climate on the west side of the island has undergone drastic changes while the climate on the east side has remained the same. It is most likely that population B will
    (1) migrate and intermix with population A
    (2) become extinct
    (3) have evolved more than population A
    (4) have evolved less than population A

12. The organisms of population A and population B are now incapable of interbreeding and producing offspring. Which biological process most likely caused this situation to occur?
    (1) artificial selection   (3) natural selection
    (2) cloning   (4) asexual reproduction

Base your answers to questions 13 and 14 on the information and graph below and on your knowledge of biology.

Scientists studying a moth population in a wooded area of New York State recorded the distribution of moth wing color as shown in the following graph. While observing the moths, scientists noted that the moths spent most of the day resting on trees and looking for food during the night. The woods contained trees with a bark color that was predominantly brown.

13. A fungus infection affected nearly all trees in the woods so that the color of the tree bark was changed to a gray-white color. Which graph shows the most probable results that would occur in the distribution of wing color in this moth population after a long period of time?

14. As a result of the fungus infection, the change in moth wing color distribution would most probably occur by the
    (1) production of sex cells by mitosis
    (2) natural selection of favorable variations
    (3) eating of pigments in fungus spores
    (4) production of mutations as a result of eating the fungus

Sources of Variation

As you may recall, the arrangement of an individual's DNA bases determines all the inherited characteristics of that individual. Any change in bases or their sequence may bring about a change in the individual. But not all of those changes can be passed on to the individual's offspring. In sexually reproducing organisms, only changes in the genes of sex cells can be passed on to the next generation and become the basis for evolutionary change. Other types of variation (such as changes to body cells) die with the individual. For example, a father who has built huge muscles due to exercise does NOT pass those large muscles to his offspring.

There are two major ways an organism can wind up with genes that differ from those of its parents. Some genetic variations arise because of mutations in the genes of an organism. Others are due to "genetic shuffling," the routine sorting and recombination of genes that occurs during sexual reproduction.

Mutation A **mutation** is a change in the base sequence of a DNA molecule. Mutations occur as random, chance events that cannot be predicted. Some mutations occur as errors in DNA as cells function. Radiation and some chemicals can also cause them. Mutations are an important source of totally new forms of genes.

When mutations occur in body cells, they affect only that individual. However, a mutation in a single-celled organism or in the sex cells of a multicellular organism can be passed on to the offspring. In organisms that reproduce sexually, only mutations in the genes of sex cells can become the basis for evolutionary change.

Nearly all mutations are harmful and may affect the offspring so severely that it cannot survive. A few mutations benefit the individual, however, and can increase its chance of surviving, reproducing, and passing the mutation to the next generation. A beneficial mutation may lead to the evolution of a new species. For example, the ancestors of polar bears probably had dark fur. If a mutation resulted in a bear with white fur, that bear probably would have died young. However, if the mutation occurred in a snowy environment, the white fur would be a useful mutation, allowing the bear to stalk its prey more effectively.

Genetic Shuffling The sorting and random recombining of genes during meiosis and fertilization results in new and different combinations of genes. These genes can be passed on to individual offspring. The process is similar to shuffling and dealing cards. The deck stays the same, but nearly every hand will be slightly different because of mixing and rearranging during shuffling. At fertilization, even more variety is introduced because now cards from "two decks" are combined. Although mutations provide new genetic instructions, genetic shuffling is the main source of the variation that exists among the members of any sexually reproducing species.

15. Which statement is basic to the theory of evolution by natural selection?

    (1) In general, living organisms maintain a constant population from generation to generation.
    (2) Changes in living organisms are almost completely the result of mutations.
    (3) Natural variations are inherited.
    (4) There is little competition between species.

16. Which statement is *not* included as part of our modern understanding of evolution?

    (1) Sexual reproduction and mutations provide variation among offspring.
    (2) Traits are transmitted by genes and chromosomes.
    (3) More offspring are produced than can possibly survive.
    (4) New organs are formed when organisms need them.

17. The modern theory of evolution states that a basis for variation within a species is provided by

    (1) mutations
    (2) asexual reproduction
    (3) cloning
    (4) overproduction

18. Sexual reproduction is related to evolution because sexual reproduction

    (1) occurs only in more recently evolved forms of animal life
    (2) increases the chances of extinction of different species
    (3) increases the chances for variations to occur
    (4) is the more usual kind of reproduction

19. Mutations can be transmitted to the next generation if they are present in

    (1) hormones   (3) body cells
    (2) gametes   (4) muscle cells

20. A new chemical was discovered and introduced into a culture containing one species of bacteria. Within a day, most of the bacteria were dead, but a few remained alive. Which statement best explains why some of the bacteria survived?

    (1) They had a genetic variation that gave them resistance to the chemical.
    (2) They were exposed to the chemical long enough to develop a resistance to it.
    (3) They mutated and became a different species after exposure to the chemical.
    (4) They absorbed the chemical and broke it down in their digestive systems.

21. Which characteristics of a population would most likely indicate the lowest potential for evolutionary change in that population?

    (1) sexual reproduction and few mutations
    (2) sexual reproduction and many mutations
    (3) asexual reproduction and few mutations
    (4) asexual reproduction and many mutations

22. Which two factors provide the genetic basis for variation within many species?

    (1) asexual reproduction and meiosis
    (2) mutations and sexual reproduction
    (3) competition and the synthesis of proteins
    (4) ecological succession and mitosis

23. Which statement best describes a current understanding of natural selection?

    (1) Natural selection influences the frequency of an adaptation in a population.
    (2) Natural selection has been discarded as an important concept in evolution.
    (3) Changes in gene frequencies due to natural selection have little effect on the evolution of species.
    (4) New mutations of genetic material are due to natural selection.

The Results of Genetic Variation

The changes that result from mutation or genetic shuffling in the sex cells may affect the offspring in several ways. Most of the changes can be categorized as structural, functional, or behavioral.

Structural Change The structure of any organism is the result of its species' entire evolutionary history. There are millions of examples of variations that have resulted in structural changes. For example, the polar bear (like other bears) has thick fur that keeps it warm in its cold environment.

Bird wing

Human arm

Whale flipper

Bat wing

Figure 5-6. Similar bone structure of different species: The limbs shown above are from different species and have different functions, but they share many structural similarities. They are all made of the same type of bones and are attached in a similar way. The whale flipper is actually much larger than the other limbs. Notice that the ulna and radius of the bat wing are almost fused.

Polar bears, however, have evolved an extra protection from the cold. The soles of their feet are also mostly covered with thick fur. This extra fur not only keeps their skin off the ice but also improves traction.

The theory of evolution has helped scientists explain many of the structural variations and similarities found in organisms. For example, in Figure 5-6, notice that each limb has one thick "long" bone, two thinner "long" bones, and a "hand" with five digits. The ancestor of these animals most likely had a similar limb structure. At one point, however, limbs began to vary, evolving into arms, legs, wings, or flippers.

Structures that are no longer used by modern organisms give scientists clues to the evolutionary history of a species. Some snakes, for example, have tiny, nonfunctional leg bones—an indication that they probably evolved from four-legged, lizard-like ancestors.

Functional Change Molecular or biochemical changes affect how an organism works. These are functional changes. For example, all working muscles emit an extremely tiny electrical output. In some eels, however, that electrical output has evolved into an adaptation that helps it find and capture food. The muscles of these eels can produce a massive shock that stuns or kills its prey.

Changes in DNA often lead to functional changes. One example is a mutation in the DNA of certain one-celled organisms that led to their ability to make enzymes that digest wood. Another is the evolution of the ability of some snakes to make a poisonous venom.

Behavioral Change Behaviors have also evolved through natural selection. Many of the specific behaviors we find in species today have become common because they resulted in greater reproductive success.

- Fighting among the males of a walrus population for a harem of females is one evolved behavior. Because of the fighting, the stronger, healthier male mates with the most females.
- The correct rate of "blinking" allows males and females of firefly species to find each other. A different pattern or rate of blinking would isolate the individual from potential mates.

The Importance of Variation

If environmental conditions change, organisms that have adapted to those conditions may die. If all the members of the species had exactly the same combination of characteristics, an environmental change could be disastrous, wiping out the entire species. The variation of organisms within a species increases the likelihood that at least some members of the species will survive in a changed environment. Once the diversity present in a species is lost, it is next to impossible to get it back. Today's endangered species have such small populations that biologists worry that they may not have the genetic diversity to adapt to even slight changes in their environment.

24. The changes in the foot structure in a bird population over many generations are shown in the diagram below.

Time → Time → Present day

These changes can best be explained by the concept of

(1) natural selection
(2) extinction
(3) stable gene frequencies
(4) cloning

25. Explain how the lack of genetic diversity found in populations of endangered species might hinder their recovery. [1]

26. The Florida panther, a member of the cat family, has a population of fewer than 100 individuals and has limited genetic variation. Which inference based on this information is valid?

(1) These animals will begin to evolve rapidly.
(2) Over time, these animals will become less likely to survive in a changing environment.
(3) These animals are easily able to adapt to the environment.
(4) Over time, these animals will become more likely to be resistant to disease.

27. Which statement could be used as evidence to show that two different species of organisms most likely developed from a single, common ancestor?

(1) They eat the same types of food.
(2) They have different digestive enzymes.
(3) They lived during the same time period.
(4) They contain similar amino acid sequences.

28. The diagrams below show the bones in the forelimbs of three different organisms.

Human   Whale   Bat

Differences in the bone arrangements support the hypothesis that these organisms

(1) are members of the same species
(2) may have descended from the same ancestor
(3) have adaptations to survive in different environments
(4) all contain the same genetic information

29. In most populations, the individuals that produce the greatest number of offspring are

(1) always the strongest
(2) usually the best adapted
(3) those that have only inheritable traits
(4) those that are the most intelligent

30. The best scientific explanation for differences in structure, function, and behavior found in different species of organisms is provided by

(1) carbohydrate electrophoresis
(2) population chromatography
(3) the theory of carrying capacity
(4) the theory of evolution

Patterns of Change

Evolution appears to follow certain patterns that appear repeatedly in the fossil record. For example:

- Changes in species are often related to environmental change.
- Species with short reproductive cycles that produce many offspring tend to evolve more quickly than species with long lifespans and few offspring.
- The failure to adapt to a changing environment may result in the death of the species.

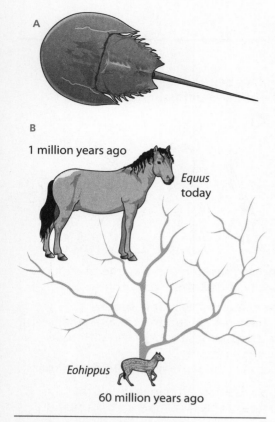

A

B

1 million years ago

Equus
today

Eohippus

60 million years ago

Figure 5-7. The rate of evolution: For some species, the rate of evolutionary change has been very slow. For example, the horseshoe crab (A) has shown little change from fossils of its ancestors that lived 300 million years ago. However, the horse (B) has evolved tremendously over the past 60 million years.

The Rate of Evolution

Most of the diversity of life on Earth today is believed to be the result of natural selection occurring over a vast period of geologic time. The amount of change seems to be linked to changes in the environment. Minimal environmental change often results in stable populations. Rapid environmental change often leads to rapid changes in species. However, for any species, it may take millions of years to accumulate enough differences from its ancestors to be classified as a new or different species. As shown in Figure 5-7, some species have hardly changed in many millions of years. Others have changed so much that the relationships may not be obvious.

The rate of evolutionary change may also be influenced by the number of offspring produced by a species. Those that have few offspring and live a long time generally evolve quite slowly. Those that have brief lifespans and numerous offspring can change so quickly that evolution may occur in just a few years.

One example of rapid change involves the evolution of antibiotic resistance by pathogenic bacteria. When a population of millions of bacteria is exposed to an antibiotic, there is a chance that a few might have a gene that makes them resistant to the antibiotic. (This gene probably occurred as a chance mutation at some earlier time. It was most likely present in some of the bacteria before the antibiotic was used, and its appearance was totally unrelated to the presence of the antibiotic.) The antibiotic could kill almost all of the bacteria except for a few that escape exposure to the antibiotic. The ones with the resistance gene would also survive.

Because the antibiotic eliminated most of the competition, the few survivors, including the resistant ones, reproduce quickly, giving rise to a new population of the bacteria. In this new population, a higher proportion of individuals is now resistant to the drug. When the same antibiotic is used on the descendants of this new population, even more resistant bacteria will survive. Now the proportion of resistant bacteria is even higher. In this case, the antibiotic has become an agent of selection. The antibiotic did not cause the original mutation that made the bacteria resistant to the antibiotic. It merely determined which bacteria would live to reproduce. Figure 5-8 shows the process.

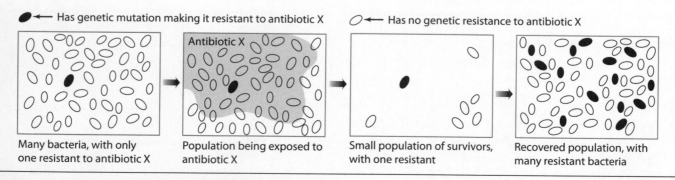

Has genetic mutation making it resistant to antibiotic X   Has no genetic resistance to antibiotic X

Antibiotic X

Many bacteria, with only one resistant to antibiotic X

Population being exposed to antibiotic X

Small population of survivors, with one resistant

Recovered population, with many resistant bacteria

Figure 5-8. How resistance to antibiotics can develop

Insects also have short reproductive cycles and produce many offspring. Many insect species have changed significantly in response to pesticide use. For example, the widespread use of the pesticide DDT led to insect species becoming resistant in just a few years. As was the case with bacteria and antibiotics, there may have been a few DDT-resistant insects in the population before the chemical was ever used. They probably had a random mutation that had no adaptive value before the use of DDT. Once the DDT was sprayed, nearly all of the nonresistant insects were killed, leaving a high proportion of resistant insects to repopulate the area. Later, if DDT was sprayed again, it was less effective against the resistant offspring of the survivors of the earlier spraying.

As a result of these kinds of rapid evolutionary events, we are finding more and more bacteria that are resistant to antibiotics and more and more insect species that are resistant to our pesticides. This has created many problems in the fields of medicine and agriculture and will continue to be a problem in the future.

Extinction

Extinction is the disappearance of an entire species. Any time the death rate of individuals within a species is greater than the birth rate, extinction is a possibility. Generally, extinction occurs when the environment changes. Temperatures change; sea levels rise and fall. Grasslands become deserts; clear lakes become polluted. The variation of organisms within a species increases the likelihood that at least some members of the species will survive the changing environmental conditions. However, when the adaptive characteristics of a species are insufficient to allow its survival in a new environment, the species will become extinct.

The fossil record shows that throughout geologic time, millions of species have evolved, survived for a while, then failed to adapt successfully, and finally became extinct. It is a surprisingly common process. In fact, from the number of fossils of extinct organisms found, it is apparent that a majority of the species that ever lived on Earth is now extinct. Figure 5-9 shows a fossil of the extinct *Archaeopteryx*, an ancestor of modern birds.

Figure 5-9. An artist's conception of how the extinct *Archaeopteryx* might have looked, and the fossilized skeleton of this animal.

Review Questions

31. The shark has changed very little in the last 50 million years. Which statement best explains why this is the case?

(1) The shark is well adapted to its relatively unchanged environment.
(2) Sharks have a high reproductive rate and show little change in their genetic makeup from one generation to the next.
(3) Sharks need to change only if humans are present in their environment.
(4) Sharks have a high mutation and genetic recombination rate.

32. Many animals exist today in a form that is almost identical to the form they had a million years ago. What is the most probable explanation for this lack of evolutionary change?

(1) Genetic mutations have occurred among these animals.
(2) The environment of these animals remained about the same.
(3) These animals reproduce by sexual reproduction.
(4) Complex organisms evolved into simpler ones.

Base your answers to questions 33 through 35 on the diagram below and on your knowledge of biology. The diagram shows an interpretation of relationships based on evolutionary theory. The letters represent different species.

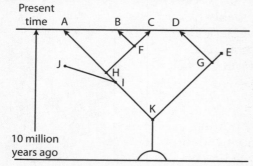

33. Explain why species B and C are more closely related than species A and C are.

34. The diagram indicates that a common ancestor for species C and E is species

    (1) F   (2) G   (3) H   (4) K

35. Which species are least likely to be vital parts of a present-day ecosystem?

    (1) A and E   (3) E and J
    (2) C and D   (4) B and F

Base your answers to questions 36 and 37 on the information below and on your knowledge of biology.

Joshua Lederberg discovered that, in a large population of Escherichia coli (E. coli) about 1 in 10 million of the offspring was naturally resistant to the antibiotic streptomycin. When these naturally resistant bacteria were isolated and grown separately, they soon formed a larger population. The entire population so formed was also naturally resistant to streptomycin.

36. The formation of the large streptomycin-resistant population is based on

    (1) variations and survival of the fittest
    (2) mutations and asexual reproduction
    (3) sexual reproduction and no mutations
    (4) survival of the fittest and cloning

37. According to modern evolutionary theory, the resistance to streptomycin probably resulted directly from

    (1) culturing the E. coli
    (2) changes in temperature under which E. coli are grown
    (3) a change in the DNA of E. coli
    (4) the presence of streptomycin in the environment of E. coli

38. A large population of cockroaches was sprayed with a newly developed, fast-acting insecticide. The appearance of some cockroaches that are resistant to this insecticide supports the concept that

    (1) species traits tend to remain constant
    (2) variation exists within a species
    (3) insecticides cause mutations
    (4) the environment does not change

39. Compounds like the pesticide DDT may bring about the evolution of new strains of organisms by

    (1) destroying food producers
    (2) acting as a natural selecting agent
    (3) mixing two different sets of genes
    (4) creating new ecological niches

40. A population of mosquitoes is sprayed with a new insecticide. Most of the mosquitoes are killed, but a few survive. In the next generation, the spraying continues, but still more mosquitoes hatch that are immune to the insecticide.

    How could these results be explained according to the present concept of evolution?

    (1) The insecticide caused a mutation in the mosquitoes.
    (2) The mosquitoes learned how to fight the insecticide.
    (3) A few mosquitoes in the first population were resistant and transmitted this resistance to their offspring.
    (4) The insecticide caused the mosquitoes to develop an immune response, which was inherited.

41. Throughout the history of Earth, which factor has probably been the chief cause of the extinction of various species?

    (1) people's interference with nature
    (2) failure to adapt to environmental changes
    (3) warfare within the species
    (4) volcanic eruptions

42. Fossil evidence indicates that many species have existed for relatively brief periods of time and have then become extinct. Which statement best explains the reason for their short existence?

    (1) These organisms lacked the energy to produce mutations.
    (2) Humans modify plant and animal species through the knowledge of genetics.
    (3) These organisms lacked variations having adaptive value.
    (4) Within these species, increasing complexity reduced their chances of survival.

Directions

Review the Test-Taking Strategies section of this book. Then answer the following questions. Read each question carefully and answer with a correct choice or response.

Part A

1 How does natural selection operate to cause change in a population?
   (1) The members of the population are equally able to survive environmental change.
   (2) The members of the population differ so that only some survive when the environment changes.
   (3) The members of the population cause environmental changes and adapt to them.
   (4) All the members of the population adapt to environmental changes.

2 Which mutation could be passed on to future generations?
   (1) a gene change in a liver cell
   (2) cancer caused by excessive exposure to the sun
   (3) a chromosomal alteration during gamete formation
   (4) random breakage of a chromosome in a leaf cell of a maple tree

3 A trait with low survival value to the members of a population will most likely
   (1) undergo a series of mutations in succeeding generations
   (2) cause the reproductive rate of the individual to increase
   (3) decrease in frequency from one generation to the next
   (4) remain unchanged in frequency through many generations

4 A change in the genetic material that produces variation in a species may be the result of
   (1) the struggle for survival
   (2) the overproduction of a species
   (3) a mutation
   (4) competition

5 The DNA sequences found in two different species are 95% the same. This suggests that these species
   (1) are evolving into the same species
   (2) contain identical proteins
   (3) may have similar evolutionary histories
   (4) have the same number of mutations

6 The process by which a species passes out of existence is known as
   (1) endangerment
   (2) deforestation
   (3) extinction
   (4) adaptation

7 The diagram below illustrates the change that occurred in the frequency of body pattern traits shown by an insect population over ten generations.

First generation   Tenth generation

10 years later

A probable explanation for this change would be that over time there was
   (1) a decrease in the adaptive value of the spotted trait
   (2) an increase in the adaptive value of the spotted trait
   (3) an increase in the population of the insect
   (4) a decrease in the mutation rate of the gene for body pattern

8 The fact that a healthy deer can outrun a timber wolf is an example of
   (1) mutation
   (2) isolation
   (3) non-random mating
   (4) natural selection

9 A maple tree releases hundreds of seeds in a single season. This is an example of
   (1) a mutation
   (2) isolation
   (3) overproduction
   (4) non-random mating

Part B

Base your answers to questions 10 through 15 on the information below and on your knowledge of biology.

The bark of trees around Manchester, England, was mostly light in color before the Industrial Revolution. Light-colored peppered moths that rested on the trees were camouflaged from bird predators, while dark-colored peppered moths were easily preyed upon. After a few years of industrialization, the tree bark became darkened from pollution. The table below represents a change in the number of light- and dark-colored moths within the peppered moth population over a period of six years from the beginning of industrialization.

End of Year	Number of Light Moths	Number of Dark Moths
1	556	64
2	237	112
3	484	198
4	392	210
5	246	281
6	225	357

Using the information in the data table, construct a line graph on the grid provided. Follow the instructions below.

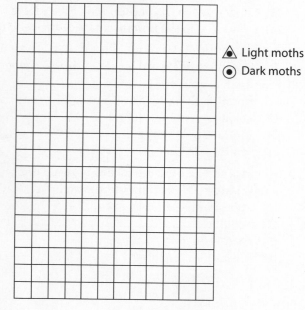

Changes in Peppered Moth Population

▲ Light moths
◉ Dark moths

Number of moths

End of year

10 Mark an appropriate scale, without any breaks, on each axis. [1]

11 Plot the data for the number of dark moths on the grid. Surround each point with a small circle and connect the points. [1]

Example:

12 Plot the data for the number of light moths on the grid. Surround each point with a small triangle and connect the points. [1]

Example:

13 At the end of which year of study was the number of dark-colored moths closest to the number of light-colored moths?
(1) 1   (2) 2   (3) 5   (4) 6

14 Which aspect of the evolutionary process is suggested by the information provided?
(1) The light-colored moths will eventually increase in number.
(2) The darker moths appeared when the tree trunks became lighter.
(3) The changing environment caused a darkening of the pigments of the moths.
(4) The darker moths increased in number when the environment became more favorable for their traits.

15 The biological concept that is most closely associated with the changes in the peppered moth population in England is known as
(1) natural selection   (3) asexual reproduction
(2) positive feedback   (4) homeostatic control

Base your answers to questions 16 through 19 on the paragraph below and on your knowledge of biology.

Two different species of crickets inhabited a meadow. One species of cricket had a straw-colored body and made up 90% of the total cricket population. The other species of cricket had a dark red body and made up 10% of the population. This proportion between the species had been constant for many years.

A new variety of grass with purple blades appeared in the meadow. The purple grass was better adapted to the meadow environment than the native green grass and replaced the green grass within a period of 50 years.

16 The appearance of the purple grass was most likely the result of
(1) asexual reproduction
(3) cloning
(2) genetic engineering
(4) mutation

17 Which graph most likely indicates the percentages of the straw-colored crickets (%S) over the 50-year period after the appearance of purple grass?

18 The evolutionary concept that would explain the changes taking place during the 50-year period in both the crickets and grasses is called
(1) common ancestry
(2) natural selection
(3) homeostatic balance
(4) selective breeding

19 What is the most likely reason for the large proportion of straw-colored crickets in the original population?
(1) The straw-colored crickets were larger and killed off most of the red crickets.
(2) Few natural enemies of the straw-colored crickets lived in the meadow.
(3) More straw-colored crickets than red were able to survive in the green grass.
(4) Red-colored crickets were not a part of the fossil record for the meadow.

20 State what could happen to a species in a changing environment if the members of that species do not express any genetic variations. [1]

Part C

21 Genetic variation is the raw material of evolution. Identify two different sources of genetic variation in a plant or animal population. [1]

Base your answers to questions 22 through 24 on the information below and on your knowledge of biology.

Humans have modified some animal species by breeding only those that possess certain desirable traits. As a result, we have racehorses and greyhounds that are faster than their ancestors.

In a similar way, many animals have been modified naturally. The giraffe has long forelegs and a long neck, head, and tongue, which make it well adapted for browsing (feeding) in the higher branches of trees. Therefore, the giraffe can obtain food that is beyond the reach of other animals, especially during droughts.

Ancient populations of giraffes varied in the relative lengths of their body parts. Those giraffes that were able to browse the highest were more likely to survive. They mated, and their offspring often inherited the structural characteristics suitable for high browsing. The giraffes that could not reach the food supply most likely died of starvation and therefore did not produce as many offspring as those that could reach higher.

22 Describe how the type of selection for traits in animals such as greyhounds and racehorses is different from the type of selection for traits that is occurring in animals such as giraffes. [1]

23 Describe two specific events of sexual reproduction that can be the source of the variations selected for in both giraffes and racehorses. [1]

24 Variation, a struggle for existence, and the survival of the fittest are all important to the evolution of species. Provide an example of each of these from the passage above. [3]

Base your answers to questions 25 and 26 on the information below and on your knowledge of biology.

Scientists have observed thousands of female leatherback turtles during egg laying. Every female leatherback exhibits the same remarkable behavior. When she first comes up on the beach to lay her eggs, she digs a deep hole, lays her eggs in the hole, and then covers the eggs with sand. She then travels about 100 meters away from the first hole and digs another. She doesn't lay any eggs in this hole, but goes through the same process of covering the hole just as if there had been eggs present.

25 Write a hypothesis to explain why the female leatherback digs two holes. [1]

26 In the past, some leatherbacks may have only dug one hole and laid their eggs in it. In terms of evolution, how can this modern behavior of digging two holes be explained? [1]

Base your answers to questions 27 and 28 on the information below and on your knowledge of biology.

Cockroaches that are resistant to many common household insecticides are more numerous than those that are killed by these same insecticides. Scientists explain the increased numbers of insecticide-resistant cockroaches with the following statement: Variations that have a high survival value tend to be passed on to the next generation of organisms in greater number than those variations that have low survival value.

27 Identify the variation that is present in the cockroach population and describe how this variation most likely came about. [1]

28 Explain how the use of insecticides is associated with the fact that the resistant cockroaches outnumber the nonresistant cockroaches. [1]

Base your answer to questions 29 through 31 on the paragraph below and on your knowledge of biology.

A scientist discovered that in a large population of pathogenic bacteria, a few were resistant to the antibiotic penicillin. By adding penicillin to the population, she soon obtained a large population that was resistant to penicillin.

29 Explain how this experiment supports the concept of evolution by natural selection. Your explanation should include the concepts of
  • selective agent [1]   • reproduction [1]
  • resistance [1]   • offspring [1]

30 Identify the chemical substance in the bacteria that provides the resistance to penicillin and makes this resistance inheritable. [1]

31 The evolutionary changes described here occurred in a relatively short period of time rather than requiring millions of years. State one reason why it is possible for bacteria to evolve so rapidly. [1]

Base your answers to questions 32 and 33 on the information below and on your knowledge of biology.

Over a period of 28 million years, various genera (related groups) of hoofed mammals called *Titanotheres* showed a continuous change in body and horn size before they eventually became extinct.

32 Describe how gradual changes in the environment might have resulted in the changes observed in *Titanotheres*. [1]

33 Explain how environmental changes could have led to the extinction of *Titanotheres*. [1]

---

34 Growers of fruit trees have always had problems with insects. Insects can cause visible damage to fruits, making them less appealing to consumers. As a result of this damage, much of the fruit cannot be sold. Insecticides have been useful for controlling these insects, but, in recent years, some insecticides have been much less effective. In some cases, insecticides do nothing to stop the insect attacks.

Provide a biological explanation for this loss of effectiveness of the insecticides. In your answer, be sure to:
  • identify the original event that resulted in the evolution of insecticide resistance in some insects [1]
  • explain why the percentage of resistant insects in the population has increased [1]
  • describe one alternative form of insect control, other than using a different insecticide, that fruit growers could use to protect their crops from insect attack [1]

Ecology

What do **You** *Think?*

Succession

Succession is the changes that occur in a species as it evolves into a series of new species.

Succession is the series of changes that take place in plant and animal communities as the habitat changes.

Succession is the series of changes a species makes as it adapts to new conditions.

Vocabulary

abiotic	ecological niche	herbivore
autotroph	ecological succession	heterotroph
biodiversity	ecology	host
biosphere	ecosystem	limiting factors
biotic	energy pyramid	parasite
carnivore	environment	population
carrying capacity	finite	predator
community	food chain	prey
competition	food web	producer
consumer	habitat	scavenger
decomposer		

Topic Overview

Our Earth is home to trillions of different organisms. None of these organisms can survive alone. All organisms—including humans—must interact with both the living and nonliving things around them. **Ecology** is the study of how organisms interact with the living and nonliving things that surround them.

Organisms and Their Environment

As you read this book, you are surrounded by your environment, which includes this book and perhaps your chair, light streaming through the window, a dog barking outside, and a pretzel on the table. If you're in class, your environment may include other students reading nearby, your teacher pacing the aisles, the drone of an airplane, the smell of the lunchroom, sunlight coming in the window, and the unseen mite picking skin flakes off your arm. In short, the **environment** is every living and nonliving thing that surrounds an organism.

Parts of an Ecosystem

Ecosystem is a short way of saying "ecological system." Scientists use the term to describe any portion of the environment. An ecosystem is made up of all the living things, such as bacteria, plants, and animals, that interact with one another. These interacting living things are termed **biotic** factors. When scientists study ecosystems, they also study the nonliving things, such as soil, water, physical space, and energy, that influence the organisms. Nonliving influences are termed **abiotic** factors.

A decaying log, a pond, a field of corn, and even a fish tank are ecosystems. In each of these ecosystems, organisms interact with both the biotic and abiotic parts of their environment. For example, frogs in a pond ecosystem may interact with insects, fish, hawks, and children chasing them with nets. They are also affected by abiotic factors, such as rainfall, the acidity of their pond, temperature, and the amount of light. Some biotic and abiotic parts of an ecosystem are shown in Figure 6-1.

Because the world contains a wide variety of physical conditions, many different kinds of environments are available to organisms. Some are shown in Figure 6-2. Most species, however, have a specific environment that is their "home." That specific environment is known as the species' **habitat.** Familiar habitats include fields, forests, oceans, streams, and deserts.

All the organisms of a species that live in the same area make up a **population.** Ants in a single anthill would be one population. All the different populations are combined to form a <u>community.</u>

Collectively, all of Earth's ecosystems make up the **biosphere**—the biologically inhabited portions of the planet. Earth's biosphere extends from the deepest ocean troughs to high above the surface of the planet. It includes all the water, land, and air in which organisms live. Throughout the biosphere, organisms interact and compete for vital resources, such as food, space, and shelter.

The fundamental concept of ecology is that all living organisms are interdependent, and they interact with one another and with the physical environment. These interactions result in a flow of energy and a cycling of materials essential for life.

Environmental Limits on Population Size

In any ecosystem, the growth and survival of organisms depends on the physical conditions and on the resources available to the organism. If they had unlimited resources, living things could produce populations of <u>infinite</u> (unlimited) size. Within any ecosystem, however, resources, such as oxygen and carbon dioxide, water, nutrients, space, and sunlight, are

Abiotic Factors

Biotic Factors

Figure 6-1. Parts of an ecosystem: The biotic part of the ecosystem includes all the living things that make up the community.

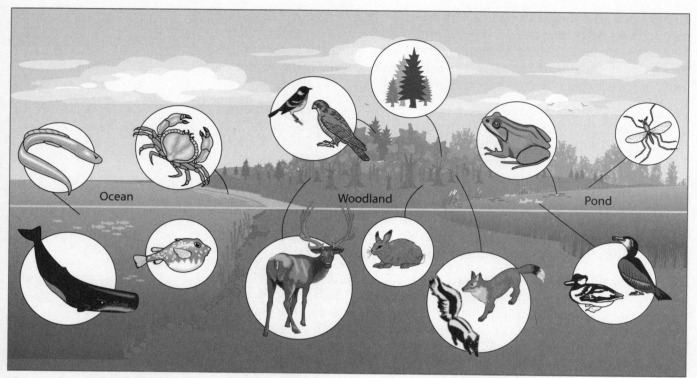

Figure 6-2. Some ecosystems in Earth's biosphere: In each ecosystem, the organisms interact with one another and with their environment. The degree to which each abiotic factor is present determines the types of organisms that can live there.

Ocean

Woodland

Pond

finite (limited). This has a profound effect on the interactions among organisms: Because the resources are finite, organisms must compete with one another to survive.

Competition is the struggle for resources among organisms. Within any one species, competition keeps the size of that species' population in check. In established ecosystems, populations tend to increase or decrease depending on the resources that are available at the time. This variation in population size tends to follow a predictable cycle. Many populations, for example, vary with the seasons. Over time, however, the size of the population remains stable.

Factors in the environment that limit the size of populations are known as **limiting factors.** Some limiting factors are abiotic; others are biotic. For example, abiotic factors, such as the amount of dissolved oxygen in a pond, may limit the kinds and numbers of fish that can live there; the amount of sunlight filtering through a forest may limit the number of green plants living on the forest floor. Some other specific limiting factors include the intensity of light, the temperature range in the environment, minerals that are available in the water or soil, the type of rock or soil in the ecosystem, and the relative acidity (measured according to the pH scale).

An important biotic factor that limits population sizes is the relationship between **predators,** which kill and eat other organisms, and **prey,** which are killed for food. As predators kill and eat their prey, they limit the growth of the prey population. If too many prey animals are killed, predators begin to starve, and their population is reduced. With fewer predators, the size of the prey population begins to recover.

The number of organisms of any single species that an ecosystem can support is referred to as its **carrying capacity**. It is determined not only by the available energy, water, oxygen, and minerals (and the recycling of such minerals), but also by the interactions of its organisms. For example, a field's carrying capacity for a population of foxes is affected not only by the climate, but also by the number and kinds of other populations present. If there are many mice for the foxes to eat, the fox population may boom. If there are many viruses affecting the health of the foxes, their population may crash. Figure 6-3 shows the population increase that normally occurs until the carrying capacity is reached.

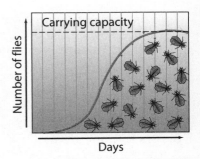

Figure 6-3. Carrying capacity: This population of insects increased until it neared its carrying capacity. Then the population became approximately stable.

Review Questions

1. All of Earth's water, land, and atmosphere within which life exists is known as

   (1) a population
   (2) an ecosystem
   (3) the biosphere
   (4) a biotic community

2. In the biosphere, what are some of the major abiotic factors that determine the distribution and types of plant communities?

   (1) temperature, sunlight, and rainfall
   (2) humidity, location, and humans
   (3) soil type, soil bacteria, and soil water
   (4) insects, carbon dioxide, and nitrogen in the air

Base your answers to questions 3 and 4 on the two graphs below and on your knowledge of biology. The first graph shows the number of days of snow cover from 1940–1960. The second graph shows the percentage of white mice in a population that was sampled during the same period.

3. The appearance of the greatest percentage of white mice occurred

   (1) before the maximum number of days of snow cover
   (2) at the same time as the maximum number of days of snow cover
   (3) after the maximum number of days of snow cover
   (4) both before and after the maximum number of days of snow cover

4. Which statement is supported by the data in the graphs?

   (1) The percentage of brown mice was greatest during the years of longest snow cover.
   (2) The percentage of mice with white fur was greatest during the years of longest snow cover.
   (3) The actual number of white mice was greatest during the years of least snow cover.
   (4) The actual number of brown mice was greatest during the years of longest snow cover.

5. The fact that an organism cannot live without interacting with its surroundings is a basic concept in the field of study known as

   (1) ecology
   (2) evolution
   (3) behavior
   (4) technology

6. When two different species live in the same area and use the same limited resources, which of the following will occur?

   (1) competition
   (2) succession
   (3) parasitism
   (4) industrialization

7. Which term includes all of the interactions that occur between the organisms and the physical factors in a pond environment?

(1) population
(2) ecosystem
(3) abiotic
(4) competition

8. The amount of salt in the air and water of coastal areas determines which species can exist there. In these areas, salt functions as a

(1) source of energy
(2) biotic factor
(3) food source
(4) limiting factor

9. This graph shows the changes in two populations of herbivores in a grassy field.

A possible reason for these changes is that

(1) all of the plant populations in this habitat decreased
(2) population B competed more successfully for food than population A
(3) population A produced more offspring than population B
(4) population A consumed members of population B

Population Interactions

There is a wide diversity of interacting species in most ecosystems. Most of the interactions occur as organisms obtain their food. Every population is linked, directly or indirectly, with all of the other populations in the ecosystem. Each population has one or more specific roles in the ecosystem. As a result, maintaining the ecosystem's diversity is essential to its stability.

Roles in the Ecosystem

The role that each species plays in an ecosystem is called its **ecological niche.** Only one species at a time can occupy a particular niche. If two species attempt to fill the same role in an ecosystem, competition results. Usually, one species will be more suited to the niche, which forces the other species to move on or face elimination. Eventually, only one species will occupy each niche.

Figure 6-4. Feeding patterns among warblers: Several warbler species feed in spruce trees, but they actually occupy different niches because each species feeds in a different part of the spruce tree.

Sometimes it appears as if different populations occupy the same niche. For example, deer and moose often live in the same area and seem to eat the same plants. A closer examination reveals that the deer and moose have different food preferences and only compete when food is very scarce. Similarly, several bird species may seem to nest and feed in the same tree. In reality, it is more probable that the birds are nesting in different parts of the tree and eating different insects. For example, the northeastern United States is home to several species of warblers. Five of those species feed on the insects that live in spruce trees. As shown in Figure 6-4, each species feeds in a different part of the tree.

Competition for a particular ecological niche often occurs when a foreign species enters an area. The new species may be more successful than the native species, partly because the newcomer may not have any natural enemies to control its population. Humans frequently bring foreign species into an area either on purpose or accidentally. One example is the zebra mussels that were brought to the Great Lakes on cargo ships. The zebra mussel has become a major problem in New York waterways.

Relationships in an Ecosystem

In every ecosystem, populations of different species are linked together in a complex web of interactions. Sometimes these relationships are competitive; occasionally they are cooperative. For example, termites have one-celled organisms in their intestinal tracts. These unicellular organisms help the termites digest their food. The tiny organisms gain a place to live and plenty of food, and the termites can make use of a food supply that they would not be able to digest without this cooperative relationship.

Other relationships benefit one organism and have no effect on the other. For example, when a shark attacks and eats its prey, small pieces of the food drift downward. Smaller fish swimming below the shark feed on these scraps. The small fish benefit, but the shark is unaffected.

Food Chains Among the most common relationships in any ecosystem are the predator-prey relationships. **Food chains,** such as those shown in Figure 6-5, illustrate the relationships between prey and predator. In simple terms, the food chain shows what eats what.

Organism's niches are partly defined by how they obtain their food. For example, photosynthetic organisms make their own food and in the process, store the sun's energy. They are known as **autotrophs** (self-feeders) or **producers**. They provide a source of food energy for almost all other living things.

Heterotrophs must acquire food by consuming other organisms. **Herbivores** are heterotrophs that survive on plant tissues; **carnivores** are heterotrophs that eat other animals. Heterotrophs are also known as **consumers.**

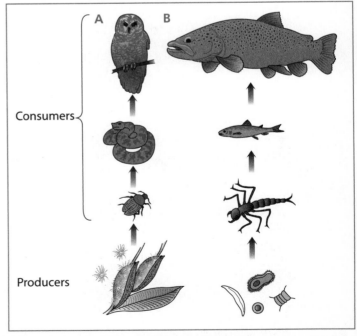

Figure 6-5. Typical food chains: A field ecosystem (A) and a pond ecosystem (B)

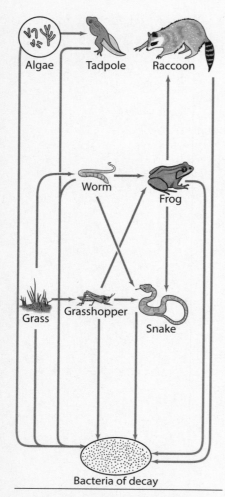

The wastes and dead bodies of all these organisms are consumed by the **decomposers**. The decomposers recycle materials that can then be reused by producers.

Two other feeding relationships between organisms do not fit into the typical predator-prey categories. These organisms are similar to predators in that they feed on other organisms, but different in that they do not kill the organisms for food. **Scavengers,** such as vultures, are consumers that eat dead organisms. They are nature's "clean-up crew." Scavengers, however, are not decomposers. Dead bodies and wastes still have to be broken down by decomposers. **Parasites** are organisms that attack other live organisms (called **host** organisms), but rarely kill them. Parasites usually live on or in the body of their host. Ticks, for example, may live on a dog and also feed on its blood.

Notice in Figure 6-5 that both food chains begin with autotrophs—the photosynthetic producers—and end with consumers. The intermediate heterotrophs (the herbivores and carnivores that rely on others for food) are often, but not always, part of food chains. All of the organisms in a food chain, if not eaten by others, are eventually consumed by decomposers. So a food chain may be as simple as: grass → decay bacteria.

Decomposers may be included at the end of a food chain, but it is important to remember that they actually consume and break down the chemical materials in all dead organisms and in the wastes of all living organisms.

Food Webs Normally, each organism feeds on more than one kind of organism. Because organisms normally have more than one food source, food chain diagrams are oversimplified. **Food webs,** as shown in Figure 6-6, are diagrams that show the more complex feeding relationships among producers, consumers, and decomposers. The food web shows the many interconnected food chains that exist in the ecosystem. Because organisms have several food choices, ecosystems often remain stable even when one population shows a major decline in numbers. The organisms that feed on the declining population simply rely more heavily on one of their other food choices until the declining population recovers.

Figure 6-6. A simplified food web near a pond

Review Questions

10. The diagram below illustrates the feeding areas of two populations in the same ecosystem during the summer and fall. Both populations feed on oak trees.

Summer

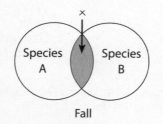

Fall

The portion of the diagram labeled X most likely indicates that

(1) these populations compete for food in the fall, but not in the summer
(2) the species are separated by a geographic barrier in the summer
(3) the supply of oxygen is greater in the summer than in the fall
(4) mating occurs between the species in the fall, but not in the summer

11. An earthworm lives and reproduces in the soil. Through its feeding, excretion, and tunneling activities, the worm adds nutrients and allows air to enter the soil. Together, these statements describe the earthworm's
    (1) habitat
    (2) nutrition
    (3) niche
    (4) environment

12. Among the populations of any natural community, the basic food supply is always a critical factor because it is
    (1) produced by all organisms
    (2) synthesized from oxygen
    (3) a means of transferring energy
    (4) present in surplus amounts

13. A consumer–producer relationship is best illustrated by
    (1) foxes eating mice
    (2) leaves growing on trees
    (3) rabbits eating clover
    (4) fleas living on a cat

Base your answers to questions 14 through 16 on the food chain below and on your knowledge of biology.

rosebush→aphid→beetle→spider→toad→snake

14. Which organism in this food chain can transform light energy into chemical bond energy?

15. At which stage in this food chain will the population with the smallest number of organisms probably be found?
    (1) spider
    (2) aphid
    (3) rosebush
    (4) snake

16. If all of the aphids were killed off due to the spraying of pesticides, what would happen to the number of toads this ecosystem could support?

17. Which group of organisms is *not* represented in the food web below?

    (1) consumers
    (2) carnivores
    (3) producers
    (4) decomposers

18. Which organisms are chiefly responsible for the recycling of dead matter?
    (1) parasites
    (2) viruses
    (3) decomposers
    (4) producers

19. In a natural community in New York State, the producer organisms might include
    (1) bacteria, fungi, and viruses
    (2) deer, rabbits, and squirrels
    (3) grasses, maple trees, and weeds
    (4) trout, peas, and earthworms

20. Which sequence illustrates a generalized food chain in a natural community?
    (1) autotroph → herbivore → carnivore
    (2) autotroph → herbivore → autotroph
    (3) heterotroph → herbivore → carnivore
    (4) consumer → autotroph → carnivore

21. In a food chain consisting of photosynthetic organisms, herbivores, carnivores, and organisms of decay, the principal function of the photosynthetic organisms is to
    (1) capture energy from the environment
    (2) provide material for decay
    (3) prevent erosion of the topsoil
    (4) release energy from organic compounds

22. A characteristic shared by both predators and parasites is that they
    (1) feed on decomposing plant material
    (2) capture and kill animals for food
    (3) live inside their hosts
    (4) attack a living food source

23. As you drive down the highway, you may see crows feeding on dead animals. As a result of this nutritional pattern, crows may be classified as
    (1) scavengers
    (2) predators
    (3) herbivores
    (4) producers

24. When the food relationships in a habitat are illustrated by means of a diagram, the result is always a complicated weblike pattern. This is due to the fact that
    (1) many consumers are adapted to use more than one food source
    (2) producer organisms always outnumber the consumer organisms
    (3) matter is lost in an ecosystem as it moves from producers to consumers
    (4) both producers and consumers require oxygen for metabolic processes

25. Although three different butterfly species all inhabit the same flower garden in an area, competition between the butterflies rarely occurs. The most likely explanation for this lack of competition is that the butterflies

(1) occupy different niches
(2) have a limited supply of food
(3) share food with each other
(4) are able to interbreed

26. In the diagram below, which organisms are components of the same food chain?

(1) trees, mountain lion, snake, and hawk
(2) trees, rabbit, deer, and shrubs
(3) grasses, cricket, frog, and mouse
(4) grasses, mouse, snake, and hawk

27. In the diagram of a food chain below, what do the arrows indicate?

(1) the direction in which organisms move in the environment
(2) the direction of energy flow through a series of organisms
(3) the order of importance of the various organisms
(4) the return of chemical substances to the environment

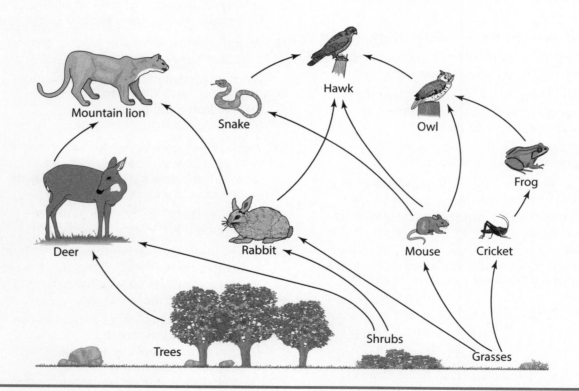

Energy Flow Through an Ecosystem

Almost all organisms use the solar energy stored in food to power their life processes. That energy, however, does not remain in the organism forever. Every second of every day, an animal that is not eating has less energy in its tissues than it had a few seconds before. This energy loss occurs because the organism is continually breaking the chemical bonds in food to use the energy to live. As it is released to make ATP and then used in the cells, much of the energy is converted to heat and is lost to the environment. Only a small amount can actually be used by the cells. As a result, each next step in the food chain has less of the original solar energy available to it.

Figure 6-7 shows how the energy is lost. Only the energy stored in the body tissues of each organism is passed to the next consumer in the chain. Because of the energy loss described above, most of the original stored energy is lost in just a few steps of the food chain. For this reason, food chains are usually quite short.

An **energy pyramid,** shown in Figure 6-8, is a diagram that illustrates the transfer of energy through a food chain or web. Each block of the energy pyramid represents the amount of energy that was obtained from the organisms below it. Only this amount of energy is available to the organisms in the next higher block. Notice that each level is smaller due to the loss of heat as the organisms carry on their life activities.

A continual input of energy, typically from the sun, is required to start the process and to keep it going. Producer organisms capture this energy and store it in the chemical bonds of the food molecules they make. The flow of energy that accompanies the transfer of the food shown in food chains and webs is essential to life on Earth. In spite of this constant drain of energy to the environment, life continues because the sun continues to provide energy.

Figure 6-7. As energy is transferred, much of it is lost to the environment as heat.

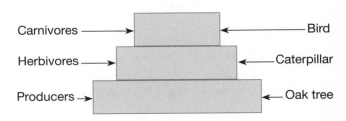

Figure 6-8. An energy pyramid: Each block in the energy pyramid illustrates the amount of energy available for use by organisms at the next level above it. (Energy for decomposers actually comes from organisms at all the levels, so they are not shown in this simplified pyramid.)

Recycling and Reusing Materials

The parts of dead organisms that are not consumed during one of the other steps in the food chain are not wasted. Decomposers extract the last bit of energy contained in the dead organisms (as well as the energy in the waste products from living organisms) and use it to sustain their life processes. As they do so, they return the raw materials contained in the once-living matter to the soil. This process of breaking down dead organisms, as well as the wastes produced by living organisms, into their raw materials and returning those materials to the ecosystem is known as decomposition.

Release of oxygen
(photosynthesis)

Sun

Release of carbon dioxide
(respiration)

Plants

Animals

Release of carbon
dioxide

(respiration)

Dead
animals

Soil nutrients
and water

Recycling of nitrogen wastes
(excretion)

Bacteria

Recycling of nitrogen compounds
(decomposition)

Figure 6-9. **The recycling of materials in ecosystems:** Dead organisms and wastes must be recycled in ecosystems so that their raw materials can be made available for re-use by producer organisms. The gas exchanges of photosynthesis and respiration, along with the action of decomposers, are crucial to the recycling process.

Two examples of organisms that fill the role of decomposers are bacteria and fungi. Because of the actions of decomposers, the atoms and molecules in living things cycle through both the nonliving and living parts of the biosphere. As they do, chemical elements, such as carbon, hydrogen, oxygen, and nitrogen, that make up the bodies of living things pass through food webs and are combined and recombined in different ways in different living organisms. For example, plants trap carbon dioxide and water molecules in energy-rich compounds (such as glucose and starch) during photosynthesis. When plants need energy to power their cell processes or are eaten by a consumer, these molecules may be broken down and used by the organism. During respiration, energy is released by the cells and molecules of carbon dioxide and water returned to the environment.

Much of the cycling of materials in ecosystems is carried out by decomposers. Figure 6-9 shows some of the ways matter cycles throughout the ecosystem.

Review Questions

28. Decomposition and decay of organic matter are accomplished by the action of

(1) green plants
(2) bacteria and fungi
(3) viruses and algae
(4) scavengers

29. Which statement best describes energy transfer in a food web?

(1) Energy is transferred to consumers, which convert it to nitrogen and use it to make amino acids.
(2) Energy from producers is converted into oxygen and transferred to consumers.
(3) Energy from the sun is stored in green plants and transferred to consumers.
(4) Energy is transferred to consumers, which use it to produce food.

30. Organisms that eat goats obtain less energy from the goats than the goats obtain from the plants they eat. This is because the goats

(1) pass on most of the energy to their offspring
(2) convert solar energy to food energy
(3) store all of their energy in milk
(4) use energy for their own metabolism

Base your answers to questions 31 and 32 on the energy pyramid below and on your knowledge of biology.

31. If birds eat insects that feed on corn, which level on this pyramid would birds occupy?

(1) A   (2) B   (3) C   (4) D

32. Which statement concerning the energy in the pyramid is correct?

(1) The producer organisms contain the least amount of energy.
(2) Stored energy decreases as it is passed from consumer to consumer.
(3) Consumers contain more energy than producers.
(4) Decomposers are the source of energy for this pyramid.

33. Most green algae are able to obtain carbon dioxide from the environment and use it to synthesize organic compounds. This activity is an example of

(1) cellular respiration
(2) autotrophic nutrition
(3) heterotrophic nutrition
(4) heterotrophic respiration

Base your answers to questions 34 through 37 on the activities described in the paragraphs below and on your knowledge of biology.

A tomato plant was placed under a sealed bell jar and exposed to light. Carbon dioxide containing radioactive carbon was introduced into the bell jar as shown in the following diagram. After an hour, the inlet valve was closed. Later, the entire plant was removed from the soil and cleaned by rinsing it in water.

A Geiger counter indicated radioactivity in the roots. These roots were then dried and chopped into very small pieces. The chopped roots were sprinkled into an aquarium containing a very hungry goldfish that was *not* radioactive.

Four days later, the fish was removed from the aquarium and a tissue section of the fish was tested with the Geiger counter. The counter indicated an above-normal level of radioactivity in the fish tissues.

34. Which cycle is primarily being studied by means of this investigation?

(1) oxygen   (3) nitrogen
(2) carbon   (4) water

35. A control setup for this investigation would be identical to the one described except for the replacement of the

(1) tomato plant with a geranium plant
(2) goldfish with a tadpole
(3) radioactive carbon dioxide with atmospheric carbon dioxide
(4) soil with distilled water

36. By which process was the radioactivity incorporated into the material that was transported to the roots?

(1) growth   (3) photosynthesis
(2) mitosis   (4) respiration

37. This investigation suggests that when plants are eaten by animals, some of the plant materials may be

(1) changed to animal tissue
(2) separated into smaller molecules before being digested
(3) eliminated by the animal in a form that allows the plant to grow again
(4) used in regulating the animal's digestive processes

38. A cycling of materials is represented in the diagram below.

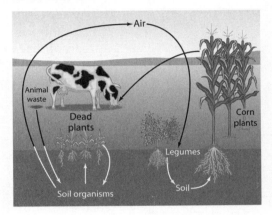

Which statement is supported by the events shown in the diagram?

(1) Materials are cycled between living organisms only.
(2) Materials are cycled between heterotrophic organisms only.
(3) Materials are cycled between the living and nonliving components of the environment only.
(4) Materials are cycled between autotrophic organisms only.

39. Which ecological principle is best illustrated by the diagram below?

(1) In an ecosystem, material is cycled among the organisms and the environment.
(2) In an ecosystem, the number of producers and consumers is equal.
(3) Competition within a species results in natural selection.
(4) An ecosystem requires a constant source of energy.

Diversity Benefits Species and Habitats

As a result of evolution, there is a great diversity of species on Earth. Almost every ecosystem is populated by many species, each occupying its own special niche. The interrelationships and interdependencies of these species help to keep ecosystems stable, and the diversity of species increases the chance that at least some organisms will survive in the face of large environmental changes.

Biodiversity is a measurement of the degree to which species vary within an ecosystem. There is a strong connection between biodiversity and the stability of an ecosystem. A natural forest, for example, contains many different species of trees. If disease or insects attack one population, nearby trees of another species are likely to survive. The mix of species in the ecosystem also makes it difficult for the disease organisms to move quickly through this environment. Here, biodiversity serves as a barrier to the spread of disease or insect attack. In contrast, on a tree farm where all of the trees are planted and are of a single species, the entire population could be seriously damaged by a single disease or insect attack.

The interactions between organisms may allow an ecosystem to remain stable for hundreds or thousands of years. In established, stable ecosystems, populations tend to increase and decrease in size in a predictable pattern. Over time, however, the size of the population remains relatively stable. For example, when the prey population increases, a large food supply causes the size of the predator population to rise. Because each predator requires many prey to meet its energy needs, the prey population rapidly decreases. Soon, with the decline in a prey population, some of the predators begin to starve. When only a few predators remain alive, the prey population reproduces and greater numbers of prey survive. The cycle begins anew. Figure 6-10 illustrates the seasonal change in a rabbit population.

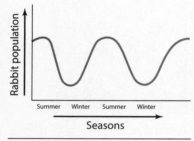

Figure 6-10. Rabbit populations: Rabbit populations may rise and fall over the course of a year, but from year to year they follow the same pattern if the environment is stable.

The loss of biodiversity in an ecosystem upsets its stability. Removing species from an environment often causes instability due to the loss of organisms that were filling critical ecological niches.

Many species may be lost when natural disasters or human activities cause large-scale destruction to habitats. Clearing large areas of tropical rain forest, for example, has disrupted many ecosystems; some may never recover. Although some species may be able to return to a damaged ecosystem, others with critical roles may be totally lost. The interdependencies between populations in the original ecosystem may have been so great that if biodiversity is lost, the ecosystem may never be restored to its original state.

Species can also be lost when humans do not consider the environmental impact of their actions. For example, offering bounties for the removal of predatory mountain lions from some environments sounded like a good idea at one time, but it led to population explosions of deer herds. Soon the deer overpopulated the area, and their overgrazing reduced the food supply so much that many deer starved. The overgrazing also led to soil erosion that caused permanent environmental damage.

When humans clear land for agricultural purposes, the loss of biodiversity may also lead to an unstable environment. Disease and insect pests present major problems to farmers whose crops are genetically similar. For these farmers, any disruption threatens to affect the entire crop. Farmers are constantly in search of ways to control insect pests and diseases in their crops, because they have created an environment that is always in danger of serious disruption. In natural ecosystems, the diversity of species provides no such concentration of one kind of food, making it far less likely that any single pest or disease will cause problems.

Biodiversity Benefits Humans

Biodiversity also represents one of the greatest resources known to humans. It ensures the availability of a rich variety of genetic material, some of which may prove valuable to humans. Though still largely untapped, the genetic diversity found in rain forests has provided humans with medicines, insecticides, and other useful resources. If we destroy ecosystems, we lose much of the biodiversity they hold. As diversity is lost, potentially valuable resources are lost with it.

Review Questions

Base your answers to questions 40 and 41 on the information and graph below and on your knowledge of biology.

During the 1970s, Canadian forests in New Brunswick were heavily sprayed to control the spruce budworms that were damaging the spruce trees. Ecologists discovered that, along with the budworm, bees of many species—including sweat bees and bumblebees—had also been killed. All of the bees were important for pollinating flowers so the plants could produce fruit. Miles away from the spruce forests, blueberry growers were devastated when their blueberry yield declined by 75 percent over the same time period as the spraying was taking place. The graph shows the biodiversity present in the Canadian spruce forests prior to, during, and after the spraying.

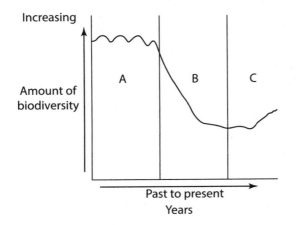

40. As the number of insect species declined due to spraying, the blueberry production decreased. Explain how these two events might be related even though the pesticide did not land directly on the blueberry plants. [1]

41. On the graph provided below, draw a line that shows the relationship of ecosystem stability to changes in biodiversity. [1]

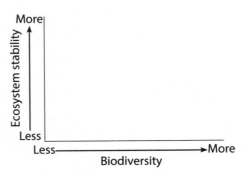

42. Explain why medical researchers are concerned when the biodiversity of an ecosystem decreases. [1]

43. The color, taste, and juiciness of a particular variety of strawberry makes it very popular. Growers are able to plant hundreds of acres of this variety, and all the plants are exactly the same, since they reproduce asexually. Explain why this lack of diversity in the strawberry field could prove to be a problem for the growers. [1]

44. The graph shows the biodiversity present in four different species living in the same area.

If the environment were to change dramatically or if a new plant disease were to be introduced, which plant species would be the most likely to have individuals that could survive the disease?

(1) Species A　　(3) Species C
(2) Species B　　(4) Species D

45. A forest community is made up of thousands of species of organisms and can exist practically unchanged for hundreds of years. This stability is due to the

(1) diversity of organisms present
(2) abundance of insects that feed on plants
(3) changes in the climate of the area
(4) lack of decomposers in the forest

Environmental Changes

Many environments, such as the bare rock on a mountaintop, have few resources that can provide homes for living organisms. Through natural processes, these environments will change over long periods of time to become habitats for many diverse species. The series of changes by which one habitat changes into another is called **ecological succession.**

In the process of ecological succession, each community causes modifications to its environment. The modifications result in changes that make it more suitable for another community. The original species that lived there may find it harder to adapt to these changes, while the new species coming in may be able to compete more successfully for the new niches.

For example, as grasses grow in an area with very shallow soil, they add organic matter, making the soil deeper and more fertile. Shrubs are then able to live in this modified environment and will eventually produce enough shade to eliminate the grasses growing below them. Over a period of many years, these gradual changes may result in the formation of a stable forest community that can last for hundreds or even thousands of years. (In dry or cold climates, succession may not advance to the forest stage, but the final stage will be a stable ecosystem that can last for many years.)

Climatic changes, natural disasters, and the activities of animals (including humans) can alter stable ecosystems. These changes may occur rapidly, perhaps due to a forest fire or flood, or slowly, as when a long-term drought or climate change occurs. Altered environments undergo a slow series of successional changes that return them to a point where long-term stability is possible. In this process, an existing community of organisms is replaced by different communities over a period of time ranging from a few decades to thousands of years.

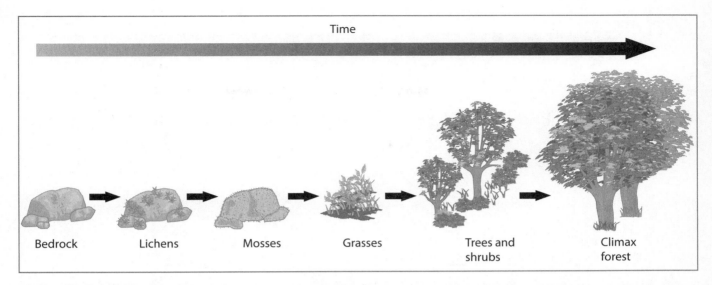

Time

Bedrock → Lichens → Mosses → Grasses → Trees and shrubs → Climax forest

Figure 6-11. Succession from bare rock to a forest: As the depth of the soil increases, it can support the root systems of larger plants.

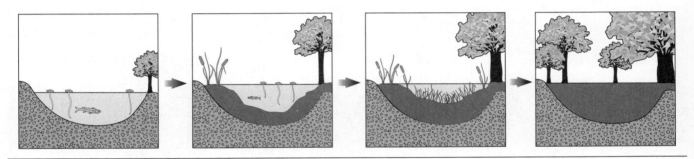

Figure 6-12. Succession from a lake to a forest

There are two commonly observed patterns of succession. A community of mostly bare rock will gradually accumulate soil, leading to a progression of vegetation types from grasses to shrubs, and eventually a forest. This process is seen in Figure 6-11.

Another commonly observed example of ecological succession is the change from a lake community to a forest. The lake will gradually accumulate sediments from erosion and the buildup of organic debris from plants and dead organisms. As the lake fills in, it becomes shallower. After many years, it may become a swamp. The filling-in continues, and eventually a mature forest may result. Successional changes from lake to forest are shown in Figure 6-12.

Base your answers to questions 46 through 49 on the sequence of diagrams below and on your knowledge of biology.

1840

1870

1900

1930

1960

1990

46. This sequence of diagrams best illustrates

(1) succession
(2) evolution
(3) the effects of acid rain
(4) a food chain

47. If no human intervention or natural disaster occurs, by the year 2050 this area will most likely be a

(1) lake   (3) desert
(2) swamp   (4) forest

48. The natural increase in the amount of vegetation from 1840 to 1930 is related to the

(1) decreasing water depth
(2) increasing amount of sunlight
(3) presence of bottom-feeding fish
(4) use of the pond for fishing

49. Describe what would happen over the fifty years following 1990 if a fire burned off all of the vegetation in the area. [1]

Base your answers to questions 50 and 51 on the information below and on your knowledge of biology.

If you travel inland from the shores of the present Lake Michigan, which was once much larger than it is today, you would travel through the following areas:

1. the present sandy beach
2. grasses
3. a cottonwood forest
4. a pine forest
5. an oak forest
6. a beech-maple forest (where the original shoreline was located)

50. The sequence of plant growth is an illustration of

(1) succession
(2) a food chain
(3) evolution
(4) an autotroph pyramid

51. Describe why the plants growing in the area of the old shoreline are beech and maple trees and no longer the grasses observed near the new shoreline. [1]

52. When a stable forest community is destroyed by fire, the community usually is

(1) not restored
(2) restored in a series of successive changes
(3) restored only if humans reforest the area
(4) changed into a permanent grassland

53. The conditions that existed in a forest before a fire will be established mainly by

(1) the water cycle
(2) the carbon cycle
(3) succession
(4) evolution

54. Which statement accurately describes ecological succession?

(1) The lack of animals in an altered ecosystem speeds up the process of natural succession.
(2) Abrupt changes in an ecosystem only result from human activities.
(3) After a major disaster, stable ecosystems can never become established again.
(4) An abrupt change in an ecosystem can lead to a long-term gradual change.

55. When Mount St. Helens erupted in 1980, a portion of the surrounding area was covered by lava, which buried all of the vegetation. Four months later, *Anaphalis margaritacea* plants were found growing out of lava rock crevices. The beginning of plant regrowth in this area is a part of the process known as

(1) species preservation
(2) evolution
(3) biotic competition
(4) succession

Base your answers to questions 56 through 58 on the diagram below, which represents the changes in an ecosystem over a period of 100 years, and on your knowledge of biology.

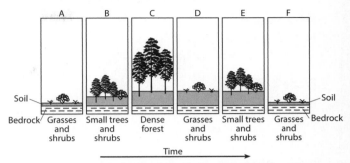

56 State one biological explanation for the changes in types of vegetation observed from *A* through *C*. [1]

57 Identify one human activity that could be responsible for the change from *C* to *D*. [1]

58 Predict what would happen to the soil and vegetation of this ecosystem after stage *F*, assuming no natural disaster or human interference. [1]

59 The diagrams below show some changes in an environment over time.

Which phrase best describes this sequence of diagrams?

(1) the path of energy through a food web in a natural community
(2) the altering of an ecosystem by a natural disaster
(3) natural communities replacing each other in an orderly sequence
(4) similarities between an aquatic ecosystem and a terrestrial ecosystem

Directions

Review the Test-Taking Strategies section of this book. Then answer the following questions. Read each question carefully and answer with a correct choice or response.

Part A

1 The members of an animal community are usually similar in
   (1) size
   (2) structure
   (3) food requirements
   (4) environmental requirements

2 Which is a biotic factor that affects the size of a population in a specific ecosystem?
   (1) the average temperature of the ecosystem
   (2) the number and kinds of soil minerals in the ecosystem
   (3) the number and kinds of predators in the ecosystem
   (4) the concentration of oxygen in an ecosystem

3 An overpopulation of deer in a certain area will most likely lead to
   (1) a decrease in the number of predators of the deer
   (2) an increase in the number of autotrophs available for food
   (3) a decrease in the incidence of disease
   (4) an increase in competition between the deer

4 A farmer abandons one of his fields, and over the years, he notices that one field community is replaced by another community. This replacement represents part of
   (1) a food chain
   (2) an abiotic community
   (3) an energy pyramid
   (4) an ecological succession

5 An ecosystem, such as an aquarium, is self-sustaining if it involves the interaction between organisms, a flow of energy, and the presence of
   (1) an equal number of plants and animals
   (2) more animals than plants
   (3) material cycles
   (4) organisms undergoing succession

6 In order to be self-sustaining, an ecosystem must contain
   (1) a large number of organisms
   (2) a warm, moist environment
   (3) a constant source of energy
   (4) organisms that occupy all of the niches

Part B

Base your answers to questions 7 through 9 on the graph below and on your knowledge of biology. The graph illustrates a comparison between pH conditions and species survival rates in certain Adirondack lakes.

The Effect of pH on Survival Rates of Selected Species in Certain Adirondack Lakes

KEY:
A–pH of a certain group of Adirondack lakes, 1880
B–pH of rainfall, 1880
C–pH of the same group of Adirondack lakes, 1980
D–pH of rainfall, 1980

–*National Geographic* (adapted)

7 Which species can tolerate the highest level of acidity in its water environment?
   (1) mussels   (3) brown trout
   (2) smallmouth bass (4) lake trout

8 In the years between 1880 and 1980, which species would most likely have been eliminated FIRST due to the gradual acidification of Adirondack lakes?
   (1) mussels   (3) brown trout
   (2) smallmouth bass (4) lake trout

9 What was the total change in pH in the rainwater from 1880 to 1980?
(1) 1.3　　(2) 1.7　　(3) 5.3　　(4) 9.7

10 Which types of organisms must be present in an ecosystem if the ecosystem is to be maintained?
(1) producers and carnivores
(2) producers and decomposers
(3) carnivores and decomposers
(4) herbivores and carnivores

11 Although three different bird species all inhabit the same type of tree in an area, competition between the birds rarely occurs. The most likely explanation for this lack of competition is that these birds
(1) have different ecological niches
(2) eat the same food
(3) have a limited supply of food
(4) are unable to interbreed

12 Producer organisms function to
(1) store more energy than they use
(2) use more energy than they store
(3) store energy but not use it
(4) use energy but not store it

13 Which foods are derived from organisms that occupy the level that contains the greatest amount of energy in an energy pyramid?
(1) bread and tomatoes
(2) shrimp and rice
(3) hamburger and French fries
(4) chicken and lettuce

14 Which organism shown in the food web below would most likely be adversely affected by a continuous decrease in the population of mice?

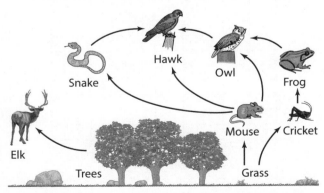

(1) grass　(2) elk　(3) crickets　(4) hawks

15 Which pair of terms would most likely apply to the same organism?
(1) heterotroph and herbivore
(2) heterotroph and autotroph
(3) autotroph and parasite
(4) producer and predator

16 In the diagram of a food web below, which organisms are most likely to be competitors?

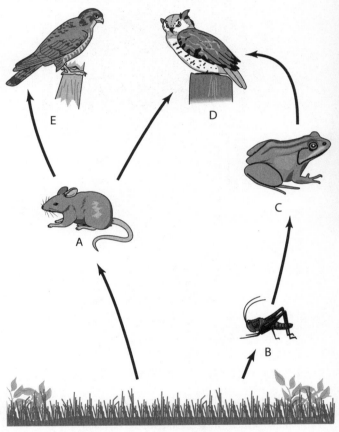

(1) A and C　　　(3) B and C
(2) B and D　　　(4) D and E

17 In the following food chain, which are the most abundant organisms?

corn plants → field mice → garter snakes → red-tailed hawks

(1) corn plants　　　(3) garter snakes
(2) field mice　　　(4) red-tailed hawks

Base your answers to questions 18 through 21 on the graphs below that show data on some environmental factors affecting a large New York lake.

18 Which relationship can be correctly inferred from the data present?

(1) As sewage waste increases, the oxygen content decreases.
(2) As sewage waste increases, the oxygen content increases.
(3) As oxygen content decreases, the carp population decreases.
(4) As oxygen level decreases, the trout population increases.

19 The greatest change in the lake's whitefish population occurred in the years between
(1) 1950 and 1955   (3) 1960 and 1965
(2) 1955 and 1960   (4) 1965 and 1970

20 Name the fish species that appears to withstand the greatest degree of oxygen depletion. [1]

21 Explain the impact of increased sewage levels on the biodiversity of the lake ecosystem. Support your answer with specific examples from the graph. [1]

Base your answers to questions 22 through 25 on the information below and data table.

A field study was conducted to observe a deer population in a given region over time. The deer were counted at different intervals over a period of 40 years. During this period, both ranching and the hunting of deer and their predators increased in the study region. A summary of the data is presented in the table.

Deer Population Changes 1900-1940

Year	Deer Population (thousands)
1900	3.0
1910	9.5
1920	65.0
1924	100.0
1926	40.0
1930	25.0
1940	10.0

Using the information in the data table, construct a line graph on the grid following the directions below.

Deer Population Changes 1900-1940

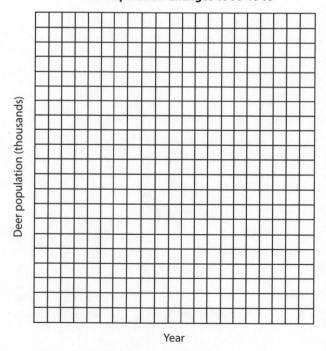

22 Mark an appropriate scale, without any breaks, on each labeled axis. [1]

23 Plot the data for the deer population on the grid. Surround each point with a small circle and connect the points. [1]

Example:

24 During which 10-year period did the greatest increase in the deer population occur?
(1) 1900–1910   (3) 1920–1930
(2) 1910–1920   (4) 1930–1940

25 State one possible action that could have been taken to help maintain a more stable population of deer in the area. [1]

Base your answers to questions 26 through 29 on the information below and on your knowledge of biology.

For 25 years, hay was cut from the same 10 acres on a farm. During these years, shrews, grasshoppers, spiders, rabbits, and mice were seen in this hayfield. After the farmer retired, he no longer cut the hay, and the field was left unattended.

26 Which description best matches the events in the former hayfield over the next few decades?
(1) The plant species will change, but the animal species will remain the same.
(2) The animal species will change, but the plant species will remain the same.
(3) Neither the plant species nor the animal species will change.
(4) Both the plant species and the animal species will change.

27 The grasshoppers, spiders, shrews, and other organisms, along with the soil minerals, amount of rainfall, and other factors, constitute
(1) an ecosystem   (3) a biosphere
(2) a species   (4) a food web

28 Just before he retired, the farmer determined the population size of several of the field species during the months of May, July, and August. The results are recorded in the table below.

Field Species	Number of Organisms		
	May	July	August
Grasshoppers	1,000	5,000	1,500
Birds	250	100	100
Grasses	7,000	20,000	6,000
Spiders	75	200	500

Draw a food chain that represents the most likely feeding relationships among four of the organisms (grasshoppers, birds, grasses, and spiders) that live in the field. [1]

29 Which graph best represents the relative population size of the field species for May?

Base your answers to questions 30 and 31 on the information below and on your knowledge of biology.

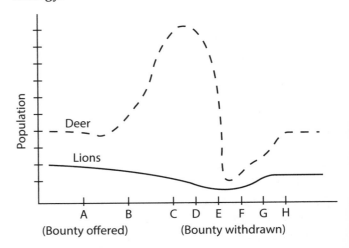

The graph shows the relative populations of mountain lions and deer in a certain geographic area that is generally favorable to both animals. At the time indicated by point A, hunters were offered a bounty payment for each mountain lion killed. Later, at the time indicated by point E, these bounties were withdrawn and hunting mountain lions was discouraged.

30 Which explanation best accounts for the fact that, according to the graph, the deer population is always higher than the mountain lion population?
   (1) The geographic location is more favorable for deer than for mountain lions.
   (2) Hunters are likely to kill more mountain lions than deer.
   (3) The organism serving as the food supply is normally more numerous than its predator.
   (4) Mountain lions usually produce more offspring than deer.

31 The graph is an illustration of the principle that
   (1) predators serve an important purpose in a balanced ecosystem
   (2) human intervention has little permanent impact on the survival of animal species
   (3) deer need the protection of humans in order to survive the attacks of their natural enemies
   (4) mountain lions do not pose the greatest danger to deer in their struggle for survival

Part C

32 Provide two reasons why it is important to preserve biodiversity. [2]

33 Explain the difference between a habitat and a niche. [2]

34 A predator affects the population of its prey, but a parasite may not have the same effect on its host population. Explain why. [1]

35 Predict what would happen to a natural community if the number of carnivores present suddenly doubled. [1]

36 If you introduced a population of rabbits into a huge field and then made sure that they had all of the food and water they needed, would the population continue to increase in size forever? Support your answer with an explanation. [1]

37 Imagine that you are stuck on a deserted island and will not be rescued for weeks. The only food you have available is two chickens and a bushel of corn. Due to environmental conditions, it is impossible for you to grow the corn. The only way to keep the chickens alive is to feed them the corn. Read the following choices, and then select the choice that provides you with the best chance of surviving until rescuers arrive. Identify your choice, and then explain your selection, addressing the pros and cons of all three choices. [4]

Choice A: You and the chickens eat the corn first, and then you eat the chickens.

Choice B: You eat the chickens first, and then eat the corn.

Choice C: You feed the corn to the chickens and eat the eggs. Later, you eat the chickens.

Base your answers to questions 38 through 41 on the information below and on your knowledge of biology.

A student uses a covered aquarium to study the interactions of biotic and abiotic factors in an ecosystem. The aquarium contains sand, various water plants, algae, small fish, snails, and decomposers. The water contains dissolved oxygen and carbon dioxide, as well as tiny amounts of minerals and salts.

38 Explain how oxygen is cycled between organisms in this ecosystem. [1]

39 Describe one specific way the fish population changes the amount of one specific abiotic factor (other than oxygen) in this ecosystem. [1]

40 Identify one source of food for the decomposers in this ecosystem. [1]

41 Describe one specific way the use of this food by the decomposers benefits the other organisms in the aquarium. [1]

42. Explain why an ecosystem with a variety of predator species might be more stable over a long period of time than an ecosystem with only one predator species. [1]

Human Impact on Ecosystems

What do You Think?

Global Warming

The hole in the ozone layer is the cause of global warming since it lets in more heat from the sun and warms the polar regions of the Earth.

Global warming is really a natural process. The Earth was first very cold and it has been getting warmer ever since.

Plants are a major cause of global warming since they give off so much carbon dioxide.

Global warming is partly the result of our burning so much fossil fuel like coal and gasoline.

Human Impact on Ecosystems

Vocabulary

carrying capacity	global warming	pollution
deforestation	industrialization	renewable resource
direct harvesting	nonrenewable resource	technology
energy flow	nuclear fuel	trade-off
fossil fuel	ozone shield	water cycle

Topic Overview

All living things affect the environment around them. Porcupines chew the bark from trees; squirrels break twigs as they leap from branch to branch. Generally, the changes to the environment are small. Humans, however, have made impressive technological achievements in the past few hundred years. As a result, we are now making significant changes in Earth's diverse environments. As the human population grows and our need for the resources to sustain our technology expands, the possibility that we will harm Earth's ecosystems increases. Our decisions about how to use—or misuse—Earth's resources will have a profound impact on all the organisms that depend on those resources.

Need for Awareness and Understanding

Human activities can create ecological problems that must be avoided or corrected. If we are to find solutions to those problems, we must encourage everyone to become environmentally literate. That means people need to understand the causes and effects of environmental problems as well as the possible solutions that could lead to environmental stability. Because environmental issues often concern many countries, resolving environmental issues frequently requires global awareness, cooperation, and action.

Our Environment

Like all living things, humans are part of Earth's natural ecosystems. We depend on our ecosystem to supply the food we eat, the water we drink, and the air we breathe. As long as our ecosystem functions normally, those essential resources will be available. We can continue to depend on the plants in the ecosystem to provide food and oxygen and to recycle the carbon dioxide we exhale. We will also be able to rely upon our ecosystem to maintain the quality of our water.

Limited Resources

Earth has a finite supply of resources. Some of Earth's resources, such as our food supply and solar energy, are renewable. Given sufficient time, renewable resources can be replaced. Other resources, such as fossil fuels and minerals, are nonrenewable resources. Once they're used, they cannot be replaced. Decisions we make today and tomorrow will determine whether or not we increase our consumption of Earth's limited resources. One way to reduce our use of resources is to control the growth rate of our population. An ever-increasing human population accelerates the use of Earth's limited resources. Making the right decisions about these issues will affect you as well as the future generations of all the organisms that share the biosphere.

Figure 7-1. **A commercial fishing trawler**

Renewable Resources Although many resources are renewable, they must be used carefully. Increased consumption can stress the natural processes that renew some resources. As a result, the resource might be unable to renew itself. For example, the fish we eat are a renewable resource. Even if many fish are captured, over time the fish populations can reproduce and recover their losses. Today, however, modern, commercial fishing (see Figure 7-1) can remove so many fish so quickly that specific populations may not have time to recover. In some cases, the reduction can be so severe that the fish population may fail to reproduce. At that point, the fish would no longer be a renewable resource.

Nonrenewable Resources Our increasing consumption of resources that cannot be replaced naturally is becoming a serious problem. Most metals, such as the aluminum we use for packaging, and other minerals, such as the silicon we use for computer chips, are nonrenewable resources. Fossil fuels, such as the gas that runs our cars and the coal that powers many factories, are also nonrenewable resources. Using too many nonrenewable resources will cause their depletion (serious reduction) within a relatively short time.

Preserving Our Resources Individuals can help maintain our supply of both renewable and nonrenewable resources by practicing the three R's: Reduce, Reuse, and Recycle. Suggestions are included in Table 7-1.

Natural Processes in Ecosystems

Several natural processes that occur in ecosystems affect the life and health of humans as well as all the other organisms that rely on the ecosystem. Some activities of humans affect these processes, and most of the changes are likely to be detrimental, or damaging, to the ecosystems. For example,

Table 7-1. How Individuals Can Preserve Resources		
The 3 R's	**Action**	**Example**
Reduce	Avoid using the resource.	Use energy efficiently; walk, bike or carpool instead of driving.
Reuse	Use the same product over and over, instead of throwing it away after one use.	Use dishes rather than paper plates. Instead of discarding your paper lunchbag, take it home and use it again.
Recycle	Don't throw it in the trash. Instead, discard the product in a way that it can be used again, or to make another product.	Paper, metal, plastic, and glass are all easily recycled. Donate unwanted clothing, books, and furniture to charitable organizations.

if **pollution**—a harmful change in the chemical makeup of the soil, water, or air—spreads to a particular habitat, some of the species that live in that habitat will suffer. The stability of the ecosystem and the variety of species that live in it might be threatened.

Maintaining Atmospheric Quality Throughout the biosphere, animals take in oxygen during respiration and release carbon dioxide. Plants and algae take in carbon dioxide during photosynthesis and release oxygen. Through the biotic processes of respiration and photosynthesis, the levels of carbon dioxide and oxygen in the atmosphere are kept in the range that is suitable for life.

Abiotic factors also help maintain the quality of the atmosphere. For example, as it falls, rain cleans the air of particles and soluble gases. The rainfall also helps maintain humidity in the atmosphere.

Soil Formation Soils form when weathering breaks down rocks and when organic materials from decaying plants and animals accumulate. Such soils support the growth of many producer organisms and serve as a habitat for decomposers. The root systems of plants hold the soil in place. If the vegetation that covers the ground is removed, the soil can be washed away by rain or blown away by wind. Soil erosion sometimes occurs during a drought when many plants die, leaving bare soil.

The Water Cycle Water continuously evaporates from the surface of the land and water and from the leaves of plants. The water vapor rises into the atmosphere and collects as clouds that can move long distances. Eventually, the vapor condenses as precipitation, which is distributed over many areas of Earth. The water collects as runoff or groundwater or evaporates. The process by which water continually moves from Earth's surface to the atmosphere and back is called the **water cycle,** and is shown in Figure 7-2. Many ecosystems maintain a supply of fresh water, which is available to all organisms, including humans.

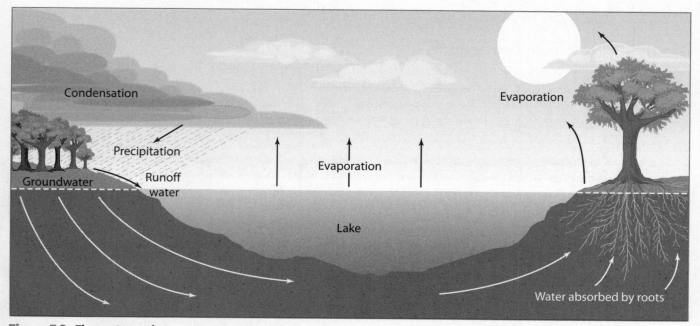

Figure 7-2. The water cycle

Waste Removal and the Recycling of Nutrients Plants that live in the soil use the soil's minerals as they grow. Nutrients are transported from one organism to another through the food chains in the ecosystem. Those that are not released into the atmosphere are eventually contained in the dead bodies and wastes of organisms. Decomposers break down the wastes and the dead bodies of organisms, removing the nutrients in the process. The nutrients are then restored to the soil, where they can then be used by other plants, continuing the cycle.

Without this natural recycling, much of the abiotic materials needed by living organisms would remain "locked up" in the bodies of dead organisms. Minerals and other nutrients would not be available for new organisms. In tropical forests, where heavy rains are frequent, decomposition and the recycling process must take place rapidly. Otherwise, the frequent rains strip the land of minerals before new plants can absorb and use them. In areas where the Amazon rain forest has been cleared and burned for planting, many nutrients have been washed away, leaving the soil unfertile.

Humans sometimes make use of this natural recycling process when they mix decaying lawn and garden wastes to make compost, which is a natural fertilizer and soil conditioner. Adding compost to the soil recycles wastes naturally and reduces the need for chemical fertilizers. It also reduces the amount of waste material in landfills and eliminates the need to burn yard waste, which pollutes our atmosphere.

The Flow of Energy Food chains, food webs, and energy pyramids illustrate the **energy flow** through ecosystems. Each organism has a role in the process and contributes to the overall stability of the ecosystem. As a result, losing all or most of the members of any species of an ecosystem could upset the stability of the whole ecosystem.

Energy is passed through the environment, but unlike nutrients, it does NOT recycle. Instead, at each feeding level in an energy pyramid, organisms lose large amounts of energy (as heat) to the environment. This energy cannot be recaptured by living things. Because of this constant energy loss, ecosystems need a constant source of new energy. That energy source is usually the sun.

People and the Environment

Because humans are part of Earth's ecosystems, they affect the way ecosystems function. They also are affected by changes in the ecosystem. Once the ecosystem is damaged, people may suffer from that damage just like any other species.

Population Growth

Most species in new environments can have a period of rapid population growth. The population increase levels off as it approaches the ecosystem's **carrying capacity,** which is the number of individuals of a species the environment can support. For example, as rabbits move into a field, their population may boom. Eventually, the food supply dwindles, and the scarcity of food leads to a reduction in the population of rabbits. Those that do not get enough to eat may become too weak to escape predators or

Figure 7-3. A population growth curve: In a new environment, the population usually increases quickly, but it stabilizes when it reaches the carrying capacity of that environment.

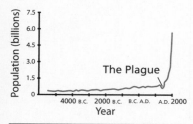

Figure 7-4. Growth curve for the human population worldwide

recover from diseases. Some may even die of starvation. The population growth levels off when the number of rabbits is balanced by the availability of food and the presence of limiting factors, such as predators. The relationship between population and the carrying capacity of an environment is shown in Figure 7-3.

Earth can only support a certain number of people. Our planet has a carrying capacity for humans just as it does for other species. The more people there are, the more resources they need. These resources come from the environment. More people also produce more waste, which must be disposed of or recycled. Overcrowding and lack of food also become problems when populations are very large.

For thousands of years, the human population grew slowly. Then about 300 years ago, our food supply began to increase, and improvements in health care and hygiene led to dramatic increases in our population. At present, the population curve inclines steeply upward. To many population scientists, the sharp increase suggests that the human population is growing at a dangerously fast rate. Compare Figure 7-4, the growth curve for the human population, with Figure 7-3, the growth curve typical for animals in an ecosystem.

If the human population continues to grow at the rate shown in Figure 7-4, Earth's carrying capacity could be reached soon. That result could be catastrophic. With no controls, the human population might even overshoot Earth's carrying capacity for our species. There might not be enough food, water, space, and/or oxygen. The resulting deaths from famine, disease, or wars over resources could reduce the human population to a small fraction of its present level. Finding ways to slow our population growth so that the growth rate levels off before Earth's carrying capacity is reached could save future generations from suffering the consequences of unlimited population growth.

Review Questions

1. Which of these resources is renewable?
   (1) wood
   (2) oil
   (3) iron
   (4) coal

2. The best way to ensure that there will be enough aluminum for all future needs is to
   (1) dig more mines and process more aluminum ore
   (2) buy more aluminum from other countries and save our own
   (3) recycle and reuse aluminum
   (4) increase space exploration and search for new sources of aluminum

3. Some ecologists are concerned that the human population has outgrown the capacity of many of Earth's ecosystems. The natural limiting factor that will most likely prevent further human population growth in many parts of the world is
   (1) habitat destruction
   (2) political intervention
   (3) food supply
   (4) social intervention

4. Which of these human activities is quite often responsible for the other three human activities?
   (1) increasing demand on limited food production
   (2) rapid increase of loss of farmland due to soil erosion
   (3) rapid increase of human population
   (4) increasing levels of air pollution

5. The graphs on the right show the size of the human population in relation to food production per acre in four different countries over the same period of time.

Which country's population appears to have reached—and is now maintaining—its population close to its carrying capacity? Explain how you can tell. [1]

Key ——————— Population size
‑ ‑ ‑ ‑ ‑ Food production/acre

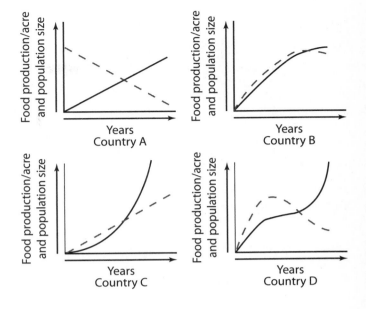

Human Activities and the Loss of Diversity

Some human activities that destroy habitats and degrade ecosystems do far more than damage individual organisms. They also destroy diversity in both the living and nonliving parts of the environment. For example, when humans use land to build a parking lot, the organisms that lived on that land are likely to die. Other organisms that ate the plants, burrowed through the ground, or nested in the nearby trees are also affected. There will be fewer resources available for a variety of species.

Many deliberate human activities, such as clearing land to plant a single crop, can change the equilibrium in an ecosystem. So can some accidents, such as inadvertently or unknowingly adding a species to an ecosystem.

Direct Harvesting The destruction or removal of species from their habitats is known as **direct harvesting.** It can sometimes lead to the extinction of a species. For example, some species that live in distant parts of the world (rain forests or deserts) are removed from their native habitats and sold to people who want them as unusual pets, ornaments, or house or garden plants. That cute monkey or beautiful parrot in the pet shop may not have been born in captivity. Instead, it may have been captured in the wild and shipped here. Many animals die in the process.

Other organisms are killed to collect a specific body part. For example, baby harbor seals are killed for their pelts, and elephants are killed for the ivory in their tusks, which people carve into jewelry or other trinkets. Direct harvesting can threaten the existence of the entire population of a species. Due to over-harvesting, some species of plants and animals have been taken from their native habitats in such large numbers that those species are now endangered. So many whales have been slaughtered that some species are now in danger of extinction.

In the past, humans have caused the extinction of several species. For example, in the early 1800s, billions of passenger pigeons lived in

Figure 7-5. The passenger pigeon: The passenger pigeon, once present in huge numbers, is now extinct because of uncontrolled hunting.

North America. (See Figure 7-5.) Each year hunters shot millions, until the population was greatly reduced. By the time people realized that the species was endangered, it was too late to save it. The last passenger pigeon died in a zoo in Cincinnati, Ohio, in 1914. Today, some endangered species are protected by law. However, because there may be a demand for products made from endangered species, <u>poaching</u> (illegally capturing or killing an organism) is a continuing problem.

Land Use As human populations grow, we use more resources to make the things we need or want, such as clothes, homes, refrigerators, MP3 players, and cars. We also need more space for places to live. More land is needed to grow food, to build roads and factories, and even to provide parks and recreational areas. As human populations and needs increase, our use of land decreases the space and resources available for other species.

Habitat Destruction Many people think that when a habitat is destroyed, the organisms simply find a new home. However, because other parts of the ecosystem are already occupied, displaced animals seldom find a new place to live. Habitat destruction occurs when people take over land for their own use. It is an important way that species can become endangered. They simply have nowhere to live! As habitats are destroyed, whole ecosystems can be damaged and entire species may become extinct. For example, pandas are endangered today because humans have greatly reduced the size of their habitat.

Deforestation, or the destruction of forests resulting from human activity, is a land use decision that causes widespread habitat destruction. People clear the forest by burning or cutting down the trees. Deforestation can provide people with land for farming and places to live. It also provides resources to use in building or manufacturing. Due to deforestation, the area covered by the world's rain forests is only about half as large as the area covered 150 years ago. (See Figure 7-6.) The wetlands, fields, and forests of New York are also threatened by development.

Biodiversity When a wide variety of different species live together in an ecosystem, it is said to have biodiversity. A reduction in biodiversity occurs when species are lost. This lost biodiversity can affect the health of whole ecosystems and food webs. It can even affect the proportion of gases in the atmosphere. Our future ability to find new medicines for treating diseases or to discover new sources of genes that could be genetically engineered into more productive and pest-resistant crops is threatened when biodiversity is lost.

Habitat destruction, such as deforestation, can lead to loss of biodiversity, but it is not the only way that human activities threaten biodiversity. For example, a farmer might plow under a meadow that is home to many species. Then the farmer might plant a single crop, such as corn or wheat, on many continuous acres of land. This practice greatly reduces the biodiversity of the area. (See Figure 7-7.) In addition, it creates an ideal environment for insects that feed on that crop. To control the insects, the farmer may need to use pesticides, which could harm other organisms living in the same or nearby environments.

Estimated Area of Rain Forest

Area (in millions of acres)

2400 · 1950 · 1975 · 2000
1800
1200
600

Figure 7-6. Habitat destruction: The destruction of rain forests, an example of deforestation, eliminates many ecosystems.

Figure 7-7. Loss of biodiversity: The corn in this field provides habitats for only a few species. The meadow that once grew here was home for hundreds of species of flowers, shrubs, trees and small animals such as insects, mice, and birds.

Imported Species Biodiversity is often reduced when people import and release a species from one environment into another. The release may be inadvertent or intentional. For example, before 1859, there were no rabbits in Australia. Then two dozen rabbits were released in Australia. By 1953, more than a billion rabbits occupied 1.2 million square miles of the continent. These rabbits ate massive amounts of vegetation ordinarily available to the native species.

Many species become pests when they are added to a new environment. Because the new organisms are not part of an existing food web in the area, they often have no natural enemies in their new environment and rapidly overpopulate the area. They then crowd out, feed on, or otherwise eliminate native species. Two examples are Japanese beetles and gypsy moths, which were accidentally released in the U.S. (See Figure 7-8.) Now they are serious pests in New York.

Once an imported species becomes a pest, it is very difficult to solve the problem. If another species is imported to control it, the second species may choose to feed on native organisms, adding another problem. Using pesticides or poisons can kill other organisms in addition to the imported one. Sometimes scientists find a disease organism that only affects the imported species. The rabbits that overran Australia were eventually controlled by a disease organism. However, there is always a risk that the species may become resistant to the disease and overpopulate again.

Because imported species are such a problem, many states and countries have laws to restrict the transport of fruits and vegetables. The goal of these laws is to avoid introducing diseases or insects that might damage local crops. Some countries require the <u>quarantine</u> (confined isolation) of certain animals and plants until officials are sure they are free of any pests that could escape into the new environment.

Scientists are working to find safer methods of pest control. One safe pest control method is setting traps that use chemical scents to attract insects. With this method, no other species are harmed and the population of the pest species can be reduced to a safe level. Breeding and releasing native predators of a pest species has also sometimes been used successfully and without harm to other species.

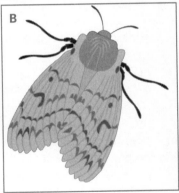

Figure 7-8. Imported species: (A) During the larval stage, the gypsy moth consumes vast quantities of leaves. (B) The adult moth lays hundreds of eggs, continuing the problem.

Review Questions

6. Ladybugs were introduced as predators into an agricultural area of the United States to reduce the number of aphids feeding on grain crops. This action is an example of
   (1) preservation of endangered species
   (2) conservation of natural resources
   (3) protection of watershed areas
   (4) use of a nonchemical means of pest control

7. An example of a human activity that has had a positive effect on the environment is the
   (1) disruption of natural habitats through deforestation
   (2) capture and sale of rare South American birds
   (3) use of reforestation to control erosion in the mountains
   (4) hunting of endangered species of animals

8. The trees in a forest aid in reducing flood damage chiefly because their
   (1) branches store water in the form of sap
   (2) leaves absorb moisture from the air
   (3) root systems hold the soil in place
   (4) stems serve to store food

9. The creation of wildlife refuges and the enforcement of game laws are conservation measures that promote increased
   (1) use of chemicals to control pests
   (2) preservation of species
   (3) use of natural controls to limit pest populations
   (4) exploitation of wildlife species

10. When land is cleared for agriculture or home construction, small isolated sections of the original habitat may remain. Explain how this reduction in habitat size and the isolation of small sections of habitat might lead to species endangerment. [1]

11. A method of agriculture presently used throughout the world where one crop is grown on many acres of land has created serious insect problems. This is primarily because this method
    (1) increases soil erosion
    (2) provides concentrated areas of one kind of food for insects
    (3) increases the effectiveness of insecticides used over long periods of time
    (4) involves the growing of crops in former desert areas

12. The least ecologically damaging method for controlling the mosquitoes that spread the diseases malaria and encephalitis is by
    (1) draining the swamps where mosquitoes breed
    (2) spraying swamps with chemical pesticides
    (3) spreading oil over swamps
    (4) introducing local fish species to the swamps where mosquitoes breed

13. Many people place bat boxes on their property to provide housing that attracts insect-eating bats. Explain how this activity has a positive effect on the environment. [1]

14. In 1859, a small colony of 24 rabbits was brought to Australia. By 1928 it was estimated that there were 500 million rabbits in a 1-million square mile section of Australia. Which statement describes a condition that probably contributed to the increase in the rabbit population?
    (1) The rabbits were affected by many limiting factors.
    (2) The rabbits reproduced by asexual reproduction.
    (3) The rabbits were unable to adapt to the environment.
    (4) The rabbits had no natural predators in Australia.

15. Humans are responsible for some of the negative changes that occur in nature because they
    (1) have controlled the use of many pesticides and other environmentally damaging chemicals
    (2) have passed laws to preserve the environment
    (3) are able to preserve scarce resources
    (4) are able to modify their physical environment to provide for human needs

16. Which of the following human activities would be the most likely to prevent certain species from becoming extinct?
    (1) Pass laws to place all endangered species in zoos.
    (2) Increase the hunting of predators.
    (3) Increase wildlife management and habitat protection.
    (4) Mate organisms from different species to create new and stronger organisms.

17. In the Cochella Valley in California, much of the desert has been converted into golf courses, housing developments, and hotels. The habitat of the Cochella Valley fringe-toed lizard is rapidly being lost. This lizard is adapted to life on fine, windblown sand. Environmentalists want to save the lizard, and developers want to continue construction. Which action would be the best long-term solution?

(1) Land in the Cochella Valley should be purchased and set aside as a preserve for the lizards.

(2) The fringe-toed lizards should be crossed with a species adapted for survival in a different habitat.

(3) The land should be developed as planned and the lizards relocated to a different valley.

(4) The land should be developed as planned and the lizards monitored to see if they can adapt to the new conditions.

18. Refer to the chart below, which illustrates some methods of pest control.

Methods of Insect Pest Control
Insect pests can be repelled or attracted with sex hormones.
Insect populations can be controlled by releasing males sterilized with X-rays.
New plant varieties can be produced and grown that are resistant to insect pests.
Insect pests can be controlled by introducing their natural enemies.

One likely effect of using these methods of pest control will be to

(1) prevent the extinction of endangered species
(2) increase water pollution
(3) reduce pesticide contamination of the environment
(4) harm the atmosphere

The Impact of Technology and Industrialization

Humans modify ecosystems through population growth, consumption, and technology. As human populations grow, they take up more space, consume more resources, and produce more wastes. The expansion of **technology** (using scientific knowledge and technical processes to meet human needs) also increases the quantity of resources people use. All these activities lead to changes in ecosystems, including the way they function. The equilibrium of stable ecosystems can be upset by human actions.

Industrialization

Industrialization is the development of an economy in which machines produce many of the products people use. These products may add to the quality of life, but their manufacture can harm the environment. In addition to contributing to pollution of the air and water, industrialization increases the demand for energy, water, and other resources, including fossil and nuclear fuels.

Higher energy demands in an industrialized society mean that more power plants must be built. Additional power plants—especially those that burn coal—add to the pollution of our air and water. **Nuclear fuel** is an energy source that results from splitting atoms. Nuclear power plants do not pollute the air or water with toxic chemicals, but they can cause thermal pollution of waterways. Also, the disposal of radioactive nuclear wastes presents a huge environmental problem.

Another problem with increased industrialization is that most factories use a lot of water. Large wells drilled for factories sometimes dry up the nearby smaller wells that individuals use to supply their homes. In some cases, withdrawing large quantities of water causes the ground to collapse, forming sinkholes. In dry climates, reducing the supply of groundwater can have serious consequences for native plants and the consumers that depend on them for food.

Figure 7-9. Water pollution: Water pollution, which can damage an ecosystem, comes from many sources.

Labels in figure: Acid rain from factory smoke; Acid water from mines; Crop dusting; Industrial waste; Barnyard waste; Nuclear reactor; Fertilizer and pesticide runoff; Sewage treatment plant; Oil pollution

Just as conservation (the three R's) can help preserve our resources, it can also help to limit the negative impact of industrialization. We can REDUCE our demand for energy and manufactured goods that we don't really need. We can REUSE manufactured products rather than discard them, and we can RECYCLE as many products as possible, conserving both energy and resources in the process.

Water Pollution

Rivers, lakes, and oceans are easy places for people to dispose of wastes, including sewage, wastes from homes and factories, and animal wastes from farms. The addition of pollutants to natural environments causes water pollution, which can change the abiotic conditions in ecosystems. For example, sewage and animal wastes can act as fertilizer, increasing the growth of plants, algae, and bacteria in aquatic systems. Plants consume oxygen all the time, day and night. However, photosynthesis, the primary source of oxygen, stops at night because it requires light. As a result, oxygen production also stops. Then, oxygen levels drop and many organisms suffocate. When these organisms die, oxygen-using decomposers begin their decay activity, which further decreases the oxygen supply. Eventually, all the organisms in this oxygen-reduced ecosystem may be lost. Figure 7-9 shows several ways water pollution can affect a natural habitat.

Toxic Wastes Many wastes dumped into waterways from cities, farms, or industries can be toxic (poisonous) to the organisms that use or live in the water. Chemical fertilizers and weed and insect killers can be washed off farmlands into streams or rivers. The chemicals can collect in the cells of organisms living in the water and along the shore. These toxic materials then move through the food chain and eventually damage or kill many kinds of organisms.

Although the level of toxic substances in the water might be low, scientists have learned that the concentration of a toxin increases as it moves through the food chain. For example, small quantities of toxic substances are absorbed into the cells of algae and other producers living in the water. When those producers are eaten by small herbivores, the toxins are stored in the herbivore's fatty tissue. There it stays until the herbivore is eaten by the next consumer in the food chain. At each level of the chain, larger and larger amounts of toxic material collect in the fatty tissue. Organisms at or near the top of the food chain are most likely to accumulate enough of these chemicals in their bodies to cause them harm. (See Table 7-2.)

For example, farmers used to spray the pesticide DDT on their crops. Rain washed some of the DDT off the land and into streams and rivers. In the water, the DDT moved up through the food chain. Soon, fish-eating birds at the top of the food chain produced eggs with very thin shells. The shells were so thin that they broke easily, which killed the next generation of birds before it even hatched.

Table 7-2. Accumulation of a Toxic Substance by Organisms in a Food Chain				
Food Chain Organisms	Plant —>	Herbivore —>	Carnivore 1 —>	Carnivore 2
Relative concentration of the toxic substance	.000003	0.04	0.5	2.0
Magnification factor (compared to the amount in the plant)	0	1,333 times as much	16,667 times as much	66,667 times as much

Thermal Pollution Some power plants and industries use water to cool their machines or materials. The warmed water is then released into a river or lake, and the water temperature in the river or lake rises. Because warm water cannot hold as much dissolved oxygen as cold water, the oxygen level in the river or lake drops as the water temperature rises. Some species may suffocate as a result of <u>thermal</u> pollution; others may be forced to try to find a new home.

The solution to most of these problems is to find better ways to deal with wastes and to reduce the need for power. Sewage can be treated before it is discharged into waterways. Toxic wastes can be separated from other materials and either recycled or stored safely. People could conserve energy by using less power. Methods could be developed for cooling industrial processes that would reduce their damage to the environment.

Air Pollution

Just as wastes dumped into rivers and oceans cause water pollution, harmful substances released into the air cause air pollution. Early in the industrial age, people thought that burning wastes just disappeared into the atmosphere, and that they didn't have to worry any more about the wastes. We now know this is not true! Most of the pollutants released into the atmosphere eventually wind up in the water cycle and return to the water or land. Like water pollution, air pollution can damage habitats and harm the organisms that live in them. Figure 7-10 shows how air pollution can affect a natural habitat.

Burning Fossil Fuels Fuels such as the coal and gas that formed from the remains of organisms that lived millions of years ago are known as **fossil fuels.** Factories, cars, and most electrical power-generating plants burn fossil fuels. When fossil fuels are burned, carbon dioxide and other gases— some containing sulfur and/or nitrogen—are added to the air.

Acid Precipitation Sulfur and nitrogen compounds that are produced when fossil fuels burn can combine with moisture in the atmosphere. When this moisture falls to Earth as <u>acid rain</u>, snow, or other precipitation, it has a low pH level and is much more acidic than normal precipitation. Some acid precipitation can be as acidic as lemon juice. When highly acidic rain or snow touches plants, it may damage them and disrupt the way they function. The damaged plants may be more susceptible to attacks by fungi or insects.

Acid precipitation can also fall into lakes and streams or run off the land into the water. In lakes, the lower pH levels can be deadly to algae, the eggs of some fish, and other organisms. Producer organisms, such as algae, are killed. Without algae suspended in it, the water looks crystal clear and pure. However, the food chains in the ecosystem have been disrupted, and

Figure 7-10. Air pollution: Trees can be damaged—or killed— by polluted air.

populations of fish and other organisms have died. Some lakes have become so acidic that nothing can live in them.

Smog Other air pollutants are produced by automobile exhaust and by industrial processes. Some of these pollutants can be toxic when inhaled. This kind of pollution becomes more serious when weather conditions trap the gases in an area for hours or even days. <u>Smog</u> is a kind of air pollution that results when certain pollutants react with sunlight. It looks like a gray or brown haze and contains many airborne pollutants. People with respiratory diseases are especially sensitive to air pollution and may be in danger when air pollution is intense.

Global Atmospheric Changes

Some pollutants in the air harm living things directly, like the trees in Figure 7-10. Others can cause worldwide atmospheric changes that threaten many habitats and the organisms that live in them.

Global Warming Sunlight passes through the gases in the atmosphere to reach Earth. But some of these atmospheric gases, called <u>greenhouse gases,</u> also trap and absorb the infrared radiation that bounces off Earth's warmed surface. For thousands of years, this process—called the <u>greenhouse effect</u>—has kept Earth warm. In recent years, however, the amount of greenhouse gases in the atmosphere has increased. As Figure 7-11 shows, the increased amount of greenhouse gases in Earth's atmosphere traps some of the heat that would normally radiate into space. The result is that Earth's average temperature is rising. This increase in temperature, called **global warming,** could lead to changes in climate patterns and even to the melting of the ice caps at the North and South Poles. Most of the recent increase in greenhouse gases has been caused by burning fuel for transportation and industry.

Carbon dioxide, a major greenhouse gas, is released when fossil fuels are burned. (See Figure 7-12.) If the greenhouse effect causes climate change, the world's food supply may suffer. Another effect could be that the ice

Figure 7-11. Global warming: Pollution caused by human activity is increasing the amount of greenhouse gases in the atmosphere. This increase can intensify the greenhouse effect, causing global warming.

caps could melt, leading to a rise in sea level and flooding in many coastal habitats.

Finding and using energy sources that do not add carbon dioxide to the atmosphere is one way to prevent further global warming. Because trees remove large quantities of carbon dioxide during photosynthesis and store it in their tissues as carbon compounds, growing more long-lived trees could also help solve the problem.

Ozone Depletion Ozone depletion is another atmospheric problem that we must solve. Like global warming, ozone depletion is a worldwide problem, and international cooperation is needed to find an effective long-term solution.

Figure 7-12. **Carbon dioxide in the atmosphere from 1750 to 2000:** The amount of carbon dioxide in the atmosphere has increased greatly since the beginning of the Industrial Revolution. The dots are data from ice core samples; the solid line represents direct measurements.

The release of certain industrial gases into the atmosphere has led to destruction of much of the **ozone shield,** the layer of ozone gas in the upper atmosphere that protects Earth from some of the sun's radiation. (See Figure 7-13.) The thinning "hole" in the ozone shield allows above normal amounts of ultraviolet radiation from the sun to reach Earth's surface. Ultraviolet radiation can cause genetic mutations and can kill cells that are exposed to it. An increase in ultraviolet radiation at Earth's surface could result in more cases of skin cancer. It could also destroy many of the producer organisms in the oceans. This would disrupt food chains and reduce the amount of oxygen released by the producers.

The main cause of ozone depletion is the release of gases called chlorofluorocarbons, or CFCs, into the atmosphere. CFCs have been used as coolants in refrigerators and air conditioners, as propellants in aerosol cans, and in the manufacture of plastic foam. Some steps have been taken to reduce the release of these gases. Researchers have found alternatives to the products that cause the most damage, and international agreements to reduce emissions of the harmful gases have been made.

Individual Choices and Societal Actions

Many people hope technology will help solve some of our environmental problems. In fact, technology has led to some improvements. For example, advances in technology have allowed farmers to greatly increase the crop yield of an acre of land. Larger crop yields mean a greater supply of food. However, some kinds of technology, such as pesticides and fertilizers, can cause pollution and have other harmful effects on the environment.

If technology cannot solve all our environmental problems, people will need to take some difficult steps to save our ecosystem. For some problems, solutions are now available, but they affect our quality of life. For example, we know how to reduce the air and water pollution caused by factories, power-generating plants, and automobiles, but the solutions are expensive and would make the

Figure 7-13. The "hole" in the ozone shield: These satellite maps show how much the "hole" in the ozone shield above the South Pole grew in just over a decade.

Figure 7-14. CFCs: Aerosol cans no longer use ozone-destroying CFCs as propellants. Safer alternatives have been found.

Figure 7-15. Public hearings: Discussion can be held to consider environmental issues and the trade-offs involved.

Figure 7-16. Recycling: Decisions on recycling are made by individuals and their communities.

products we buy cost more. We also know how to conserve energy, but many people are unwilling to give up their large cars, brightly lit neighborhoods, and air-conditioned comfort and to turn off their radios, computers, and televisions.

For each environmental problem, people must learn to assess the risk to the ecosystem. For each solution, they must learn to analyze the costs and benefits. Then they must determine which **trade-off,** or compromise, is acceptable and which is simply too dangerous to the welfare of future generations.

The Impact of New Technologies

New laws restrict the introduction of certain new technologies or major construction projects. The individual or company seeking permission to make a change that affects the environment must prepare a statement known as an environmental impact statement. This statement includes an analysis of how the project or technology will affect the environment and is usually discussed at public hearings. Then members of the public or their elected representatives vote on whether or not to allow the new technology or construction project to go forward. Appropriate decisions can be made only if the public is environmentally literate and has a clear understanding of the ecological issues. If an incorrect decision is made, it may be impossible to undo the damage that might result.

Today's Decisions Affect the Next Generation

The decisions we make today can have a huge impact on our environment. Those decisions, right or wrong, will affect the people living today as well as future generations.

The loss of some species may seem unimportant. However, the loss of that single species might have a huge impact on the ecology of an area. If the loss of species continues, large-scale destruction of natural environments will result, with serious consequences for the future. For example, the destruction of large forests or the loss of algae in ocean waters affects not only the organisms that live in those ecosystems but organisms elsewhere too. Those losses may compromise Earth's ability to produce enough oxygen and remove enough carbon dioxide to maintain an atmosphere that meets the needs of all of its inhabitants, including humans.

Many important decisions about the environment are made by states and nations, but a surprising number of important decisions are made each day by individuals. For example, individuals decide whether to burn their garden waste or turn it into compost, whether to toss the soda can into the trash or recycle it, whether to grab a fresh sheet of paper or write a note on an old envelope.

Much of the impact of our technology and population growth on Earth's ecosystems has been detrimental. If our environmental problems are not recognized and solved, the long-term damage will be irreversible and severe. On the other hand, cooperation by individuals and nations can help maintain the stability of the ecosystems upon which all life depends. Making people aware of the successful results of the collective actions of many separate individuals may be the most promising approach to solving ecological problems.

19. Plants help maintain the quality of the atmosphere by

    (1) storing carbon dioxide
    (2) opening holes in the ozone shield
    (3) causing global warming
    (4) storing oxygen

20. Greenhouse gases in the atmosphere

    (1) keep Earth warm
    (2) are released mostly from trees
    (3) are valuable as fuels
    (4) reduce holes in the ozone shield

21. Which human activity has probably contributed *most* to lake acidification in the Adirondack region of New York State?

    (1) passage of environmental protection laws
    (2) reforestation projects in lumbered areas
    (3) production of chemical air pollutants by industry
    (4) use of biological insect controls to eliminate pests

22. Identify one part of the water cycle that the burning of fossil fuels, such as coal and oil, directly affects. Support your answer. [1]

23. Explain how the runoff waters from farm land and golf courses might be dangerous to organisms living in ponds, rivers, or streams. [1]

24. Explain why water shortages occur frequently in parts of New York State even though the water supply is nearly constant. [1]

25. The number of industries along New York State's rivers is increasing. What is the most likely consequence of increased industrialization?

    (1) a decrease in the amount of water needed by industry
    (2) a decrease in the amount of water pollution
    (3) an increase in the destruction of natural ecosystems
    (4) an increase in the amount of water available for recreational use

26. To preserve the biosphere for future generations, humans must

    (1) make use of technology to develop new pesticides
    (2) put all wild animals in game preserves
    (3) explore ways to drain and fill wetlands along the seacoast
    (4) understand how living things interact with their environment

27. The use of technology often alters the equilibrium in ecosystems. With which of the following statements would most scientists agree?

    (1) Humans should use their knowledge of ecology to consider the needs of future generations of humans and other species.
    (2) Humans should develop new technology to expand the influence of humans in natural communities.
    (3) Humans should learn how to control every aspect of the environment so that damage due to technology will be spread evenly.
    (4) Humans should develop the uninhabited parts of Earth for human population expansion.

28. Which illustrates the human population's increased understanding and concern for ecological interrelationships?

    (1) importing organisms in order to disrupt existing ecosystems
    (2) allowing the air to be polluted only by those industries that promote technology
    (3) removing natural resources from the Earth at a rate equal to or greater than the needs of an increasing population
    (4) developing animal game laws in order to limit the number of organisms that may be killed each year

29. When living organisms obtain water and food from their environment, they may also take in toxic pesticides. Low concentrations of some pesticides may not kill animals, but they may damage reproductive organs and cause sterility. The data table below shows concentrations of a pesticide in tissues of organisms at different levels of a food chain.

Concentration of Pesticide in Tissues	
Organisms	Pesticide Concentration (parts per million)
producers	0.01 — 0.03
herbivores	0.25 — 1.50
carnivores	4.10 — 313.80

What does this information suggest to a person who is concerned about health and is deciding on whether to have a plant-rich or an animal-rich diet? Support your answer using the information provided. [1]

Directions

Review the Test-Taking Strategies section of this book. Then answer the following questions. Read each question carefully and answer with a correct choice or response.

Part A

1 Today's lifestyles have led to increased demands for disposable products. The packaging of these products has caused environmental problems most directly associated with
   (1) food web contamination
   (2) atmospheric depletion
   (3) solid waste disposal
   (4) the use of nuclear fuels

2 Some modern agricultural methods have created serious insect problems, primarily because these methods
   (1) increase soil loss
   (2) provide concentrated areas of food for insects
   (3) aid in the absorption of water
   (4) grow crops in areas where formerly only insects could live

3 The decline and extinction of many predatory animal species is most probably the result of
   (1) an overabundance of prey species
   (2) the introduction of a new species of animal into an area
   (3) the disruption of natural food chains
   (4) the decreased use of chemical pesticides

4 Modern methods of agriculture have contributed to the problem of soil depletion because many of these methods
   (1) require smaller amounts of mineral and fertilizer application
   (2) interfere with the natural cycling of elements
   (3) use many varieties of cloned plants
   (4) depend on the practice of planting and harvesting

5 Which action that humans have taken in attempting to solve an ecological problem has had the most negative effect?
   (1) seeking better means of birth control in the human population
   (2) applying scientific farming techniques to oceans
   (3) producing stronger and more effective pesticides
   (4) developing new techniques for the disposal of sewage and industrial and chemical wastes

6 Japanese beetles, a major insect pest in the United States, do relatively little damage in Japan because they
   (1) are kept in check by natural enemies
   (2) are kept in check by effective pesticide sprays
   (3) hibernate during the winter months
   (4) have gradually adapted to the environment

7 Gypsy moths were accidentally introduced into North America. The most probable reason these insects have become serious pests in North America is that they
   (1) were bred by research scientists and are resistant to all pesticides
   (2) are protected by environmental laws and feed on other insect species
   (3) have few natural enemies and reproduce successfully
   (4) are affected by natural controls and feed on plants

8 The survival of many plants and animals has been aided most by
   (1) increasing the height of industrial smokestacks to spread air pollutants away from the immediate vicinity of combustion
   (2) reduction in the number of restrictive pollution control laws
   (3) heavy use of pesticides to kill all of the insect pests that compete with humans for food sources
   (4) development of research aimed toward the preservation of endangered species

9 DDT is an insecticide that accumulates in the fatty tissues of animals and is transferred through food chains. Its concentration increases at each link of a food chain. Which organism in a food chain is most likely to accumulate the highest concentration of DDT?
   (1) rabbit (a herbivore)
   (2) corn (a producer)
   (3) field mouse (a consumer)
   (4) owl (a predator)

10 What is the most likely cause of the change in life expectancy shown in the graph below?

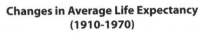

Changes in Average Life Expectancy (1910-1970)

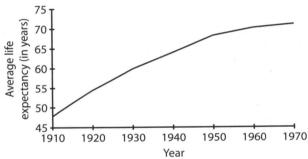

   (1) poor land-use management that has affected the quality of the topsoil
   (2) technological oversights that have had an impact on air quality
   (3) a decrease in natural checks, such as disease, on the population
   (4) widespread use of pesticides, such as DDT, in water supplies

11 A desired outcome derived from an understanding of the principles of ecology would be
   (1) the elimination of most predatory species
   (2) an increase in world human population
   (3) a decrease in disruptions of existing wildlife habitats
   (4) an increase in the amount of industrialization

Part B

Base your answers to questions 12 through 14 on the paragraph below and on your knowledge of biology.

A scientist studied a river and forest area downstream from a large city with an increasing human population. During the study, the scientist made observations that could be classified as:

   (A) Most likely a negative result of human activity
   (B) Most likely a positive result of human activity
   (C) Probably not influenced by human activity to any extent

Select the letter of the phrase from the list above that best fits the observation for each question. A letter may be used more than once or not at all.

12 Measurement of the levels of nitrates and phosphates (fertilizer chemicals from sewage) in the river that flows through the forest showed the following results:

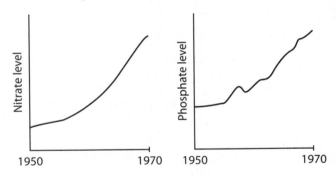

Which phrase from the choices listed above best fits this observation? [1]

13 After 1970, measurements showed that the concentration of dissolved oxygen in the river increased, while the concentration of suspended particles decreased. Which phrase from the choices listed above best fits this observation? [1]

14 The population of hawks declined, while their food sources increased. High levels of pesticides were found in the reproductive tissues of the hawks. Which phrase from the choices listed above best fits this observation? [1]

Base your answers to questions 15 through 18 on the diagram below and on your knowledge of biology. The diagram represents the growth rate of a mouse population introduced into an abandoned field ecosystem.

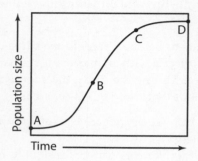

15 At what points is food most likely a limiting factor in the rate of mouse population growth?
(1) A and B
(3) C and D
(2) B and C
(4) B and D

16 At what point is the rate of population growth the greatest?
(1) A
(2) B
(3) C
(4) D

17 At what point would the mouse population be the greatest in the ecosystem?
(1) A
(2) B
(3) C
(4) D

18 Compare the growth rate of the mouse population in the abandoned field to the growth rate of the human population. In your comparison be sure to identify
• how it is similar [1]
• how it is different [1]

Base your answers to questions 19 and 20 on the information below and on your knowledge of biology.

Oak trees in the northeastern United States have survived for hundreds of years, in spite of attacks by native insects. Recently, the gypsy moth, which has a caterpillar stage that eats leaves, was imported from Europe. The gypsy moth now has become quite common in New England ecosystems. As a result, many oak trees are being damaged more seriously than ever before.

19 State one biological reason that this imported insect is a more serious problem for the trees than other insects that have been present in the area for hundreds of years. [1]

20 Identify the diagram that represents the stage of development of the gypsy moth in which it destroys the most deciduous trees and conifers in New York State. Support your choice with a biological explanation. [1]

(1)   (2)   (3)   (4)

21 Certain insects are kept under control by sterilizing the males with X-rays so that sperm production stops. Explain how this technique reduces the survival of this insect species. [1]

Base your answers to questions 22 and 23 on the information and graph below and on your knowledge of biology.

The screw-worm fly is a destructive parasite of livestock. The graph shows the results of an experiment in which one population of screw-worm flies was treated with pesticides and another group of equal size was treated with ionizing radiation, which made the male flies sterile.

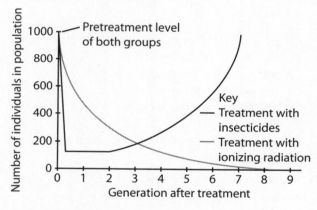

22 At what point after treatment will the group treated with pesticide probably reach its pretreatment population?
(1) first generation
(3) third generation
(2) seventh generation
(4) eighth generation

23 At what point after treatment will the sterility method be more successful against screw-worm flies than the pesticide method?
(1) immediately
(3) third generation
(2) second generation
(4) sixth generation

Base your answers to questions 24 and 25 on the information in the paragraph below and on your knowledge of biology.

A single protist (a one-celled organism) was placed in a large test tube containing nutrient broth. The tube was kept at room temperature for 24 hours. Samples from the tube were observed periodically during the 24 hours, using the low power of a compound light microscope. The data are summarized in the table below.

Age and Number of Protists in Culture	
Age of the Population in Hours	Number of Protists in the Population
0	1
6	2
8	3
10	4
13	8
16	16
18	32
20	64
22	128
24	256

24 Which graph best represents the data given in the table?

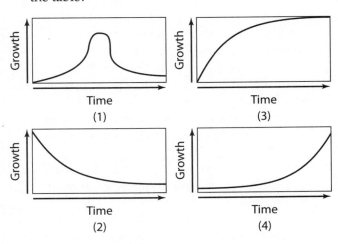

25 Which graph most resembles the growth of the human population at the present time?
(1) 1   (2) 2   (3) 3   (4) 4

26 The use of ionizing radiation in an attempt to control the screw-worm fly is a form of a pest control method referred to as biological control. The use of ladybugs to control aphids, milky spore disease to reduce Japanese beetle populations, and sex attractants to lure pest insects into traps are also examples of biological control strategies used against insect pests. State one reason why the use of biological control methods is often better than the use of chemical pesticides. [1]

Base your answers to questions 27 through 31 on the reading passage below and on your knowledge of biology.

The ecological balance of the Great Lakes has been seriously altered by human civilization, which has disrupted species in food chains from the producers (microscopic plankton) to the predator fish. This disruption has caused a reduction in the natural game fish populations of the lakes.

For example, the Atlantic salmon was formerly found in Lake Ontario. The salmon's passage to Lake Erie was blocked by Niagara Falls. The fish was a prize catch for fishermen, but no Atlantic salmon have been caught in Lake Ontario since 1890. Soil that eroded from farmland covered the salmon's gravel spawning grounds with silt, trees that shaded the streams where the young salmon lived were torn down as forests were cleared, and dams built for sawmills prevented the salmon from traveling upstream to spawn.

As the population of Atlantic salmon and other deepwater fish declined, two alien marine species—the alewife and the sea lamprey—appeared in Lake Ontario. These intruders most likely entered by way of the Hudson River, the Erie Canal, and the Oswego River. Lack of predators and the abundant food supply led to a rapid increase in the populations of these species until they were the dominant species in the lake. Furthermore, the completion of the Welland Canal, linking Lake Erie with Lake Ontario, in 1932 gave these species access to the remainder of the Great Lakes. By the early 1970s, about half the fish caught throughout the Great Lakes were alewives. The lamprey's increasing population devastated the desirable fish in the lakes, harming the fishing industry.

Government agencies, such as the United States Fish and Wildlife Service, took action at this point to restore game fish to the lakes and return sport fishing to this region. They developed a lampricide that proved fatal to the young sea lampreys, but had no harmful effects on other species. They also started stocking the lakes with predator game fish such as Coho salmon, Chinook salmon, and steelhead trout. As a result of these actions, the populations of the alewife and the sea lamprey have both decreased, and sport fishing has returned to Lake Ontario.

27 Which event would most likely have occurred if microscopic plankton had been removed from Lake Ontario when Atlantic salmon were abundant?
(1) Predator fish would have thrived.
(2) Game fish would have increased their spawning activities.
(3) Food chains would have been disrupted.
(4) The water level in the lake would have increased.

28 Which fish species was *not* introduced into the Great Lakes for sport fishing?
(1) Coho salmon   (3) alewife
(2) Chinook salmon   (4) steelhead trout

29 Which graph represents the effect of the spread of human civilization on the population of Atlantic salmon in Lake Ontario?

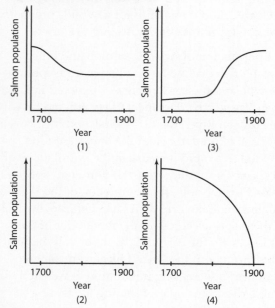

30 State one way humans contributed to the change in the Atlantic salmon population in Lake Ontario. [1]

31 Explain the role humans played in the appearance of the alewife and the sea lamprey in Lake Erie. [1]

Part C

32 For over 100 years scientists have monitored the carbon dioxide concentrations in the atmosphere in relation to changes in the atmospheric temperature. The graphs below show the data collected for these two factors.

Concentration of Carbon Dioxide in the Atmosphere

Average Atmospheric Temperature Change per Year

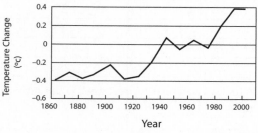

Discuss the overall relationship between carbon dioxide concentration and changes in atmospheric temperature and the effect of these factors on ecosystems. Your answer must include:
• a statement identifying the overall relationship between the concentration of carbon dioxide and changes in atmospheric temperature [1]
• one way in which humans have contributed to the increase in atmospheric carbon dioxide [1]
• one specific negative effect the continued rise in temperature would be likely to have on an ecosystem [1]
• one example of how humans are trying to reduce the problem of global warming [1]

Base your answers to questions 33 and 34 on the information below and on your knowledge of biology.

Cattail plants that grow in freshwater swamps in New York State are being replaced by an imported species of plant called purple loosestrife. The two species have very similar environmental needs.

33 Since cattails and loosestrife occupy the same niche, it is predicted that eventually only one of the two species will exist in New York freshwater swamps. State one reason why loosestrife will probably out-compete the cattails and be more successful. [1]

34 Explain why loosestrife plants replacing the native cattails could potentially cause a decrease in many swamp wildlife populations and perhaps even lead to the elimination of some species from New York State. [1]

---

35 Scientists have discovered a link between deforestation and global warming.
- Explain what is meant by the terms *deforestation* and *global warming*. [1]
- Describe the connection between the two terms. [1]

36 Describe two ways in which the destruction of the rainforest in South America could affect a hospital patient in New York State? [1]

37 The graph below shows the percentage of solid wastes recycled in New York State between 1987 and 1997.

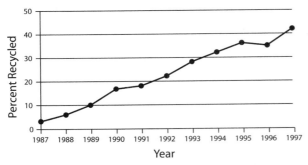

Discuss the impacts of recycling. In your answer be sure to:
- explain what recycling is and provide one example of a material that is often recycled [2]
- state one specific positive effect recycling has on the environment [1]

- state one specific reason that the percentage of solid wastes recycled increased between 1987 and 1997 [1]

38 Human activities continue to place strains on the environment. One of these strains on the environment is the loss of biodiversity.

Explain what this problem is and describe some ways humans are involved in both the problem and the possible solutions. In your answer be sure to:
- state the meaning of the term *biodiversity* [1]
- state one *negative* effect on humans if biodiversity continues to be lost [1]
- suggest one practice that could be used to preserve biodiversity in New York State [1]

Base your answers to questions 39 and 40 on the information below and on your knowledge of biology.

Plankton is the name given to the algae and microscopic life that grow in great numbers on and near the surface of the ocean. Plankton serve as the basis of food chains for oceanic life. Scientists have become concerned with the increase in ultraviolet (UV) radiation reaching the surface of the Earth in recent years. They fear that UV rays may negatively impact the plankton.

39 Explain why the amount of UV radiation reaching the surface may be on the increase, especially near the North and South Poles. [1]

40 Describe the effect any large-scale plankton destruction will have on larger species living in these same areas of the ocean where the UV levels have been increasing. [1]

---

41 Destruction of the ozone shield is generally considered a negative aspect of human involvement with the ecosystem. In your answer be sure to:
- Explain how solving this problem will require increasing global awareness and cooperation [1]
- Identify two trade-offs that may have to be considered in decisions regarding what to do about the problem [2]

Base your answers to questions 42 and 43 on the diagram below and on your knowledge of biology. The diagram represents a part of a food web in a Long Island ecosystem.

The numbers in the diagram show the concentration of the insecticide DDT in parts per million (ppm) in the body tissues of the various organisms.

Eel (0.28)

Osprey (13.8)

Water plant (0.08)

Fluke fish (1.28)

Merganser (22.8)

Mud snail (0.26)

Blowfish (0.17)

Cormorant (26.4)

42 Explain why the water plant contains the pesticide DDT. [1]

43 Explain why the amounts of DDT in the three bird species are so much higher than in the other organisms of this food web. [1]

Base your answers to questions 44 through 46 on the information below and on your knowledge of biology.

The planning board of a community held a public hearing in response to complaints by residents concerning a waste-recycling plant. These residents claim that the waste-hauling trucks were polluting air, land, and water and that the garbage has brought an increase in rats, mice, and pathogenic bacteria to the area. The residents were insistent that the waste-recycling plant be closed permanently.

Other residents recognized the health risks but felt that the benefits of waste recycling outweighed the health issues.

44 Identify *two* specific health problems that could result from living near the waste recycling plant. [1]

45 State *one* cause of a health problem that can be associated with the presence of the waste recycling plant. [1]

46 State *one* ecological benefit of recycling wastes. [1]

47 Ladybugs were introduced as predators into an agricultural area of the United States to reduce the number of aphids (pests that feed on grain crops). Describe the positive and negative effects of this method of pest control. Your response must include at least:
• *two* advantages of this method of pest control [1]
• *two* possible dangers of using this method of pest control [1]

48 Choose *one* ecological problem from the list below.

Ecological Problems
Global warming
Destruction of the ozone shield
Loss of biodiversity

Discuss the ecological problem you chose. In your answer be sure to state:
• the problem you selected and *one* human action that may have caused the problem [1]
• *one* way in which the problem may negatively affect humans [1]
• *one* positive action that could be taken to reduce the problem [1]

Scientific Inquiry and Skills

What do **YOU** *Think*?

Experimental Design

I am doing an experiment to determine the effect of different colors of light on photosynthesis. The dependent variable will be how fast the plants use carbon dioxide.

I am doing an experiment to determine the effect of temperature on the activity of a starch-digesting enzyme. The independent variable will be how fast the enzyme breaks down starch.

I am doing an experiment to determine the effect of different amounts of fertilizer on plant growth. My control group will get the most fertilizer.

TOPIC 8

Scientific Inquiry and Skills

Vocabulary

assumption	dependent variable	model
bias	evidence	observation
conclusion	experiment	opinion
control	hypothesis	peer review
controlled experiment	independent variable	research plan
data	inference	scientific literacy

Topic Overview

Science is both a body of knowledge and a way of knowing things. Through intellectual and social activities, human thinking is applied to discovering and explaining how the world works. Science originates when people ask questions. Scientists use scientific inquiry and skills to seek answers to questions about the world. This involves formulating hypotheses, designing and conducting experiments, collecting data, and analyzing the data to form conclusions. Scientists also rely on peer review by other scientists to confirm the validity of their results.

What Is Science?

At one time, "scientific" knowledge was just a collection of opinions and unrelated ideas attempting to explain observations. For example, many people gazing out over the ocean were certain that Earth was flat as shown in Figure 8-1. A few individuals were equally sure that Earth was round. The topic was hotly debated. Those believing that Earth was flat offered for **evidence** (support for the idea that something is true) the fact that some ships never returned home. They believed that these ships had been destroyed when they sailed over Earth's edge. Those who believed that Earth was round also had evidence. They had observed boats approaching land and noticed that the tops of the sails were visible before the hull of the boat.

Another common idea once was that living organisms could come from nonliving things. Some people believed that when conditions were just right, frogs formed from the mud, water, and gases in the bottom of a pond. People also thought that if you left some grain and a dirty shirt in a wooden box, mice would develop after a period of time. Many people were certain that reproduction was not necessary for life to form. This idea, too, was discussed and debated.

Today, scientists do more than debate whether or not a new opinion or idea seems to make sense. They develop explanations using observations as evidence. New information is combined with what people already

Figure 8-1. Ships at sea: At one time a flat Earth seemed to make sense.

know. Learning about the historical development of scientific concepts and about the individuals who have contributed to scientific knowledge helps people understand the thinking that has taken place. At first, it might seem silly to believe that Earth is flat, but based on observations made at the time and the tools available at the time, it's not surprising that many people believed in a flat Earth. The emergence of life from pond mud seemed equally reasonable.

Scientific Inquiry

Scientific investigation involves the following:

- questioning
- observing and inferring
- experimenting
- collecting and organizing data
- finding evidence and drawing conclusions
- repeating the experiment several times
- peer review

Questioning is at the heart of science. Progress in science depends on people who not only wonder how the world works but who also take the time to develop questions that can be tested and answered.

Observations and Inferences

Observations are things or events that are made using any of the senses or tools, such as thermometers, graduated cylinders, balances, or rulers. As more and better tools are developed, the ability of scientists to observe the natural world increases. For example, the invention of both the microscope (Figure 8-2) and, later, the electron microscope increased our ability to observe the structure of living organisms. This led to the realization that all living things are composed of cells.

Figure 8-2. The microscope: With the invention of the microscope, scientists could finally observe microorganisms.

Inferences Conclusions or deductions based on observations are **inferences.** Inferences may be very subtle. An inference can also be thought of as an idea or conclusion based on the results of an experiment or observation. For example, you may infer that a slug that remains motionless for several hours is dead.

Assumptions A good experiment keeps assumptions to a minimum. An **assumption** is the belief that something is true. Assumptions also may be very subtle, and at first you may be unaware you are making them. For example, when doing a seed germination experiment, you might assume that all 100 seeds planted will germinate when watered and kept under favorable conditions. The idea that 100% of the seeds will grow is an assumption. An assumption that could be made during a slug feeding experiment is that slugs will eat every day if provided with desirable food.

Opinions Ideas people have that may or may not have any basis in fact are **opinions.** Opinions are often **biased,** or influenced by an assumption that may or may not be correct. Although everyone has opinions, which should be respected, a good way to avoid bias is to leave opinions out of data collection and analysis.

The Scientific View Understanding the scientific view of the world is essential to personal, societal, and ethical decision making. To think scientifically, you must critically analyze events, explanations, and ideas. You should use these skills—as well as ideas from other disciplines—to develop personal explanations of natural events. You should also create visual models and mathematical formulations to represent your thinking.

Keep in mind that asking questions to develop an explanation is a continuing and creative process. Sometimes conflicting explanations arise from the same body of evidence. For example, plants seem to grow better when talked to daily. Some explain this by crediting the voice or words. Others point out that simply breathing carbon dioxide on the plant helps it grow. Science is a search for the truth. Scientific thinking can keep you from being misled and making poor judgments.

Review Questions

1. A student performed an experiment involving two strains of microorganisms, strain A and strain B, cultured in various temperatures for 24 hours. The results of this experiment are shown in the data table below.

Microorganism Growth and Temperature		
Temperature (°C)	Microorganism Growth (Number of Colonies)	
	Strain A	Strain B
25	10	11
28	10	7
31	11	3
34	12	0

Based on the results of the experiment, the student inferred that strain A was more resistant to higher temperatures than strain B was. What, if anything, must the student do for this inference to be considered a reasonable conclusion?

(1) nothing, because this inference is a valid scientific fact
(2) repeat this experiment several times and obtain similar results
(3) repeat this experiment several times using different variables
(4) develop a new hypothesis and test it

2. The graph below represents the results of an investigation of the growth of three identical bacterial cultures incubated at different temperatures.

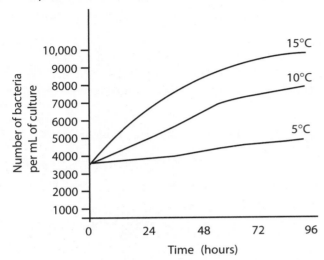

Which inference can be made from the graph?

(1) Temperature is unrelated to the reproductive rate of bacteria.
(2) Bacteria cannot grow at a temperature of 5°C.
(3) Life activities in bacteria slow down at high temperatures.
(4) Refrigeration will most likely slow the growth of these bacteria.

3. A student prepared the following list of steps for performing a laboratory investigation. She omitted one important step for completing the investigation.

Steps to Follow in an Experiment
Define a problem.
Develop a hypothesis.
Select suitable lab materials and perform a controlled experiment to test the hypothesis.
Collect, organize, and graph the experimental data.
?

State the procedure that is missing in the chart. [1]

4. When heavy rains occur while apple orchards are in bloom, the apple crop the following fall is much smaller than normal. This information can best be described as

(1) an inference   (3) a prediction
(2) a hypothesis   (4) an observation

5. Which of the steps listed below would be first in a scientific investigation?

(1) Perform the experiment.
(2) Analyze the experimental data.
(3) Formulate a hypothesis.
(4) Define the problem to be investigated.

Inquiry Skills and Understandings

Everyone needs to understand certain concepts about science and inquiry. **Scientific literacy** involves applying critical thinking skills to everyday life, particularly to claims related to health, technology, and advertising. For example, imagine you are watching a television commercial with your family. The advertiser claims its company has developed a cream that makes hair grow when applied to the scalp. According to the commercial, people with thin hair or no hair have both used the cream with success.

Before rushing out to buy this product, you should think about the claims and begin to question some of what you heard. Next, think about how you can get answers to your questions. Then you should evaluate whether or not the information is to be believed. Here is a way to approach the problem:

1. *Inquiry involves asking questions, and locating, interpreting, and processing information from a variety of sources.*

You may begin by thinking about the following questions:

• How many people were tested?
• What is in the product?
• How long do you have to use it to get results?
• Does it have any side effects?

Next, you ask your friends, and no one knows anything about the product. You also find that your state's consumer product information agency has no information about the company or the hair growth product. Then, you may go to the Internet and find that the company has a Web page that claims 50% of the people using the product grew a full head of hair after ten applications.

Now ask yourself: Are you ready to use the product based on the information you have found? Do you know enough about the product to make an informed decision? You might want to find answers to more questions.

- How many people actually took part in the study? In other words, 50% of how many people grew hair?
- What caused the participants to have thinning hair or to be bald? Did they have a medical condition that needed attention?
- How long has the company been in business?
- Why hasn't the consumer information agency heard of them and their product?
- Was the cream tested scientifically with careful experimental techniques and design?

Keep in mind that careful scientific inquiry involves doing research to find answers to questions and explanations of natural phenomena. Much of the research in the hair product example was done by finding information without actually doing a laboratory investigation.

2. *Inquiry involves making judgments about the reliability of the source and relevance of information: Scientific explanations are accepted when they are consistent with experimental and observational evidence.*

When evaluating evidence and making decisions about how useful your information is, keep the following in mind.

- All scientific explanations are tentative. They can be changed or updated as new evidence emerges. What seems to be true today may be disproved tomorrow.
- Each new bit of evidence can create more questions than it answers. This leads to an increasingly better understanding of how things work.
- Good scientific explanations can be used to make accurate predictions about natural phenomena.
- Beyond the use of reasoning and consensus, scientific inquiry involves the testing of proposed explanations using conventional techniques and procedures. In other words, logic is not enough. Questions should be answered using a good experimental design and thoughtful interpretation.

For example, suppose you read in a magazine about a newly developed HIV vaccine that is said to be effective on monkeys. You should ask:

- Are these results preliminary and tentative, or are they the final results of extensive studies?
- How was the testing done? How many animals were used? For how long have they remained healthy?

- Is HIV in monkeys the same as HIV in humans? Is this the solution to the HIV epidemic in humans or just an early step?

3. *Answers can be found through a research plan and hypothesis testing.*

Developing a Research Plan A **research plan** involves finding background information, developing a hypothesis, and devising an experimental process for testing a hypothesis. Before investing time and resources on research, it is important to find out what others have already learned. (See Figure 8-3.) Most research plans begin with a thorough library search. This search may include the use of electronic information retrieval (the Internet and library databases), a review of the literature (scientific journals), and feedback from the investigator's peers. This background work is done so that the researcher has a thorough understanding of the major concepts being investigated and any similar investigations.

Figure 8-3. Research: A review of the literature must be done before the investigation can be designed. Useful resources include primary science journals, professional Web sites, and library databases.

Making Hypotheses Inquiry involves developing and presenting proposals, including formal hypotheses, to test explanations. A good **hypothesis** attempts to explain what has been observed in a way that can be tested. It is a tentative answer to a question. Experiments cannot prove a hypothesis; they can only either support the hypothesis or fail to support it.

Most hypotheses would make sense if the words "I think that" were added to the beginning of the statement. Try adding "I think that" to the beginning of each hypothesis in the following chart.

A good hypothesis can also help determine the organization of an experiment as well as what data to collect and how to interpret those data. Testing a hypothesis is valuable even when the hypothesis is not supported by experimental results, since new information is gained in the process of testing any hypothesis.

Examples of Hypothesis Statements
This hormone will make plants grow faster.
The presence of this chemical in our drinking water does not harm us.
If this hormone is applied to plant leaves, then the plant will grow faster.
If this chemical is safe, then it will not harm us when it is added to our drinking water.

Designing an Experiment

Once the background work has been done and the hypothesis developed, the actual experiment must be designed. An **experiment** is a series of trials or tests that are done to support or <u>refute</u> (disprove) a hypothesis.

Let's say that you suspect that applying the chemical IAA (a growth hormone) to plant leaves will increase the growth rate of the plant. Your hypothesis might read as follows: *If IAA is applied to the leaves of plants, then the plants will grow more rapidly than those that do not have IAA applied to their leaves.* Once you have written your hypothesis, you must make decisions about variables and experimental techniques.

The Dependent Variable What is it that you will measure? In this experiment, you will measure the effect of IAA on plants. What you will measure is called the **dependent variable,** since it depends on what you do to the plants. Since you asked about how the plants will grow, you will need to measure how large the plants are at the beginning as well as at regular intervals until the conclusion of the experiment. You will also have to decide how to make the measurements. Will you measure only the height of the stem, or will you also measure the size of the leaves? What units will you use?

Independent Variables Factors that might influence the dependent variable are **independent variables.** This is the variable the investigation manipulates. If you are investigating the effect of IAA being applied to the leaves, you must decide on the concentration of IAA. How often will it be applied to the leaves, and how will you apply it? You may even decide to test several concentrations of IAA. In this example, the frequency of applications and the concentration of IAA are independent variables.

Controlling Variables How will you control the independent variables that might affect your interpretation of the results? A **control** is an established reference point used as a standard of comparison. It allows you to make comparisons that generate valid information. For example, you should start with plants that are of the same kind and are about the same age and size as in Figure 8-4. All of the plants should be healthy, grown in the same kind of soil, and provided with the same amount of water and light. If you neglect to control all independent variables, one or more of them may affect plant growth, and you may reach a false conclusion concerning IAA.

A **controlled experiment** is one in which the possible variables have been carefully considered and regulated so the results are due only to the independent variable you are testing.

Experimental plants

Control plants

Figure 8-4. Experimental controls: The control group will have distilled water applied to their leaves in place of IAA. It is important to apply something to the leaves of the control group or they would be treated differently in two ways from the experimental group. The plants will be the same type, size, and age as those in the experimental group. They will be grown in the same soil, with the same amount of light and water.

Keep in mind that there should only be one variable being tested at one time. You can test different concentrations of IAA, or you can test the frequency of applying IAA, but you cannot test both on the same plants at the same time. You also cannot test both the impact of fertilizer AND the impact of IAA on the same plants at the same time.

Developing Experimental Techniques Selecting, acquiring, and building apparatus, as well as considering safety precautions and planning how to avoid bias, are important parts of this stage in the development of the research plan. For example, in the IAA study, you need to decide how many plants to use. Would one plant for each concentration of IAA be enough? Should you use 100 plants for each concentration? Think about these possibilities. With only one plant, genetic differences could cause variations in growth. Could one of the plants have been infected with a fungus while still an embryo? Would using multiple plants help to cancel out this type of problem? How many trials will you need?

Is one trial enough, or would five or six trials be better? Large sample sizes with repeated trials provide much more accurate information, and there is less probability of error due to chance. Large sample sizes and multiple trials are more likely to produce valid results.

When designing an experiment, think of the steps in the following Experimental Design Guide as a way to assist you in your planning. Remember that you should first formulate the question you want to answer or the problem you want to solve. Then review the literature to learn about the topic you are investigating.

Experimental Design Guide	
What is your hypothesis?	The hypothesis is a testable statement. It should suggest a possible answer to the question you are investigating.
What is your dependent variable?	What should change and/or be measured as a result of the experiment? Make a data table to record the data as they are collected.
What is your independent variable?	What is the treatment? Are you only changing one factor at a time to see its effect? Will there be several groups, with each testing one treatment—such as several pH values, colors of light, or temperatures?
Describe how you will control the experiment.	What other possible factors may vary that could also affect the results and make your experiment inconclusive?
What steps will you take to conduct this experiment?	Make a list of procedures and materials needed to conduct the experiment. Be sure to address safety issues.

Review Questions

6. A drug company tested a new medication before putting it on the commercial market. Pills without medication were given to 500 test subjects in group A, and pills with medication were given to 500 subjects in group B. In this experiment, the individuals in group A served as the

   (1) host group
   (2) dependent variable
   (3) control
   (4) hypothesis

7. In order to find the percentage of organic matter in soil from several different locations, a student collected the samples, weighed them immediately, roasted them for several minutes in a flame to burn off organic matter, and weighed them again. The student concluded that the difference between the first and second weights represented the weight of the organic matter in the soil. The most serious mistake that the student made in this experiment was in

   (1) taking large samples
   (2) weighing the samples before roasting them
   (3) failing to dry the samples before first weighing them
   (4) assuming that roasting could remove the organic matter

8. In an investigation to determine the effects of environmental pH on the germination of dandelion seeds, 25 dandelion seeds were added to each of five petri dishes. Each dish contained a solution that differed from the others only in its pH, as shown below. All other environmental conditions were the same. The dishes were covered and observed for 10 days. The data table the student designed is shown below.

The Effect of pH on Seed Germination		
Petri Dish	pH of Solution	Number of Seeds Germinated
1	9	
2	8	
3	7	
4	6	
5	5	

State the independent variable in this investigation. [1]

Base your answers to questions 9 through 11 on the information below and on your knowledge of biology.

A student placed five geranium plants of equal size in five environmental chambers. Growing conditions were the same for each plant except that each chamber was illuminated by a different color of light of the same intensity. At the end of 20 days, plant growth was measured.

9. State a possible hypothesis for this experiment. [1]

10. What control should be used in this experiment? [1]

11. Describe one modification you would make in the design of this experiment to make the results more reliable. [1]

12. A new drug for the treatment of asthma is tested on 100 people. The people are evenly divided into two groups. One group is given the drug, and the other group is given a glucose pill. The group that is given the glucose pill serves as the

(1) experimental group (3) control
(2) limiting factor   (4) indicator

13. As part of a laboratory experiment, a thin slice of peeled raw potato weighing 10 grams is placed in an oven at 80°C. After 5 hours, the potato sample is removed from the oven and weighed again. The purpose of this experiment might be to

(1) test for the presence of starch in living tissues
(2) isolate cells in various stages of cell division
(3) determine the water content of potato tissue
(4) study the rate of photosynthesis in potatoes

14. Describe the function of a control group in an experiment. [1]

15. A student wants to shorten the ripening time for tomatoes. He predicts that the more water the seedlings receive, the faster the tomatoes will ripen. To test this prediction, he grows 20 tomato plants in a garden in full sunlight that has dry soil and 20 in a garden in a shadier location where there is greater moisture content in the soil. He then records the time it takes for fruit to develop and ripen on the plants in each garden location.

State a serious error the student made with the design of this experiment. [1]

16. In attempting to demonstrate the effectiveness of a new vaccine, a scientist performed these experimental procedures:

- One hundred genetically similar rats were divided into two groups of 50 rats each (group A and group B).
- Each rat in group A was given an injection of the vaccine in a glucose-and-water solution.
- Each rat in group B was given an injection of the glucose-and-water solution containing no vaccine.
- After several weeks, all rats in both groups were exposed to the disease for which the vaccine was developed.

Identify the dependent variable that was studied in this experiment. [1]

17. Scientists breed mice to be as genetically alike as possible to use in experiments. Explain why scientists would want mice that are genetically alike.

In your answer be sure to explain:

- The advantage of using genetically alike mice [1]
- Why cloned mice would be even better [1]

Collecting and Organizing Data

In science, **data** generally refers to the results of trials, or tests, completed during experiments such as that in Figure 8-5. Scientific inquiry involves the ability to use various methods of recording, representing, and organizing data. Data can be organized into diagrams, tables, charts, graphs, equations, and matrices. Scientists must then be able to interpret the organized data and make inferences, predictions, and conclusions based on those data.

A data table is an important initial stage in making sense of the information you will collect while doing an experiment. When constructing a table to record your data, keep the checklist in mind.

Data Table Checklist

✓ Title the table in a way that relates the independent variable to the dependent variable. For example: The Effect of Fertilizer Concentration (the independent variable) on Plant Growth (the dependent variable).

✓ Column headings include the dependent and independent variables. They may also include trial or setup numbers or other information.

✓ Column headings need to indicate units of measurement.

✓ The independent variable is typically recorded in increasing order.

✓ The dependent variable is recorded to correspond with the independent variable.

Figure 8-5. Data collection: Making measurements and carefully recording data are important parts of doing an experiment.

The next step is to construct a graph like the one in Figure 8-6 that allows you to see trends or patterns in your mathematical data. Almost every day you interpret graphs. Television, newspapers, and other media often use graphs to illustrate ideas. Advertisers use graphs to convince us to use their pain reliever or allergy medication. They know that a carefully constructed graph can provide us with a large amount of information quickly. Examining columns of numbers in a data table is time consuming and sometimes difficult. Looking at a graph allows us to make comparisons quickly and to draw conclusions.

Graph Construction Checklist

Title
✓ Title your graph so that the reader knows what it is illustrating. You can often use the same title you used on the data table.

Vertical axis
✓ Dependent variable is on the vertical axis.
✓ Vertical axis is labeled, including units of measure.
✓ Scale on the vertical axis is appropriate, without any breaks, and spaced at even intervals.

Horizontal axis
✓ Independent variable is on the horizontal axis.
✓ Horizontal axis is labeled, including units of measure.
✓ Scale on the horizontal axis is appropriate, without any breaks, and spaced at even intervals.

Points
✓ Points are plotted accurately.

Data
✓ Data points are connected, and the line does not go beyond. (You only know what you measured; beyond that is speculation.)

Legend
✓ Legend indicates the meaning of each line if there is more than one. Often you are expected to surround data points with small circles or triangles.

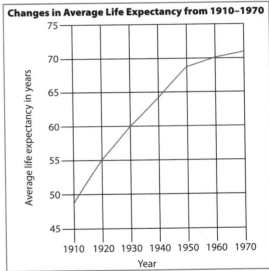

Figure 8-6. Everyday use of graphs: Interpreting graphs like this one is part of everyday life.

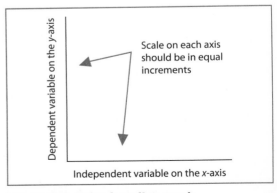

Figure 8-7. Rules for a line graph

There are four basic types of graphs:

- pie or circle graph
- bar graph
- histogram
- line graph

A scientist must decide which type of graph will be the most effective for presenting data so that the conclusion will be clear. Different rules are used in drawing each type of graph. However, there are a few rules common to all line and bar graphs.

Rule 1: The dependent variable is plotted on the vertical, or *y*-axis. Remember that the dependent variable is what you find out as a result of doing the experiment. It is what you measure during the experiment.

Rule 2: The independent variable is plotted on the horizontal, or *x*-axis. This is the factor you varied to find its effect on the test organisms or situation.

Rule 3: The spacing between the numbers on both axes must be in equal increments, without any breaks. Figure 8-7 shows how to apply the three rules to a line graph. Use the Graph Construction Checklist when constructing a graph.

The Results

A careful examination of the experimental results involves the ability to look at relationships between the predicted result contained in the hypothesis and the actual result.

Drawing Valid Conclusions After carefully considering how well the predicted result and the actual result of the experiment correspond, a decision about the outcome—a **conclusion**—can be made. A scientist needs to determine whether the hypothesis has been supported.

Scientists often use statistical analysis techniques to find the likelihood that their results were produced by chance. If the results differ only slightly, errors in measurement, genetic differences among the test organisms, or chance may be the reason. Once a significant pattern or relationship has been discovered as a result of data analysis, a scientist next tries to explain why these results were obtained.

A **model** can often be used to explain the results of an experiment. A model is a way of explaining or demonstrating what might be happening and to predict what will occur in new situations. A model explains how DNA carries the genetic code and how traits are passed from one generation to the next. As more is learned about the structure and function of DNA, parts of the model are confirmed or changed. See Figure 8-8.

Figure 8-8. A model of DNA

Reporting Results One assumption of science is that other individuals could arrive at the same explanation if they had access to similar evidence. Experiments that cannot be repeated exactly with the same results have little worth.

Research must be shared in such a clear manner that other scientists can repeat the investigation and try to get the same results. When reporting the results of an experiment, a scientist must pay close attention to details. The experimental results may be used by hundreds of other scientists to repeat the experiment. Thus, each step of the experiment must be described accurately and in exact detail.

If you wanted to repeat an experiment done by a friend, would you be able to do it if your friend told you to heat the mixture "for a little while"? Or if you had to add some soap powder to the mixture, would it be acceptable for your friend to tell you to "add two pinches"? If you expect to obtain the same results, your friend must provide precise instructions, such as to heat the mixture at a temperature of 75°C for 5 minutes, and then add 2 grams of a certain kind of soap powder.

Figure 8-9. Peer review: Scientists examine one another's work to ensure that the results are correct.

Scientific inquiry also requires the ability to develop a written report for public scrutiny. Scientists report their findings in scientific journals or during presentations at professional meetings. The report describes the hypothesis, including a literature review of previous studies, the experiment performed, its data and the scientist's conclusion, and suggestions for further study. Based on the results of the experiment and public discussion and review, inquiry may also require the scientist to revise the explanation and think about additional research. A **peer review,** in which several scientists examine the details of an experiment, is an important part of the scientific process. Scientists are expected to question explanations proposed by other scientists. Peers analyze the experimental procedures, examine the evidence, identify faulty reasoning, point out statements that go beyond the evidence, and suggest alternative explanations for the same observations. Peer review is one of the systems of checks and balances in science.

Keep in mind that all scientific explanations are subject to change as more is learned. Scientists know and accept this as a part of the way they work. With new information, they must be willing to change their thinking and, therefore, their explanations.

Evidence is a collection of facts offered to support the idea that something is true. Scientists accept evidence when it is supported by many facts. Until they have a large collection of evidence to support their thinking, scientists must remain neutral.

Sometimes claims are made that are not supported by actual evidence. Scientific claims should be questioned if

- the data are based on samples that are very small, biased, or inadequately controlled
- the conclusions are based on the faulty, incomplete, or misleading use of numbers

For example, enough organisms must be used in an experiment and the difference in data between the control and experimental group must be significant enough so that genetic differences, random chance, and inaccuracies in measurement cannot be responsible for the results. Wherever appropriate, a statistical analysis of the results should be done. This could be something as simple as finding the average, calculating the percentage of difference, or determining the frequency. Claims should also

be questioned if

- fact and opinion are intermingled
- adequate evidence is not cited
- conclusions do not follow logically from the evidence given

Further Science Understandings

Well-accepted scientific theories are supported by many different scientific investigations, often involving the contributions of individuals from different disciplines. In developing a theory, scientists carry out many investigations. They may vary in degree of complexity, scale, and focus. Research by different scientific disciplines can bring to light multiple views of the natural world. The resulting theory can encompass many different aspects of natural events. For instance, the theory of evolution began with the observations of one naturalist. But over the years scientists—including botanists, biologists, geologists, oceanographers, and others—researched numerous aspects of the theory to reach one general scientific idea.

Review Questions

18. A student conducted an original, well-designed experiment, carefully following proper scientific procedure. In order for the conclusions to become generally accepted, the experiment must

(1) contain several experimental variables
(2) support the original hypothesis
(3) be repeated to verify the reliability of the data
(4) be conducted by a scientist

19. A student tossed a coin five times and observed results of four tails and one head. He concluded that when a coin is tossed, there is an 80% chance of getting a tail and a 20% chance of getting a head. The conclusion would be more valid if

(1) only two tosses of the coin had been used
(2) the weight of the coin had been taken into consideration
(3) a greater number of tosses had been used
(4) the surface the coin landed on had been taken into consideration

Base your answers to questions 20 through 22 on the experiment described below and on your knowledge of biology.

After watching the behavior of earthworms in soil, a biology student suggested that the penetration of air into the soil promotes the root development of plants. The student then set up the following experiment.

20. The important data to be recorded in this experiment will come from the observation of the increase in

(1) leaf size
(2) stem size
(3) number of leaves
(4) number of roots

21. State the hypothesis being tested in this experiment. [1]

22. State one way this experiment could be improved to make the results more reliable. [1]

Base your answers to questions 23 through 25 on the experiment described below and on your knowledge of biology.

A group of 24 frogs was separated into two equal groups. Group A was placed in an environment in which the temperature was a constant 35°F. Group B was placed in a similar environment, except the temperature was a constant 65°F.

Equal amounts of food were given to each group at the start of the experiment and again every 24 hours. Immediately before each daily feeding, the excess food from the prior feeding was removed and measured. This allowed the scientist to determine the daily amount of food each group of frogs consumed. Each day, the heart rate and breathing rate of the frogs were checked. At the end of the experiment, the following bar graphs were prepared:

23. Using one or more complete sentences, state the hypothesis the scientist was most likely investigating in this experiment.

24. After examining the graphs, the scientist could reasonably assume that at a low temperature the frogs would

    (1) become more active
    (2) produce less carbon dioxide
    (3) eat more food
    (4) use more oxygen

25. The independent variable in this experiment was

    (1) heart rate
    (2) breathing rate
    (3) amount of food consumed
    (4) temperature of the environment

Base your answers to questions 26 through 29 on the information below and on your knowledge of biology.

A student was working on an investigation to measure the relative activity of an enzyme at various pH values. He collected the following data: pH 2, enzyme activity 10; pH 8, enzyme activity 50; pH 12, enzyme activity 10; pH 4, enzyme activity 20; pH 6, enzyme activity 40; pH 10, enzyme activity 40

26. Identify the independent variable in this experiment. [1]

27. Organize the data by filling in the data table provided. Follow these directions when completing your data table.

    • Provide an appropriate title for the data table. [1]
    • Fill in the first box in each column with an appropriate heading. [1]
    • Arrange the data so that pH values are in increasing order. [1]

Title:	

28. Using the information in the data table, construct a line graph on the grid provided, following the directions below:

    • Provide an appropriate title for the graph. [1]
    • Make and label an appropriate scale, without any breaks, on each axis. [1]
    • Plot the data on the grid. Surround each data point with a small circle and connect the points. [1]

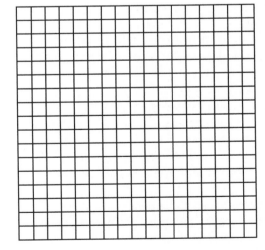

29. According to the data, this enzyme would probably work best at what pH values?

    (1) 7 and 8   (3) 6 and 7
    (2) 2 and 12   (4) 4 and 10

Practice Questions
for the New York Regents Exam

Directions
Review the Test-Taking Strategies section of this book. Then answer the following questions. Read each question carefully and answer with a correct choice or response.

Part A

1 One ounce each of protein, carbohydrate, and fat are burned separately in a calorimeter to determine Caloric content. The results are shown in the data table.

Caloric Content of Substances	
Organic Compound	Number of Calories Produced
Protein	147
Fat	271
Carbohydrate	152

Which statement represents a valid conclusion based on the data?
(1) An ounce of fat contains about twice as many Calories as an ounce of protein.
(2) Protein is a better energy food than carbohydrate.
(3) Carbohydrates, fats, and proteins all yield approximately the same number of Calories per unit of weight.
(4) Proteins and carbohydrates provide the most Calories per ounce.

2 Which laboratory procedure would be best for demonstrating the effect of light intensity on the production of chlorophyll in pea plants?
(1) using 10 plants of different species, each grown in the same intensity of light
(2) using 10 plants of different species, each grown in a different intensity of light
(3) using 10 plants of the same species, each grown in the same intensity of light
(4) using 10 plants of the same species, each grown in a different intensity of light

3 In an early trial of the Salk vaccine for polio, 1,830,000 school children participated. This original trial was an attempt to determine whether the Salk vaccine was effective in preventing polio. Of the 1,830,000 children involved, only 440,000 received the vaccine. The remainder were not given the vaccine because they
(1) had a natural immunity
(2) already had polio
(3) served as a control
(4) were allergic to the vaccine

4 A scientific study showed that the depth at which some microscopic plants were found in a lake varied from day to day. On clear days, the plants were found as far as 6 meters below the surface of the water but were only 1 meter below the surface on cloudy days. Which hypothesis would these observations support?
(1) Light intensity affects the growth of microscopic plants.
(2) Wind currents affect the growth of microscopic plants.
(3) Nitrogen concentration affects the growth of microscopic plants.
(4) Precipitation affects the growth of microscopic plants.

5 A scientist tested a hypothesis that white-tailed deer would prefer apples over corn as a primary food source. The findings of the test, in which the scientist claimed that the deer preferred apples, were published. Which research technique, if used by the scientist, might result in this claim being questioned?
(1) The scientist observed four deer in different locations at various times of the day.
(2) The scientist observed a total of 500 deer in 20 different locations at various times of the day.
(3) The scientist observed 200 deer in various natural settings, but none in captivity.
(4) The scientist observed 300 deer in various locations in captivity, but none in natural settings.

6 Tomato plants in a garden are not growing well. The gardener hypothesizes that the soil is too acidic. To test this hypothesis accurately, the gardener could
(1) plant seeds of a different kind of plant
(2) move the tomato plants to an area with less sunlight
(3) change the pH of the soil
(4) reduce the amount of water available to the plant

Part B

7 A scientist performed an experiment using the steps below.

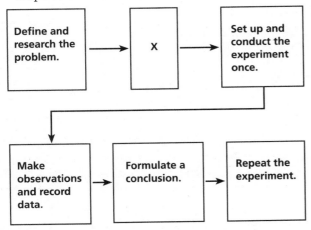

State the directions that belong in box X. [1]

Identify the Steps of Development that best correspond to the statements below (questions 8 through 11). The steps are in no particular order and may be used more than once or not at all.

Steps of Development:
A. *Test the hypothesis with an experiment.*
B. *State the results.*
C. *Draw a conclusion from the results.*
D. *Form a hypothesis.*

8 Beans will grow faster if you fertilize them at regular intervals than if you only fertilize the ground once before you plant them. [1]

9 If I add more catalyst to the reaction, the reaction will speed up. [1]

10 A scientist took saliva from his dog's mouth and mixed it with a solution of starch and warm water. He took the same amount of saliva from his own mouth and mixed it with the contents of a second tube of starch and warm water. One hour later, the contents of both tubes were checked for sugar. [1]

11 In an experiment, caterpillars consumed 8 grams of lettuce leaves and 0.4 grams of tomato leaves. [1]

12 The data table below contains information on the growth of eight white pine trees, planted in eight different locations, after a period of time.

Data Table			
Tree Number	Trunk Diameter 1.2 Meters Above Soil Surface (m)	Soil pH	Elevation Above Sea Level (ft)
1	0.54	4.0	1,200
2	0.79	6.5	1,650
3	0.64	4.5	1,400
4	1.04	5.0	1,350
5	0.96	5.0	1,350
6	0.82	4.5	1,250
7	0.80	5.5	1,400
8	0.52	5.0	1,600

Which statement is best supported by the data in the table?
(1) White pines grow best at higher elevations.
(2) White pines are not found at elevations below 1,000 feet.
(3) White pines have a long life span.
(4) White pines can grow in acidic soil.

13 In experiments designed to test new drugs on human patients, doctors usually give one group the new drug while the other group is given a sugar pill—or placebo—instead. Explain why it is important to give the placebo to the second group rather than giving them no pill at all. [1]

14 To investigate the effect of a substance on plant growth, two bean plants of the same species were grown under identical conditions with Substance X added to the soil of one of the plants. At the end of 2 weeks, the plant grown with Substance X added was 12.5 centimeters tall, and the plant grown without Substance X was 12.2 centimeters tall. The researcher concluded that the presence of Substance X causes plants to grow taller.

State one reason why this conclusion may not be valid. [1]

Part C

Use the information below and your knowledge of biology to answer questions 15 through 17.

A biology student wanted to investigate the effects of fish oil fertilizer on the growth of plants. A month ago, she planted 10 bean plants. Five of the plants were fertilized once a week with 1 mL of the fertilizer mixed in 10 mL of water. The other five plants were given 11 mL of water each week in place of the fertilizer. All other conditions were kept exactly the same for both groups of plants.

The information the biology student collected during the experiment appears in Tables 1 and 2.

		Growth (cm)				Total Growth (cm)	Average Growth per Week (cm)
Table 1: Height Gain in Centimeters — Fertilizer Added — Experimental Plants							
Plant	Height (cm) on Day 1	Week 1	Week 2	Week 3	Week 4	Total Growth (cm)	Average Growth per Week (cm)
A	15.0	2.6	1.4	3.0	2.5	9.5	2.4
B	10.0	1.1	1.5	2.0	2.5	7.1	1.8
C	17.0	3.0	2.0	1.9	1.9	8.8	2.2
D	12.0	2.1	2.2	1.8	2.3	8.4	2.1
E	16.0	2.3	2.0	1.7	2.4	8.4	2.1
Totals	—	11.1	9.1	10.4	11.6	42.2	10.6

		Growth (cm)				Total Growth (cm)	Average Growth per Week (cm)
Table 2: Height Gain in Centimeters — No Fertilizer Added							
Plant	Height (cm) on Day 1	Week 1	Week 2	Week 3	Week 4	Total Growth (cm)	Average Growth per Week (cm)
F	16.0	2.0	1.0	2.0	1.2	6.2	1.6
G	11.0	1.0	1.1	1.0	1.5	4.6	1.2
H	18.0	2.0	1.2	1.1	1.3	5.6	1.4
I	11.0	1.1	1.4	1.2	1.3	5.0	1.2
J	17.0	1.3	1.0	1.4	1.4	5.1	1.3
Totals	—	7.4	5.7	6.7	6.7	26.5	6.7

15 The student wrote the following hypothesis before designing the experiment: "Adding fish oil fertilizer to the soil will affect the growth of bean plants." Do the results of the experiment support her hypothesis? Use data from the two tables to support your answer. [1]

16 Explain why the student should compare average plant height gain instead of comparing individual plants. [1]

17 Explain why the extra water was used in place of the fertilizer in the No Fertilizer group of the plant growth experiment. [1]

18 A scientist wants to determine the best conditions for hatching brine shrimp eggs. In a laboratory, brine shrimp hatch at room temperature in glass containers of salt water. The concentration of salt in the water is known to affect the number of brine shrimp eggs that will hatch.

Design an experiment to determine which of three saltwater concentrations (2%, 4%, or 6%) is best for hatching brine shrimp eggs. In your experimental design, be sure to:
- State the number of containers to use in the experiment, and describe what would be added to each container in addition to the eggs. [1]
- State *two* factors that must be kept constant in all the containers. [1]
- State what data must be collected during this experiment. [1]
- State *one* way to organize the data so that they will be easy to analyze. [1]
- Describe a result that would indicate the best salt solution for hatching brine shrimp eggs. [1]

19 A laboratory setup for a demonstration is represented in the diagram below.

Describe how an indicator can be used to determine if starch diffuses through the membrane into the beaker. In your answer, be sure to include:
- the procedure used [1]
- how to interpret the results [1]

Base your answers to questions 20 through 23 on the information below.

Acid rain can have a pH between 1.5 and 5.0. The effect of acid rain on the environment depends on the pH of the rain and the characteristics of the environment. It appears that acid rain has a negative effect on plants. The scale below shows the pH of normal rain.

Provide the information requested below that should be included in a research plan to test the effect of pH on the early growth of bean plants in the laboratory.

20 State a hypothesis. [1]

21 Identify the independent variable. [1]

22 State two factors that should be kept constant. [1]

23 Construct a data table to organize the results. [1]

Base your answers to questions 24 and 25 on the information and data table below and on your knowledge of biology.

Trout and black bass are freshwater fish that normally require at least 8 parts per million (ppm) of dissolved oxygen (O_2) in the water for survival. Other freshwater fish, such as carp, may be able to live in water that has an O_2 level of 5 ppm. No freshwater fish are able to survive when the O_2 level in water is 2 ppm or less.

Some factories or power plants are built along rivers so that they can use the water to cool their equipment. They then release the water (sometimes as much as 8°C warmer) back into the same river.

The Rocky River presently has an average summer temperature of about 25°C and contains populations of trout, bass, and carp. A proposal has been made to build a new power plant on the banks of the Rocky River. Some people are concerned that this will affect the river ecosystem in a negative way.

The data table below shows the amount of oxygen that will dissolve in fresh water at different temperatures. The amount of oxygen is expressed in parts per million (ppm).

Data Table	
Temperature (°C)	Fresh Water Oxygen Content (ppm)
1	14.24
10	11.29
15	10.10
20	9.11
25	8.27
30	7.56

24 State one effect of temperature change on the oxygen content of fresh water. Support your answer using specific information from the data table. [1]

25 Explain how a new power plant built on the banks of the Rocky River could have an environmental impact on the Rocky River ecosystem downstream from the plant.

Your explanation must include the effects of the power plant on:
- water temperature [1]
- dissolved oxygen [1]
- fish species [1]

Base your answers to questions 26 and 27 on the information in the newspaper article below and on your knowledge of biology.

Patients to test tumor fighter

Boston—Endostatin, the highly publicized experimental cancer drug that wiped out tumors in mice and raised the hopes of cancer patients, will be tested on patients this year.

"I think it's exciting, but … you always have the risk that something will fail in testing," said Dr. Judah Folkman, the Harvard University researcher whose assistant, Michael O'Reilly, discovered endostatin.

Endostatin and a sister protein, angiostatin, destroy the tumors' ability to sprout new blood vessels. This makes cancer fall dormant in lab animals, but no one knows if that will happen in humans.

The Associated Press

26 Explain why it is necessary to test these experimental drugs on human volunteers as well as on test animals. [1]

27 State one reason that mice are often used by scientists for testing experimental drugs that may be used by humans. [1]

28 Many people who are in favor of alternative medicine claim that large doses of vitamin C introduced into a vein speed up the healing of surgical wounds Describe an experiment to test this hypothesis. Your answer must include at least:
- the difference between the experimental group of subjects and the control group [1]
- two conditions that must be kept constant in both groups [1]
- data that should be collected [1]
- an example of experimental results that would support the hypothesis [1]

Laboratory Skills

What do **You** *Think?*

Laboratory Procedures

When you are looking at cells with a microscope always start focusing with the high power objective lens, then if the cells appear too large, switch to a lower power.

You shouldn't eat food or drink soda in a classroom laboratory unless you make sure you wash your hands first.

Paper chromatography is used to separate mixtures of molecules that are of different sizes.

Gel electrophoresis is used to cut DNA into smaller fragments.

Laboratory Skills

Vocabulary

balance

chromatography

compound light microscope

dichotomous key

dissection

electronic balance

electrophoresis

graduated cylinder

indicator

magnification

mass

metric ruler

microscope

stain

stereoscope

triple-beam balance

volume

Topic Overview

Biologists are always trying to add to our understanding of the world in which we live. To do this, they make observations and do experiments. To help them collect data from these observations and experiments, they rely on a variety of tools and techniques. These tools, like microscopes, extend our senses, allowing us to collect data that would otherwise be unavailable. Scientists have also developed specific techniques that give us valuable information about the cells, molecules, and processes of living organisms.

Tools for Measurement

During laboratory investigations, you are often required to make measurements of length, mass, and volume. You need to know the proper pieces of equipment to select and the appropriate procedures and units to use.

Measuring Length Typically a **metric ruler** is used to determine the length of an object. To measure length, use either centimeters (cm) or millimeters (mm). You should know how to convert millimeters to centimeters and vice versa.

The metric ruler shown in Figure 9-1 is <u>calibrated</u>—or scaled—in centimeters (cm). The lines indicated by the numbers 1, 2, 3, and so on each represent a distance of 1 centimeter. The smaller divisions each equal 1 millimeter (10 mm = 1 cm). A line equal to 5 cm is shown above the ruler in Figure 9-1.

Figure 9-1. Metric ruler: The tool used for measuring length in centimeters and millimeters (not shown to scale)

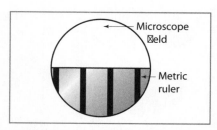

Figure 9-2. Microscope field with metric ruler (not shown to scale)

Micrometers (μm), are very tiny units that are used to measure objects through the microscope. One thousand micrometers equal one millimeter.

Figure 9-2 shows a metric ruler as seen under the low-power objective of a microscope. The distance across the field of view is approximately 3.2 millimeters, or 3,200 micrometers (since 1.0 mm = 1,000 μm).

If the cells observed on the slide in Figure 9-3 are being viewed through the same low-power objective, the field of view is still 3.2 millimeters. The approximate length of each cell is therefore about 1 millimeter or 1,000 micrometers, since about 3 cells fit across the diameter (widest part) of the field.

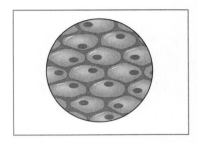

Figure 9-3. Microscope field with cells

Measuring Volume A **graduated cylinder** is often used to measure a liquid's **volume**, or the space it occupies. Liters and milliliters are typically used to indicate volume in the metric system, while quarts and ounces are used in the English system. Graduated cylinders are calibrated in milliliters (mL).

Water and many other fluids form a meniscus (curving surface) when placed in the narrow tube of a graduated cylinder. To correctly read the volume of the liquid, place the cylinder on a flat surface. Then read from the bottom of the curved meniscus at eye level. The volume of liquid in the graduated cylinder in Figure 9-4 is 13 mL.

Measuring Temperature In the biology laboratory, temperature is often measured in degrees Celsius. The freezing point of water is 0°C; the boiling point is 100°C. Human body temperature is 37°C, which is the temperature indicated on the thermometer in Figure 9-5.

The correct volume is 13 mL.

Figure 9-4. Graduated cylinder: You can find the volume of a liquid using a graduated cylinder.

Measuring Mass In the biology laboratory, **mass**—the quantity of matter in something—is often measured with a **balance**, which is a tool that works by comparing an object of unknown mass with an object of known mass. The triple-beam balance or an electronic balance is typically found in a high school laboratory.

A **triple-beam balance** (Figure 9-6) has a single pan and three bars (beams) that are calibrated in grams. One beam, the 500-gram beam, is divided into five 100-gram units. Another beam is divided into ten units of 10 grams totaling 100 grams. The front beam is divided into 10 major units of 1 gram each. Each of these divisions is further divided into 0.1-gram units.

Figure 9-5. Thermometer: This Celsius thermometer shows human body temperature.

Figure 9-6. Triple-beam balance

Figure 9-7. Electronic balance

Before using a balance, make sure that the pan is empty and that the pointer and all of the <u>riders</u> (devices that are moved along the beams) are on zero. To determine the mass of an object, it is first placed on the pan. Then, starting with the 500-gram beam, the masses on the beams are adjusted until the pointer is again pointing to zero. The mass of the object is equal to the sum of the readings on the three beams.

An **electronic balance** measures mass automatically. To use an electronic balance, first turn it on and wait until it shows a zero mass. (This may require using the re-zero button shown on Figure 9-7.) Place the object with the unknown mass on the pan. Read the mass.

Never place a substance directly on a balance pan. Instead, protect the balance with a weighing paper or dish. With a triple-beam balance, first find the mass of the weighing paper. Then find the mass of the substance AND the weighing paper. Subtract the mass of the weighing paper from the total mass of the paper plus the substance. The remainder is the mass of the substance.

For an electronic balance, put the weighing paper on the balance and then use the re-zero button to set the balance to zero. Next, put the substance on the paper and read the mass. The re-zero button automatically subtracts the mass of the weighing paper from the total. The reading on the balance is the actual mass of the substance.

Review Questions

1. The crab shown in the illustration below has four pairs of walking legs and one pair of pincer legs. The crab is shown in its normal walking position.

In this position, what is the distance between the ends of the front pair of walking legs? (One of the front pair of walking legs is identified with an "X" in the illustration.)

(1) 8.5 cm   (3) 7.5 cm
(2) 85 cm   (4) 75 cm

2. Identify which piece of laboratory equipment you would use to accurately measure 10 grams of glucose. [1]

3. Which piece of laboratory equipment would be used to most accurately measure the volume of a liquid?

(1) beaker   (3) test tube
(2) balance   (4) graduated cylinder

4. A student measured a larva using a metric ruler, as represented in the diagram below.

What is the length of the larva?

(1) 26 cm   (2) 26 mm   (3) 16 cm   (4) 16 mm

5. Which of the graduated cylinders below contains a volume of liquid closest to 15 mL?

(1) (2) (3) (4)

6. Which diagram below shows a correct measurement?

(1)

(2) (3)

(4)

7. The diagram below shows a triple-beam balance with a mass on the pan.

With the riders in the positions indicated, what is the mass of the object on the pan of the balance?

(1) 9 grams   (3) 249 grams
(2) 200 grams   (4) 942 grams

8. Draw a meniscus to represent a water level of 6 mL on the diagram below of a graduated cylinder. [1]

Microscope Skills

The **microscope** is a tool that uses a lens or a combination of lenses to make an object easier to see. It allows for the examination of objects too small to be seen with the unaided eye. Microscopes also permit the close observation of fine details. For example, without a microscope you can see the legs and wings of a fly. With a microscope you can also see the hairs covering the fly's body, the pads and clawlike structures on its feet, and the framework of its wings. This is possible for two reasons. A microscope magnifies the specimen and also allows you to distinguish between objects that are close together. **Magnification** is the ability of a microscope to make an object appear larger.

Types of Microscopes

There are many different types of microscopes. The two most commonly found in a high school laboratory are the compound light microscope and the stereoscope. The primary difference between the two is that with a compound light microscope, light must pass through or reflect off the specimen being examined.

Stereoscopes With a stereoscope (Figure 9-8), light is reflected off the specimen. A **stereoscope**, sometimes called a <u>dissecting</u> <u>microscope</u>, has two <u>ocular</u> eyepiece lenses, one for each eye, and one or more <u>objectives</u> (the other lenses of the microscope). The amount of magnification is low, but the image is three-dimensional and is not reversed as it would be with a compound microscope. Stereoscopes are often used to observe parts of specimens such as insects, worms, or flowers.

Figure 9-8. A stereoscope

Compound Microscopes The typical **compound light microscope** has one ocular lens, at least one objective lens, and a light source. Light passes through the object being examined, through the objective lens, and then through the eyepiece.

The image you see is magnified by both lenses—the ocular lens and the objective lens. The total magnification is calculated by multiplying the magnification of the ocular by the magnification of the objective. For example, if you use a microscope that has a 10x eyepiece and a 40x objective, the magnification of a specimen would be 400x.

Eyepiece × Objective = Total Magnification

10x   × 40x   = 400x

Figure 9-9. A compound microscope: Each part is labeled with a number. The names and functions of the parts are given in Table 9-1.

Table 9-1. Names and Functions of Parts of a Compound Microscope	
1 Eyepiece or Ocular Lens	• lens nearest the eye and used to "look through" • usually magnifies 10x
2 Objective Lenses	• lenses located closest to specimen • usually 2 or 3 • commonly magnify at 4x, 10x, and 40x
3 Stage	• flat surface (platform) on which the slide is placed • stage clips hold the slide in place
4 Diaphragm	• located under the stage • controls the amount of light passing up through the specimen
5 Light Source	• might be a mirror or a light bulb • provides light that passes up through the specimen and makes it visible
6 Coarse Adjustment	• used to focus only under low power (up to 100x) • never used when the high-power objective is in place for viewing • usually the larger knob; causes a large amount of movement of the lenses
7 Fine Adjustment	• the only focus you should use with high power • used to sharpen the image under low power • also used to see different layers of a specimen • usually the smaller of the focus knobs; causes a small amount of movement of the lenses

Microscope lenses may get dirty from contact with fingers, specimens, stains, and so on. Do not use paper towels or your shirt to clean them! Only use lens paper to clean the lenses of a microscope. Lens paper will not scratch the soft glass of the lens.

Techniques for Using Microscopes

Due to the action of microscope lenses, there are a number of things you need to remember when viewing objects through a compound light microscope.

- The image will be upside-down and backwards, as shown in Figure 9-10.
- You must move the slide in the direction that is opposite the way the organism appears to be moving. In other words, if the organism appears headed toward the upper right side of your field of view, you must move the slide down and to the left to keep it in view. See Figure 9-11.
- The field becomes darker as you increase the magnification. You will need to increase the amount of light passing through the specimen as you go from low power to high power. The diaphragm, located under the stage, can be used to do this.
- Since the field becomes smaller under high power, center the object you are viewing before switching to a higher power. Otherwise the object may be outside of the field of view.

Focusing When observing specimens through the compound light microscope, first use the low-power objective. Do this even if higher magnification is needed to make your observations.

1. First, place the slide on the stage of your microscope. Position the slide so that the specimen is over the opening in the stage. Anchor the slide with the stage clips.
2. Move the coarse adjustment so that the low-power objective is as close to the slide as you can get it without touching the slide. Some microscopes have a built-in "stop" that prevents you from getting the objective lens too close to the slide. You should look at the objective and the slide while doing this. Never lower the objective while looking through the eyepiece.
3. Look through the eyepiece with both eyes open and turn the coarse adjustment so that the low-power objective and slide move apart. The specimen should come into view.
4. Next, turn the fine adjustment to bring the specimen into sharp focus.
5. To focus the specimen under higher magnification after locating it under low power, move the slide so that what you are interested in seeing is located in the center of your field of view. Remember that as you increase the magnification, the object appears larger, but you see less of its edge. The field of view becomes smaller when you

A   B

Figure 9-10. Microscope view: The letter "e" as seen on a slide (A) and as seen through the microscope (B). (Only the change in position of the letter is shown, not magnification.)

Organism swims toward the upper right.

Move slide this way to keep the organism in view.

Figure 9-11. Moving the slide to follow a moving object

Figure 9-12. **Specimen under low and high power:** Note that the high power field is narrower (only 4 cells can be seen), but the cells appear larger, and more detail is visible.

Figure 9-13. Preparing a wet-mount slide

Figure 9-14. Staining a wet-mount slide

switch from low power to a higher power. See Figure 9-12.

6. Watch from the side of the microscope and slowly turn the high-power objective into place. Be sure that the high-power objective is not going to touch the slide. High-power objectives are longer than low-power objectives and can easily hit the slide—be careful.

7. If the objective is not going to hit the slide, click it into position. As you look through the eyepiece, the specimen should be visible. Use the fine adjustment to sharpen the focus. Remember never to use the coarse adjustment when using the high-power objectives. You could damage the microscope lens and break the slide.

Preparing Wet-Mount Slides Only specimens that are small and thin can be seen through a compound light microscope. However, thin slices may quickly dry and shrivel. To avoid this, a temporary wet-mount slide can be prepared by using the following steps:

1. Using a <u>pipette</u> (eye dropper), add a small drop of water to the center of a clean, glass slide.

2. Place the object to be viewed in the water. (It should be lying flat rather than folded over.)

3. Use <u>forceps</u> to position a <u>coverslip</u>, as shown in Figure 9-13. Using forceps will keep you from getting fingerprints on the coverslip. Fingerprints could interfere with your ability to view the image clearly.

4. Lower the coverslip slowly. This technique will prevent the formation of air bubbles under the coverslip.

Staining Specimens When you examine cells and cell parts through a microscope, they often appear to be transparent. You need to adjust the light and the focus so that you can see differences in thickness and density. Although adjusting the amount of light passing through the specimen may help, stains are often used to create greater contrast. Different types of cells and cell parts vary in their ability to soak up various stains. For example, certain cell parts turn darker in the presence of iodine stain. Other parts do not become darker.

To add a stain, such as methylene blue, to a wet-mount slide, place a drop of the stain beside one edge of the coverslip. Next touch a small piece of paper towel to the opposite edge of the coverslip. The towel absorbs water and draws the stain across the slide under the coverslip. This technique allows you to keep the slide on the stage of the microscope. You do not need to prepare a new slide. See Figure 9-14.

Identifying and Comparing Cell Parts It is important to remember that cells have specific structures that perform specific jobs. Many of these structures in Figures 9-15 and 9-16 are visible through a compound light microscope. Some of the parts you can either expect to see or see evidence of are the following:

Figure 9-15. **Typical plant cell:** Structures that can be seen through a microscope

- **Nucleus**—usually observed as a rounded, dense, dark-staining structure. It can be located anywhere in the cell, not just in the middle.
- **Cytoplasm**—typically fills the cell. It appears to be clear in some cells and very grainy in others. Cell organelles, which may or may not be visible, are suspended in the cytoplasm.
- **Cell membrane**—found surrounding the cytoplasm. It is the outer boundary of animal cells and is located between the cell wall and the cytoplasm in plants and some other organisms.
- **Cell wall**—The nonliving cell wall on the outside of the cell membrane in plant cells is a supportive structure. Many bacteria form a different type of protective cell wall.
- **Chloroplasts**—green, oval structures found in the cytoplasm of some plant cells and photosynthetic one-celled organisms.
- **Vacuoles**—often seen as clear areas in the cytoplasm. Plant cells contain very large fluid-filled vacuoles that occupy much of the inside of the cell. Some single-celled organisms may contain specialized vacuoles for digestion and for regulating water balance.
- **Chromosomes**—most easily observed in cells undergoing mitosis or meiosis as in Figure 9-17. They are usually dark-staining and threadlike.

Figure 9-16. **Animal cells:** As seen through a compound light microscope

Additional Laboratory Techniques

There are many techniques that are useful in the biology laboratory. Some of the most common are electrophoresis, chromatography, and the application of stains and indicators. Dichotomous keys are especially useful for field research.

Electrophoresis Gel **electrophoresis** is a very powerful tool and is widely used by scientists in many disciplines—not just biologists. It allows scientists to separate mixtures of large molecules according to size. DNA and proteins are the two types of molecules most often separated by gel electrophoresis.

When setting up a protein gel, a sample of biological material containing proteins is prepared by breaking open the cells in order to release the proteins. Next, the proteins are treated with both chemicals and heat. One of the chemicals used coats the protein molecules and gives them a negative charge. Then, very small amounts of the prepared sample are placed in wells at the top of a special gel positioned in a gel electrophoresis apparatus. (The wells are similar to the holes you would get by pressing the teeth of a comb part way into a block of gelatin dessert.) The gel is placed between two electrodes that are connected to a power supply. This causes one end of the gel to take on a positive charge and the other to take on a negative charge.

Figure 9-17. **Plant cells undergoing mitotic cell division:** A indicates chromosomes, and B indicates a nucleus before the cell undergoes mitosis.

Standard markers of known sizes are injected in this well for reference purposes.

Other wells contain samples from different individuals.

Negative end

Large protein molecules

Small protein molecules

Positive end

Figure 9-18. Protein gel electrophoresis: Protein gels are typically run vertically, with the gel block standing on end.

Positive end

Negative end

Wells

Small DNA fragments   Large DNA fragments

Figure 9-19. DNA gel electrophoresis: DNA gels are typically run horizontally, with the gel block lying flat.

Positively charged molecules in the sample move toward the negative electrode, while negatively charged protein molecules move toward the positive electrode. The type of gel used in protein electrophoresis is made up of long molecules that form a tangled mesh. Smaller molecules are able to work their way through the gel more quickly than larger molecules. Therefore, molecules are separated by both their size and electrical charge. See Figure 9-18.

DNA gel electrophoresis is a little different. The analysis of an individual's DNA begins with the use of special enzymes to cut the DNA at specific points in the sequence of bases. This produces fragments of DNA that are of different lengths. These pieces of DNA will vary in size and number from one individual to another due to the uniqueness of each genetic code.

Next, small amounts of the DNA samples are placed in wells located on one side of a semisolid gel. See Figure 9-19. Typically the DNA gel is made of <u>agarose</u>—the same gelatine-like substance used to culture bacteria but without the nutrients. The gel is located between two electrodes that are connected to a power supply. This causes one end of the gel to take on a positive charge and the other to take on a negative charge when the current is turned on. The negatively charged DNA fragments move toward the positive electrode.

As with the protein gel, the smaller the fragment, the more rapidly it moves through the gel. Small pieces of DNA will travel farther and be located farther from the well where they were initially injected. This allows the DNA fragments to form a distinct pattern that becomes visible through staining or a variety of other techniques.

The information provided by both DNA and protein gels looks very much like a bar code. The patterns formed from different protein samples or the DNA of different individuals can provide information about relatedness. DNA has been used to determine who the father and/or mother of a child actually is in paternity cases or in instances where a couple suspects that the child given to them in the hospital is not their child. It has also been used to determine guilt or innocence during criminal investigations. The source of blood, semen, or skin can be identified with this technique. DNA left at a crime scene can be compared to a suspect's DNA to determine if the suspect was at the crime scene.

In the case of endangered species, scientists can use DNA electrophoresis to learn which groups are being devastated by poachers, since skins from members of the same group will have similar DNA patterns. Gel electrophoresis can also be used to determine and to identify the genes responsible for specific genetic diseases such as sickle cell disease.

Chromatography Like gel electrophoresis, **chromatography** is a technique used for separating mixtures of molecules. In one type of chromatography commonly used in the biology laboratory, the mixture being separated is placed on a paper to which it sticks. For example, chlorophyll extract from plant leaves is placed on filter paper or special chromatography paper. It is done by placing a small dot of the concentrated chlorophyll extract near one end of a strip of the paper. Then, the end of the paper nearest the dot of extract is placed in a solvent. In the case of chlorophyll, the <u>solvent</u> could be alcohol. The solvent cannot touch the dot when it is initially set up, or the chlorophyll would simply wash away into the solvent.

As the solvent soaks into the paper and moves upward, substances in the mixture that do not stick tightly to the paper will be picked up by the solvent and moved along quickly. Substances that are more tightly held to the paper and less attracted to the solvent will also be picked up but will move along more slowly. This results in the formation of bands of the different substances on the chromatography paper. If the substances in the mixture are colorless, they can be viewed by combining them with reactive chemicals that will give them color. The chlorophyll extract consists of several plant pigments that are very colorful and easy to distinguish.

In summary, the rate at which a substance moves along the paper in a given solvent can be used to separate it from other substances. By comparing the distances moved with those of known substances in the same solvent, the unknowns can be identified. See Figure 9-20.

Stains and Indicators **Stains** can be used to make cell structures more visible. In fact, chromosomes were so named for the fact that they are easily stained. Commonly used stains are iodine and methylene blue. Iodine darkens certain cell structures. It is especially useful when examining plant cells through the microscope. Methylene blue stains structures in the nucleus. It is useful when observing many types of cells.

An **indicator** is a substance that changes color when it contacts certain chemicals. The examples in Table 9-2 represent only a few of the indicators commonly used in the biology laboratory.

Other indicators can be used to determine how much sugar there is in a solution or the amount of carbon dioxide present. Swimming pool owners use indicators to tell them how much chlorine is in the water. Some of the pregnancy test kits that pharmacies sell also use indicators.

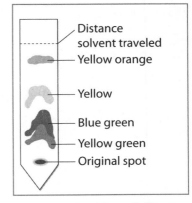

Figure 9-20. Chlorophyll chromatography

Labels: Distance solvent traveled; Yellow orange; Yellow; Blue green; Yellow green; Original spot

Table 9-2. Indicators Used in the Biology Laboratory	
Indicator	**What It Tests**
pH paper	A piece of pH paper is dipped in the solution to be tested. Its color is then matched to a color scale. Specific colors indicate whether the solution is acidic (pH values from 0 to 6), neutral (pH 7), or basic (pH values from 8 to 14).
Iodine (Lugol's) solution	A color change from golden brown to blue-black indicates the presence of starch in the tested solution.

Dichotomous Keys A key is used to sort, name, and/or classify a particular organism. By working through a series of steps, organisms are eliminated until the one of interest is finally identified. Each step of a **dichotomous key** typically consists of two statements that divide the things being identified/classified into two groups. Each statement is followed by a direction that indicates either what step to go to next or the name of the organism.

To make your own dichotomous key, you would need to start out with two statements that divide the organisms being classified into two groups.

1a	Requires petroleum fuel	go to Step 2
1b	Requires only muscle power	bicycle
2a	Has wings and flies	jet
2b	Has no wings and does not fly	go to Step 3
3a	Has two wheels	motorcycle
3b	Has more than two wheels	car

Figure 9-21. A dichotomous key is used to sort, name, or classify.

Each statement would be followed with a direction about the next step to take. At the next step, you again divide the organisms into two groups that are again followed by directions about the next step to go to or the identity of the organism or object. For example, Figure 9-21 shows how you might construct a key to classify a bicycle, car, jet, and motorcycle.

Pretend that you do not know a motorcycle from a bicycle from a jet, from a car. All you could do is examine each one of the objects, make observations, and determine how they work. Once you did that, you would be ready to place names on each of the four items.

Notice that if you did not work through the key step by step, it would be very easy to misname an object. If you thought about a bicycle as having two wheels and scanned down the list with no attention to following the steps, you could easily mistake the bicycle for a motorcycle. You would spot step 3a, which says, "Has two wheels" and say to yourself, "Yep, that's the bicycle." You would totally miss the fact that the object in step 3a must run on petroleum fuel. Always start at the beginning of a key.

Review Questions

Base your answers to questions 9 through 11 on the diagram and information below, and on your knowledge of biology.

- Distance solvent traveled
- Yellow orange
- Yellow
- Blue green
- Yellow green
- Original spot

Several drops of concentrated green pigment extract obtained from spinach leaves were placed near the bottom of a strip of highly absorbent paper. When the extract dried, the paper was suspended in a test tube containing solvent so that only the tip of the paper was in the solvent. As the solvent was absorbed and moved up the paper, the various pigments within the extract became visible, as shown in the diagram.

9. A valid conclusion that can be drawn from this information is that spinach leaves

(1) contain only chlorophyll
(2) contain pigments in addition to chlorophyll
(3) contain more orange pigment than yellow pigment
(4) are yellow-orange rather than green

10. The technique used to separate the parts of the extract in the diagram is known as

(1) staining   (3) chromatography
(2) dissection   (4) electrophoresis

11. In which organelle would most of these pigments be found?

(1) nucleus   (3) ribosome
(2) mitochondrion   (4) chloroplast

12. A student observed a one-celled organism in the field of view of a compound light microscope as shown in the adjacent diagram.

On the diagram, draw an arrow to indicate the direction the organism would seem to move if the student moved the slide on the stage to the left and down. [1]

13. To test for the presence of glucose, a student added the same amount of Benedict's solution to each of four test tubes. (Benedict's is a glucose indicator that is a royal blue color when no glucose is present. To determine if glucose is present, Benedict's must be mixed in the unknown solution and heated for several minutes.)

Two of the test tubes contained unknown solutions. The other two test tubes contained known solutions. The chart below shows the color results obtained after the solutions were heated in the four test tubes in a hot water bath.

Data Table		
Tube	Contents	Color After Heating
1	Unknown solution + Benedict's solution	Royal blue
2	Unknown solution + Benedict's solution	Red orange
3	Water + Benedict's solution	Royal blue
4	Glucose + water + Benedict's solution	Red orange

The student could correctly conclude that

(1) all of the tubes contained glucose
(2) tubes 1 and 2 contained glucose
(3) tube 1 did not contain glucose, but tube 2 did
(4) tube 2 did not contain glucose, but tube 1 did

14. A student viewing a specimen under the low-power objective of a compound light microscope switched to high power and noticed that the field of view darkened considerably.

Which microscope part identified on this microscope would the student adjust to brighten the field of view?

(1) A   (2) B   (3) C   (4) D

15. A student studied the upper layer of cells of a tissue sample on a slide, using the high-power objective of the compound microscope shown.

Which part of the microscope should the student adjust to observe the lower layer of the sample?

(1) A   (2) B   (3) C   (4) D

16. State the purpose of using stains in a wet-mount slide preparation. [1]

17. The eyepiece of a compound light microscope has a magnification of 10X and the low-power objective and high-power objective lenses have magnifications of 10X and 30X, respectively. If the diameter of the low-power field measures 1500 micrometers, the diameter of the high-power field will measure either 4500 micrometers or 500 micrometers.

Select the correct diameter. Support your answer. [1]

Base your answers to questions 18 and 19 on the diagram below of some internal structures of an earthworm and on your knowledge of biology.

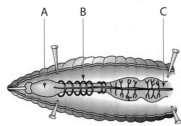

18. Which laboratory equipment should be used to observe the surface details of structures A, B, and C of the earthworm?

(1) stereoscope
(2) compound light microscope
(3) graduated cylinder
(4) triple-beam balance

19. Structure A has a diameter of 3 millimeters. What is the approximate diameter of the blood vessel indicated by C?

(1) 2.5 mm   (3) 1.5 mm
(2) 2.0 mm   (4) 0.5 mm

Base your answers to questions 20 and 21 on the illustration below and on your knowledge of biology. The image is a representation of an animal cell as it would appear when viewed with compound light microscope

20. Identify the organelle indicated by letter X. [1]

21. What technique could be used to make the organelle indicated by letter X more visible? [1]

22. While focusing a microscope on high power, a student crushed the coverslip. The student probably

(1) shut the light off
(2) turned up the light intensity
(3) rotated the eyepiece
(4) used the coarse adjustment

23. An experimental setup is shown in the diagram below.

Setup with light

Setup without light

Which hypothesis would most likely be tested using this setup?

(1) Green water plants release a gas in the presence of light.
(2) Roots of water plants absorb minerals in the absence of light.
(3) Green plants need light for cell division.
(4) Plants grow best in the absence of light.

Base your answers to questions 24 through 27 on the photograph below and on your knowledge of biology. The photograph shows onion root-tip tissue viewed under the high-power objective of a compound light microscope.

24. The photograph illustrates stages in the process of

(1) meiosis in root tips
(2) mitotic cell division in plants
(3) water conduction in onions
(4) chlorophyll production in chloroplasts

25. Identify the structure indicated by arrow A. [1]

26. Identify the structure indicated by arrow B. [1]

27. Describe one adjustment that could be made to the microscope to make the field of view brighter. [1]

28. Pieces of pH paper were used to test the contents of three test tubes. The results are shown in the diagram below.

Which statement about the tubes is correct?

(1) Tube A contains a base.
(2) Tube B contains a base.
(3) Tube B contains an acid.
(4) Tube C contains an acid.

29. When viewed with a compound light microscope, which letter would best illustrate the way in which the microscope inverts and reverses the image?

(1) A (2) W (3) F (4) D

30. Gel electrophoresis is a technique used to
(1) cut DNA into pieces of various sizes
(2) separate DNA fragments by charge and size
(3) move DNA fragments from one species to another
(4) make copies of chromosomes

Observing Plant and Animal Specimens

Classroom experiences involving plants and animals range from observation to dissection. Opportunities to observe plants and animals require consideration and appreciation for the organism. The abuse of any live organism for any purpose is intolerable.

Dissection and Preserved Specimens

The dissection of plant and animal specimens provides a framework upon which to organize biological knowledge. **Dissection** (or the examination of preserved specimens) provides a way to

- observe similarities and differences that exist among species
- understand the relationship between biological form and function
- expose and identify the internal structures of organisms

To dissect a specimen correctly, you need:

- the knowledge of what equipment to use and how to use it properly
- a work area that is clean and well organized both before and after the activity

Equipment commonly used during dissection activities is described in Table 9-3.

Equipment	Use
Table 9-3. Dissection Equipment	
Dissecting pan	Resembles a cake pan but has a wax or a rubber-like substance in the bottom. The specimen is placed on the waxy surface.
Dissecting pins	Large pins with a "T" shape used to anchor the specimen during the dissection
Scalpel	A sharp instrument used to slice open the specimen so that the internal parts can be observed
Scissors	Used for cutting open the specimen and to remove parts. May have two sharp points or one blunt and one sharp point.
Probe/ Teasing needle/ Dissecting needle	Used to move structures around while they are still intact. The probe can be used to lift some organs so that others located below them are observable. The probe or dissecting needle is also used to point out different structures when showing specific features to someone else. Another function is to "tease" or gently tear apart structures such as muscle tissue.
Tweezers/ Forceps	Used to lift out small parts, to move structures, and to pry parts open
Safety goggles	Wrap-around shatter-proof glasses used to protect eyes from accidental splashes of preservative when dissecting as well as in other lab situations.

Review Questions

31. State one scientific purpose for dissecting an organism. [1]

32. For what purpose would the equipment in the following illustration most likely be used?

(1) dissecting an earthworm
(2) removing cell organelles
(3) identifying and classifying a single-celled organism
(4) observing mitosis on prepared slides

33. Along with a dissecting pan, which group of equipment would be most useful to a student planning to dissect a preserved specimen?

(1) dissecting pins, compound light microscope, and pH paper
(2) pH paper, eye dropper, and safety goggles
(3) safety goggles, scissors, and compound light microscope
(4) safety goggles, stereoscope, and scissors

34. What is the best use for the dissection instrument illustrated in the diagram below?

(1) cutting through bones
(2) spreading apart muscle tissue
(3) cutting through thick muscles
(4) removing blood plasma

Laboratory Safety

Laboratory investigations are, for some students, the most exciting part of the Living Environment course. However, they sometimes involve potentially dangerous activities and materials. As a result, careful attention to safety procedures is critical.

Using Safety Equipment

You should know how to properly use the safety equipment located in your biology laboratory. It is critical to be aware of the location in your laboratory of each of these:

- fire extinguisher
- safety shower
- eye wash station
- fire blanket
- emergency gas shutoff

Use the safety equipment provided for you. Goggles should be worn whenever a lab calls for the use of chemicals, preserved specimens, or dissection. If indicated by your teacher, you should also wear a safety apron when using chemicals. Some activities, such as those involving chemicals or live or preserved organisms, also require the use of special gloves.

Safety in the Laboratory

Read all of the directions for an investigation before you start to work. If you are unsure about any part of the lab procedures, check with your teacher. As a general rule, do not perform activities without permission; do only what the instructions and your teacher direct you to do.

- Do *not* eat or drink in the laboratory.
- When you are heating a test tube, always slant it so that the open end of the tube points away from you and others. Never heat a closed container, such as a test tube that has been closed with a stopper.
- Never inhale or taste any of the chemicals you are using in a laboratory. This includes the specimens you are dissecting.
- If you spill a chemical or get any on your skin, wash it off immediately. Also, report the incident to your teacher.
- Tell your teacher about any personal injury no matter how minor it may seem.
- Tie back long hair, and keep loose clothing away from laboratory equipment, chemicals, and sources of heat and fire.
- Never expose flammable liquids to an open flame. Use a hot water bath (such as a large beaker of water heated on a hot plate) if you need to heat flammable liquids (such as alcohol). See Figure 9-22.
- Know what equipment to use when handling hot glassware. Do not use bare fingers to pick up hot test tubes or beakers. Use test tube holders and beaker tongs.
- Do not use glassware that has cracks or large chips. Tell your teacher about the damage and get a replacement.
- Do not pour chemicals back into stock bottles or exchange stoppers on the stock bottles.
- Use laboratory apparatus as it is intended to be used. For example, do not stir a solution using a thermometer, plastic ruler, or your pen.
- Do not use electrical equipment around water. If electrical cords seem to have exposed wires or if you get a shock handling electrical equipment, notify your teacher immediately. Do not attempt to disconnect the equipment yourself.

Figure 9-22. Hot water bath: A hot water bath is used to heat test tubes that contain a flammable liquid such as alcohol.

Cleaning Your Work Area

- Turn off the gas and water after you are done with them. Disconnect any electrical devices.
- Clean your work area by returning materials to their appropriate places, washing glassware according to your teacher's instructions, and wiping off the lab surface.
- Dispose of chemicals according to the instructions provided by your teacher.
- Wash your hands thoroughly!

Review Questions

35. If a student spills nitric acid on her arm, she should *first*
(1) report the accident to the school nurse
(2) report the spill to her teacher
(3) rinse her arm with water
(4) allow the acid to evaporate

36. When they are not being used during a laboratory investigation, electrical devices should be
(1) put away
(2) turned off
(3) unplugged
(4) covered

37. A student performing an experiment noticed that the beaker containing the water being heated had a small crack. It was not leaking. What should the student do?

(1) Stop heating the beaker and try to fix the crack.
(2) Stop heating the beaker and report the crack to the teacher.
(3) Stop heating the beaker and immediately take the beaker to the teacher.
(4) Continue heating as long as the liquid does not start to leak out of the crack.

38. The diagram below shows a student conducting a laboratory experiment. Describe one safety procedure the student should be following that is *not* represented in the diagram. [1]

39. The diagram below shows a student heating some test tubes with chemicals in them during a laboratory activity. Describe one error in the laboratory procedure shown in the diagram. [1]

40. An *unsafe* procedure for heating a nutrient solution in a flask would be to

(1) heat the solution at the lowest temperature on a hot plate
(2) stopper the flask tightly to prevent evaporation of the solution
(3) use a Bunsen burner to heat the solution
(4) stir the solution while it is heating

41. Chlorophyll can be removed from leaves by boiling them in alcohol, a flammable solvent. In addition to wearing safety goggles, which is the safest procedure to follow?

(1) A stoppered test tube of leaves and alcohol should be held over the Bunsen burner.
(2) A stoppered test tube of leaves and alcohol should be placed in a large beaker of alcohol and heated on a hot plate.
(3) A beaker of leaves and alcohol should be placed on a tripod over a Bunsen burner.
(4) A beaker of leaves and alcohol should be placed into a larger beaker of water and heated on a hot plate.

42. Which safety procedure should a student follow during a dissection?

(1) The student should wear gloves and hold the specimen in the palm of her hand while cutting the specimen open.
(2) The student should cut the specimen open while holding it under running water.
(3) The student should apply additional preservative to the specimen.
(4) The student should direct the cutting motion away from her body.

Directions

Review the Test-Taking Strategies section of this book. Then answer the following questions. Read each question carefully and answer with a correct choice or response.

Part A

1 The diagram below shows a wasp positioned next to a centimeter ruler.

What is the approximate length of a *wing* of this wasp?
(1) 10 mm   (3) 3.5 cm
(2) 1.4 cm   (4) 35 mm

2 When preparing a wet-mount slide of onion cells, a student put a drop of Lugol's iodine stain on the slide. Lugol's iodine stain was added to
(1) prevent the formation of air bubbles
(2) make cell structures more visible
(3) increase the magnification
(4) increase the rate of photosynthesis in the cells

3 A student views some cheek cells under low power. Before switching to high power, the student should
(1) adjust the eyepiece
(2) center the image being viewed
(3) remove the slide from the stage
(4) remove the coverslip from the slide

4 Bromthymol blue turns yellow in the presence of carbon dioxide. This characteristic makes it possible for bromthymol blue to function as
(1) a measure of volume
(2) an indicator
(3) a catalyst
(4) an energy source

5 Which statement describes two unsafe laboratory practices represented in the diagram below?

(1) The flame is too high, and the test tube is unstoppered.
(2) The opening of the test tube is pointed toward the student, and the student is not wearing goggles.
(3) The test tube is unstoppered, and the student is not wearing goggles.
(4) The beaker has water in it, and the flame is under the tripod.

6 A student sees the image shown below when observing the letter "f" with the low-power objective lens of a microscope.

Which of the four diagrams below most closely resembles the image the student will see after switching to high power?

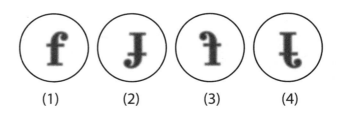

(1)   (2)   (3)   (4)

Part B

7 The diagram below represents the field of view of a compound light microscope. Three single-celled organisms are located across the diameter of the field.

Knowing that 1 mm = 1000 micrometers, what is the approximate length of each single-celled organism?
(1) 250 micrometers
(2) 500 micrometers
(3) 1000 micrometers
(4) 1500 micrometers

8 When stained with certain dyes, cell structures known as nucleoproteins appear black. These dyes would most likely be used to
(1) identify specific nucleoproteins within cells
(2) stain all types of cell organelles
(3) determine the chemical composition of nucleoproteins
(4) indicate the presence of nucleoproteins

9 A student, not wearing safety goggles, gets some unknown chemical in his eye. What is the most appropriate action he should take?
(1) Put on safety goggles immediately.
(2) Ask his lab partner to see if his eye looks OK .
(3) Go to the eyewash station and use it to rinse his eye thoroughly.
(4) Rub the eye gently and see if it hurts or stings.

10 A student is heating a test tube containing an indicator solution and glucose. The student is wearing safety goggles and a laboratory apron. Describe another safety procedure that this student should be following. [1]

11 While she is using a Bunsen burner, a student's sleeve catches fire. State two things the student should have done to avoid this kind of accident. [1]

12 The diagram below represents part of the process of

(1) gel electrophoresis
(2) genetic engineering
(3) homeostatic control
(4) cell culturing

13 A student is viewing a single-celled organism under the low-power objective of a compound light microscope. Describe an adjustment the student would need to make to see the organism clearly *after* switching from low power to high power. In your description include the name of the part of the microscope that would be used to make the adjustment. [1]

14 What is the volume of the liquid in the graduated cylinder shown below?

(1) 23 mL   (2) 26 mL   (3) 27 mL   (4) 28 mL

15 The diagrams below show four different one-celled organisms (shaded) in the field of view of the same microscope using different magnifications. Which illustration shows the largest one-celled organism?

Base your answers to questions 16 through 18 on the information below, the key, and on your knowledge of biology.

Biologists use keys to accurately classify unknown organisms such as the unidentified female mosquito shown in the following diagram. These keys are designed to categorize organisms according to structural characteristics. The key shows various characteristics used to identify the differences among *Anopheles, Deinocerites, Culex, Psorophora,* and *Aedes mosquitoes.*

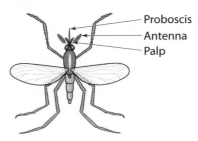

Unknown female mosquito

1a Antennae very bushy — Male mosquito	**1b** Antennae not bushy — Go to 2
2a Palps much shorter than proboscis — Go to 3	**2b** Palps as long as proboscis — Female *Anopheles*
3a Tip of abdomen blunt, without points — Go to 4	**3b** Tip of abdomen with points — Go to 5
4a Antennae much longer than proboscis — Female *Deinocerites*	**4b** Antennae shorter than proboscis — Female *Culex*
5a Many long scales present on hind legs — Female *Psorophora*	**5b** Hind legs without long scales — Female *Aedes*

16 According to the key, which feature distinguishes male from female mosquitoes?
(1) palp length
(2) leg scales
(3) abdomen points
(4) antennae appearance

17 According to the key, which characteristics are necessary to identify a female *Anopheles* mosquito?
(1) antennae, palps, and proboscis
(2) wings, proboscis, and scales on legs
(3) eyes, scales on legs, and abdomen tip
(4) palps, abdomen tip, and wings

18 According to the key, the unknown female mosquito belongs to the group known as
(1) *Deinocerites*   (3) *Psorophora*
(2) *Culex*   (4) *Aedes*

Part C

19 Some students did a lab to test the vitamin C content of several fruits. They squeezed the juice from some of the fruits and cut others up and placed them in a blender to obtain a juice sample. Juice for each fruit was kept in a clean, labeled beaker. Pipettes were used to transfer the juices to test tubes for analysis.

During the laboratory cleanup, one student drank some of the juice left in one beaker. State why this was an unsafe procedure. [1]

20 Below is a drawing of a hypothetical electrophoresis gel. Included on the gel are some bands for several different individuals.

- Decribe where the smallest fragments of DNA would be located on the gel in the illustration. [1]

- Discuss two practical applications of information that can be obtained through this process. [1]

21 The dichotomous key begun below should allow users to classify the organisms illustrated. Complete the key using only information shown in the illustration. [3]

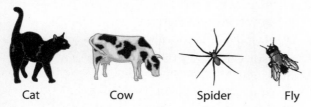

Cat   Cow   Spider   Fly

Dichotomous Key
1a. Wings present·····································Fly 1b. No wings present····························· go to 2

Base your answers to questions 22 through 24 on the information and diagram below and on your knowledge of biology.

The diagram below shows the results of a test that was done using DNA samples from three bears of different species. Each DNA sample was cut into fragments using a specific enzyme and placed in the wells as indicated below. The DNA fragments were then separated using gel electrophoresis.

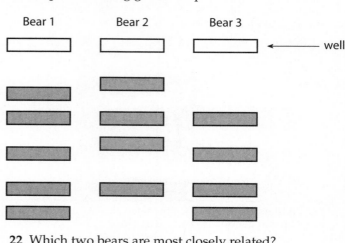

22 Which two bears are most closely related? Support your answer with data from the test results. [1]

23 Identify one additional way to determine the evolutionary relationship of these bears. [1]

24 Identify one procedure, other than electrophoresis, that is used in the laboratory to separate the different types of molecules in a liquid mixture. [1]

Part D of The Living Environment Regents Examination, is composed of multiple-choice and/or open-ended constructed-response questions, based on the NY State-required laboratory activities.

Questions and Answers About Part D of the Regents Examination

1. **How important are the required laboratory activities?** Everyone taking the Living Environment Regents Examination is expected to have satisfactorily met the laboratory requirement and completed the four laboratory activities. Questions on Part D of the Regents Examination assess content and skills related to these required laboratory activities. Everyone who has completed these activities should have available for review the *Student Laboratory Packet* supplied by the Regents for each of the labs. The packet contains background information, procedures, questions, and answers that were filled in as you carried out the laboratory activity. These packets should be used for review purposes, along with the information provided in this Appendix.

2. **How do the required labs help me in the Living Environment course?** Performing the required laboratory activities accomplishes two basic things. First, you learn and/or practice important laboratory skills associated with the biological sciences. Second, the lab activities are each associated with specific concepts contained in the *Living Environment Core Curriculum*, helping you better learn, understand, and apply those concepts.

3. **How can this Appendix help me prepare for the Part D questions?** To best prepare for the questions on Part D, you need to review your completed *Student Laboratory Packet* for each required laboratory activity along with the information presented here. You should have all four completed packets (with correct answers) available as you work through this Appendix.

4. **What should I know about each of the Required Laboratory Activities?** The most critical thing is that you have actually completed each activity and observed firsthand the results of each part. The next thing is to review the content and skills associated with each activity by working through the rest of this Appendix. In many cases, the content or skills are already found elsewhere in this book. References and notes are provided to show you where to look. Specific information and skills related to each activity is provided in this section.

The questions on Part D may be *applications* of the skills and content associated with the activity. For example, although red onion cells are used in the diffusion laboratory activity, a question involving the basic concepts of diffusion using another kind of plant cell would be appropriate as a Part D question.

It is important to note that you do *not* have to know, for test purposes, all of the content information provided with each activity. Much of it is included in the activity so that you can understand the important concepts. Only a few concepts in the required labs that are not in the Core Curriculum are actually testable. Each of these will be clearly noted in this Appendix.

Laboratory Activity #1: Relationships and Biodiversity

In this activity, you conducted a number of tests to compare various characteristics of a hypothetical "endangered plant species" with 3 other species that were related to it. From the data, you then determined which species might be the most likely to produce the substance "Curol" that has important medical uses. The final segment of the activity focused on biodiversity, both its benefits and how the loss of biodiversity can be an environmental problem.

Skills and/or content associated with the laboratory activity	Procedures and suggestions for review Note: Pages noted below are either in *Brief Review in the Living Environment* (BR) or in your *Student Lab Packet (SLP)*.
Making/recording observations of plant tissues	See pages 146–148 and page 179 (BR) for information about observations, inferences, assumptions, and opinions.
Making/recording observations of tissue samples with a microscope	Review focusing and other microscope skills on pages 169–172 (BR). In this activity you examined plant tissues with the microscope to look for similarities and differences.
Comparing samples to determine similarities and differences	You compared the flowers, leaves, seeds, and stem cross-sections in an attempt to determine which one was most closely related to *Botana curus (B. curus)*. If a Regents question illustrates parts of specific organisms, you could be asked to use your observations to determine relationships between them.
Use of paper chromatography	Review what you did during the laboratory activity on pages 2–3 (SLP). Review the process on page 175 (BR). Be prepared to answer questions about why goggles were required or about correct vs. incorrect technique related to chromatography, such as: What if the water (solvent) level was above the pigment spots when the paper was put in the cup? (answer: the pigment would wash away and not go up the paper)
Use of an indicator (to test for enzyme M)	You were testing for an enzyme that was present in *B. curus* to see if any of the other plants also produced it. The presence of this enzyme in any of the other plants might suggest a closer relationship to *B. curus*. Review information about indicators on page 175 (BR).
Use of simulated gel electrophoresis of DNA from plant samples	Review what you did during the laboratory activity on pages 3–4 (SLP), then review the technique of electrophoresis on pages 173–174 (BR). Be prepared to answer questions about how enzymes are used to cut the DNA into fragments as described in the lab activity. Also know how to interpret gel electrophoresis results: e.g., what do the bands represent and what information do they convey, or, where would the smallest fragments be on a gel?
Translating the DNA code to a particular protein sequence	Review what you did during the laboratory activity on page 7 (SLP). You first used the base pairing "rule" for DNA to RNA transcription—G goes with C, and A goes with U (not T) to get the mRNA sequences. Then you used the Universal Genetic Code Table provided by your teacher to look up which amino acid each three-letter mRNA sequence represented. This enabled you to get a particular amino acid sequence for each species, so that you could compare them and determine possible genetic relationships. Similar DNA suggests common ancestry. Review the information on pages 47–48 (BR) regarding proteins and DNA in cells.
Using branching tree diagrams to show relationships	Review question 6 on page 6 (SLP), then review Figure 5–2 on page 81 (BR). Read pages 87–88 (BR). Read the information about Practice Questions 13–14 on pages x–xi (BR).
Human actions and biodiversity	Re-read the passage on page 7 (SLP), then review your answers to questions 8–10. Review pages 110–111 (BR) and pages 127–129 (BR) regarding the benefits of biodiversity, and the section: *Extinction*, on page 91 (BR).

Questions and comments regarding Laboratory Activity #1

After reviewing your *Student Lab Packet* and the sections of this book as noted above, check yourself by answering the following questions found in this book on the pages noted.

p. 49; 8, 9, 13, 16, 17
p. 50; 18, 20, 21, 22
p. 54; 35
p. 55; 1, 6
p. 56; 8
p. 81; 4
p. 82; 5
p. 89; 27, 30
p. 101; 5
p. 111; 40, 41, 42
p. 112; 44, 45

p. 120; 32
p. 143; 36
p. 176; 9, 10, 11
p. 177; 13, 14, 15
p. 178; 22
p. 179; 29, 30
p. 183; 3
p. 184; 12, 13
p. 185; 20
p. 186; 22, 23, 24

You should also be able to:

- explain how you used your lab data to determine which plant species is the closest relative to *B. curus.*
- explain why finding a close relative to *B. curus* is important.
- list several forms of structural evidence that can be used to indicate biological relationships (such as similarities in embryos, flower form, or leaf shape).
- explain why structural evidence is often less useful than molecular evidence to determine biological relationships.
- use a genetic code table to convert a DNA sequence, to a mRNA sequence, to an amino acid sequence. (Ask your teacher for a copy of the table you used in the activity and practice with it.)
- explain why closely related species often share many molecular/biochemical similarities.
- answer questions related to why and how biodiversity may be lost, why such a loss is important, and how human activities often play a role in the loss of biodiversity.
- discuss why tradeoffs must be considered when the destruction of habitats/native species is involved.

Part D Review Questions: Lab 1

Base your answers to questions 1 through 4 on the information below and on your knowledge of biology.

To demonstrate techniques used in DNA analysis, a student was given two paper strip samples of DNA. The two DNA samples are shown below.

Sample 1:
ATTCCGGTAATCCCGTAATGCCGG
ATAATACTCCGGTAATATC

Sample 2:
ATTCCGGTAATCCCGTAATGCCGGA
TAATACTCCGGTAATATC

The student cut between the C and G in each of the shaded CCGG sequences in sample 1 and between the As in each of the shaded TAAT sequences in sample 2. Both sets of fragments were then arranged on a paper model of a gel.

1. The action of what kind of molecules was being demonstrated when the DNA samples were cut? [1]

2. Identify the technique that was being demonstrated when the fragments were arranged on the gel model. [1]

3. The results of this type of DNA analysis are often used to help determine
   (1) the number of DNA molecules in an organism
   (2) if two species are closely related
   (3) the number of mRNA molecules in DNA
   (4) if two organisms contain carbohydrate molecules

4. State one way that the arrangement of the two samples on the gel model would differ. [1]

5. R, S, and T are three species of birds. Species S and T show similar coloration. The enzymes found in species R and T show similarities. Species R and T also exhibit many of the same behavioral patterns.

   Show the relationship between species R, S, and T by placing the letter representing each species at the top of the appropriate branch on the diagram to the right. [1]

Base your answers to questions 6 through 8 on the diagram below and on your knowledge of biology. Letters _A_ through _L_ represent different species of organisms. The arrows represent long periods of geologic time.

6. Which two species are the most closely related?

   (1) J and L   (3) F and H
   (2) G and L   (4) F and G

7. Which species was best adapted to changes that occurred in its environment over the longest period of time?

   (1) A   (3) C
   (2) B   (4) J

8. Which two species would most likely show the greatest similarity of DNA and proteins?

   (1) B and J   (3) J and K
   (2) G and I   (4) F and L

Base your answers to questions 9 through 11 on the information below and on your knowledge of biology.

Paper chromatography can be used to investigate evolutionary relationships. Leaves from a plant were ground and mixed with a solvent. The mixture of ground leaves and solvent was then filtered. Using a toothpick, twenty drops of the filtrate (material that passed through the filter) were placed at one spot on a strip of chromatography paper.

This procedure was repeated using leaves from three other species of plants. A separate strip of chromatography paper was prepared for each plant species. Each of the four strips of chromatography paper was placed in a different beaker containing the same solvent for the same amount of time. One of the laboratory setups is shown below.

9. State one reason for using a new toothpick for the filtrate from each plant. [1]

10. State one way the four strips would most likely be different from each other after being removed from the beakers. [1]

11. State how a comparison of these resulting strips could indicate evolutionary relationships. [1]

Base your answers to questions 12 through 14 on the information below and on your knowledge of biology.

Scientists found members of a plant species they did not recognize. They wanted to determine if the unknown species was related to one or more of four known species, A, B, C, and D. The relationship between species can be determined most accurately by comparing the results of gel electrophoresis of the DNA from different species.

The chart below represents the results of gel electrophoresis of the DNA from the unknown plant species and the four known species.

Results of Gel Electrophoresis of DNA from Five Plant Species				
Unknown Species	Species A	Species B	Species C	Species D

Key
— = Band in the gel

12. The unknown species is most closely related to which of the four known species? Support your answer. [1]

13. Identify one physical characteristic of plants that can be readily observed and compared to help determine the relationship between two different species of plants. [1]

14. Explain why comparing the DNA of the unknown and known plant species is probably a more accurate method of determining relationships than comparing only the physical characteristic you identified in question 13. [1]

Laboratory Activity #2: Making Connections

In Part A of this activity, you learned to take your pulse rate. Then you compared pulse rate data for the class. You next experienced muscle fatigue by rapidly squeezing a clothespin. In Part B, you designed a controlled experiment to determine which of two claims about exercise and pulse rate is correct.

Skills and/or content associated with the laboratory activity	Procedures and suggestions for review **Note:** Pages noted below are either in *Brief Review in the Living Environment (BR)* or in your *Student Lab Packet (SLP)*.
Taking pulse rate	You should be familiar with the procedure to find a person's pulse rate on page 2. (SLP) Review the information on human systems on pages 10–13 (BR).
Data tables and graphs	Review the data table and histogram you prepared on page 3 (SLP). Also review the questions and your answers on page 4 (SLP). Review the information about collecting and organizing data on pages 154–156 (BR).
Muscle fatigue	Review the information, questions, and your answers to them on pages 5 and 6 (SLP).
Designing a controlled experiment and a report on the findings	Review the background information on page 7 (SLP) to help you recall how you determined the hypothesis your experiment tested. Review the steps for the design of a controlled experiment and how to organize the final report on pages 8–9 (SLP), then read over your final laboratory report for this activity, noting how you addressed each step of the design and report organization. Review the information on pages 149 through 158 (BR) regarding experimental design and the reporting of results and conclusions.

Questions and comments regarding Laboratory Activity #2

After reviewing your *Student Lab Packet* and the sections of this book as noted above, check yourself by answering the following questions found in this book on the pages noted.

p. 14; 38
p. 16; 15
p. 149; 3, 5
p. 153; 6, 8
p. 154; 9, 10, 11, 12, 14, 15, 16
p. 158; 18, 19
p. 159; 23, 24, 25, 26, 27, 28
p. 161; 7, 8, 9, 10, 11, 12, 13
p. 162; 14

You should also be able to:

- explain what your pulse rate tells you about activities occurring within your body.
- explain why a higher level of activity would affect a person's pulse rate. Be sure to state specifically how the functioning of muscle cells is affected by blood flow through various parts the body including the respiratory and digestive systems.
- explain what muscle fatigue is, what happens to cause it, and how it can eventually be overcome—see page 5 (SLP).

- explain why different individuals may have different resting pulse rates and that not all people experience muscle fatigue with the same amount of muscle activity.
- explain why evidence is important in determining whether or not a claim someone makes is true.
- describe your actual experiment, including the question, hypothesis, independent and dependent variables, and your conclusions. You should also be able to suggest at least one additional experiment that could be done to answer a question that came about as a direct result of the experiment you conducted. (Such a question might involve the effect of more activity on the test subjects, having more test subjects, or choosing a greater variety of test subjects.)

Part D Review Questions: Lab 2

15. On a television talk show, a guest claims that people who exercise vigorously for 15 minutes or more every day are able to solve math problems more rapidly than people who have no vigorous exercise in their daily routine.

Describe a controlled experiment that could be conducted to test this claim. In your description be sure to:

- state the purpose of the experiment [1]
- state why the sample to be used should be large [1]
- describe how the experimental group will be treated and how the control group will be treated [2]
- state the specific data to be collected during the experiment [1]
- state one way to determine if the results support the claim [1]

16. A student measures his pulse rate while he is watching television and records it. Next, he walks to a friend's house nearby and when he arrives, measures and records his pulse rate again. He and his friend then decide to run to the mall a few blocks away.

On arriving at the mall, the student measures and records his pulse rate once again. Finally, after sitting and talking for a half hour, the student measures and records his pulse rate for the last time. Which graph below best illustrates the expected changes in his pulse rate according to the activities described above?

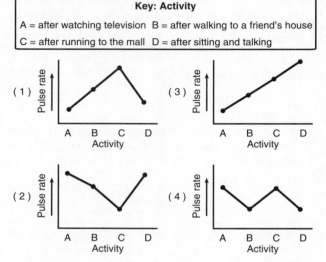

Key: Activity

A = after watching television B = after walking to a friend's house
C = after running to the mall D = after sitting and talking

17. A student squeezed a clothespin as many times as possible in a 30-second time period. The student repeated this procedure nine more times in quick succession. The data obtained are in the chart below.

Trial	Number of Squeezes in 30 Seconds
1	32
2	29
3	28
4	27
5	26
6	25
7	23
8	21
9	19
10	17

State one hypothesis that this data would support concerning the relationship between number of trials and number of squeezes in 30 seconds. [1]

Base your answers to questions 18 and 19 on the information below and on your knowledge of biology.

In an investigation, 28 students in a class determined their pulse rates after performing each of three different activities. Each activity was performed three times during equal time intervals. The average results are shown in the graph below.

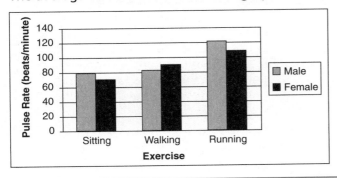

18. Before constructing the graph it would have been most helpful to organize the results of the investigation in
    (1) a research plan   (3) a data table
    (2) an equation   (4) a generalization

19. Some students concluded that males always have a higher pulse rate than females. Does the graph support this conclusion? Justify your answer. [1]

Laboratory Activity #3: The Beaks of Finches

The Beaks of Finches lab is a simulation of how natural selection works. Various tools are used in this activity to represent some beak variations that might be present in a population. Competition between participants leads to finding which tool(s) are best suited for obtaining enough food for the individuals with that tool (beak variation) to survive. The activity concludes with data about actual beak variations present today in different species of finches—the result of competition over many years on the Galapagos Islands.

Skills and/or content associated with the laboratory activity	Procedures and suggestions for review **Note:** Pages noted below are either in *Brief Review in the Living Environment (BR)* or in your *Student Lab Packet (SLP)*.
Predicting	Review the procedures and questions on page 2 (SLP) to recall why you could expect a particular tool to be useful for the job specified.
Collecting and organizing data, making predictions	Review what you did during the Round One competition on page 3 (SLP). You could be asked to place data in a data table provided, as you did in this activity. Review the information on p. 154–156 (BR).
Analyzing and interpreting data	Review what you did during the Round Two competition on page 3 (SLP). The competition in Round Two was expected to make it harder to collect as many seeds in the same time interval as you had in Round One. State whether or not your results supported this expectation. Include data from the table in your answer. Read the introduction to The Mechanics of Evolution and Overview of Evolution on page 82 (BR) and on pages xiii–xiv (BR) about data table question strategies.
Summarizing results	Review questions 1–9 and your answers on pages 4–6 (SLP). Read the information on page 82 (BR), then on page 83–84 (BR) read the three sections and review the information in figures 5–4 and 5–5. Read pages 99–101 (BR); *Environmental Limits on Population Size*.
Galapagos Island Finches—Interpreting charts	Review the chart on page 6 (SLP), noting the "design" of each beak compared with the way it functions and the preferred food. Review the questions about the chart along with your responses to them. Be prepared to answer similar questions in association with this chart or a similar chart or diagram.

Questions and comments regarding Laboratory Activity #3

After reviewing your *Student Lab Packet* and the sections of this book as noted above, check yourself by answering the following questions found in this book on the pages noted.

p. 84; 6	p. 101; 6
p. 85; 11, 12	p. 102; 9
p. 87; 16	p. 104; 10
p. 93; 1, 3, 5, 7	p. 158; 19

You should also be able to:

• identify a specific procedure or action you carried out in this lab that is directly associated with *each* of the following concepts associated with evolution: variation, competition, survival, adaptation, and the role of the environment as an agent of natural selection. For help, see question #9 on page 6 (SLP).

• describe how being assigned a tool is more like how adaptations occur in nature than being allowed to choose a particular tool for the task.

• predict how the addition of small pebbles to the dish (that could not be used as food) could affect the results as the (food) seeds were being collected.

• explain how the characteristics of a particular bird's beak could affect its survival.

• explain why a bird has no control over the type of beak it has.

• explain how a particular beak could be useful in one environment and nearly useless in another.

• explain why migration to a new environment may enable an individual who cannot successfully compete in its original location to survive.

• explain why an individual with a beak that does not enable it to compete successfully for food cannot simply get a new beak that would make it better adapted.

• describe two characteristics of a bird, other than its beak, that would vary among individuals in the population and be a factor in the ability of individual birds to survive. Select one of these characteristics and state how it would specifically be important to the individual's survival.

• name two species on the beak chart, on page 6 (SLP), that would be likely to compete when food is scarce. Explain the basis for your answer.

Part D Review Questions: Lab 3

20. A hawk has a genetic trait that gives it much better eyesight than other hawks of the same species in the same area. Explain how this could lead to evolutionary change within this species of hawk over a long period of time. In your answer, be sure to include an explanation of:

• competition within the hawk population [1]

• survival of various individuals in the population [1]

• how the frequency of the better-eyesight trait would be expected to change over time within the population [1]

• what would most likely happen to the hawks having the better-eyesight trait if they also had unusually weak wing muscles [1]

21. In members of a bird species living on a remote island, the greatest number of beak variations in the population would most likely be found when

(1) there is a high level of competition for limited resources

(2) homeostasis is limited by a severe climate

(3) they have a large and varied food supply

(4) they are prey for a large number of predators

22. The different tools used during the beaks of finches lab represented

(1) feeding adaptations in finches

(2) nest construction adaptations

(3) variations in seed size

(4) variations in ecosystems

Base your answer to question 23 on the portion of the mRNA codon chart and information below.

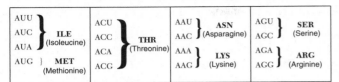

Series I represents three mRNA codons. Series II includes a mutation of series I.

Series I AGAUCGAGU
Series II ACAUCGAGU

23. How would the amino acid sequence produced by the mutant strand (series II) compare to the amino acid sequence produced by series I?

(1) The amino acid sequence would be shorter.
(2) One amino acid in the sequence would change.
(3) The amino acid sequence would remain unchanged.
(4) More than one amino acid in the sequence would change.

Base your answers to questions 24 through 26 on the passage below and on your knowledge of biology.

When Charles Darwin traveled to the Galapagos Islands, he observed 14 distinct varieties of finches on the islands. Darwin also observed that each finch variety ate a different type of food and lived in a slightly different habitat from the other finches. Darwin concluded that the finches all shared a common ancestor but had developed different beak structures.

24. The 14 varieties of finches are most likely the result of

(1) absence of biodiversity
(2) biological evolution
(3) asexual reproduction
(4) lack of competition

25. The second sentence best describes

(1) an ecosystem
(2) a predator/prey relationship
(3) a niche
(4) a food web

26. The different beak structures mentioned in the last sentence were most likely influenced by

(1) selection for favorable variations
(2) environmental conditions identical to those of the common ancestor
(3) abnormal mitotic cell division
(4) characteristics that are acquired during the bird's lifetime

Laboratory Activity #5: Diffusion Through a Membrane

The Diffusion Through a Membrane activity initially focuses on making a model "cell" and determining how certain materials move through the membrane surrounding it. Indicators are then used to test various solutions to determine which materials moved and where they ended up. Red onion cells were treated with salt solution and distilled water to determine the effect of such substances on live cells.

Skills and/or content associated with the laboratory activity	Procedures and suggestions for review **Note:** Pages noted below are either in *Brief Review in the Living Environment (BR)* or in your *Student Lab Packet (SLP)*.
Making a model "cell"	Review the procedures by which you made a model "cell" out of dialysis tubing (or a plastic bag). The "cell" contained both glucose and starch while the beaker contained starch indicator solution and water—see p. 2 (SLP). Read pages 5–8 (BR) regarding cell organelles, including the cell membrane. Read p. 166–168 (BR), *Tools for Measurement*.
Using starch and glucose indicator solutions	Review the procedures (p. 3 SLP, Table One) for testing for starch and glucose using the indicator. Notice that, in each case, a color change indicated the presence of the substance, and that the glucose test required heating before a result could be observed.

Determining indicator results	Table 2 (p. 3 SLP) summarizes the tests and results for each indicator. Be sure you can explain why it is necessary to test both the substance you want the indicator to "find" and any other substances that are also present. Read p. 175 (BR); *Stains and Indicators*.
Observing and interpreting results	Review your Model Cell Observations (p. 4 SLP) and the diagrams you filled in. Then carefully review your answers to questions 1–7 on pages 4–5 (SLP). Be sure you now understand which molecules moved through the membrane and know how you could tell. Also be sure you know how this information was used to determine the relative sizes of the molecules.
Making a wet-mount slide (of onion cells)	Review the procedures for making a wet mount slide. (p. 6 SLP) Read pages 169–172 (BR); *Microscope Skills*.
Drawing and labeling microscope images	Review the drawings you made for questions 6, 10, and 15. (p. 7 SLP) Note the differences in each drawing and review what you did each time to cause the changes you observed and drew.
Adding liquids to wet-mount slides	Review the procedure for this technique. (p. 6 SLP) You should be able to describe this process and predict the effect a substance being added would have on the cells.
Applying skills and concepts	Review the Analysis Questions and your answers to them. (p. 8–9 SLP) Just as you did for these questions, you should be able to apply the main concepts from this activity to questions like these if they appear on Part D of the Regents examination.

Questions and comments regarding Laboratory Activity #5

After reviewing your *Student Lab Packet* and the sections of this book as noted above, check yourself by answering the following questions found in this book on the pages noted.

p. 6; 11
p. 9; 22, 23, 25, 26, 27, 28
p. 10; 30, 31, 32, 33, 35
p. 15; 4, 5, 6, 7, 8, 9, 10
p. 16; 11
p. 18; 28, 29

p. 168; 3, 4
p. 169; 5, 6, 8
p. 177; 13, 14, 15, 16, 17
p. 178; 22
p. 183; 2, 4

You should also be able to:

- explain why dialysis tubing or a plastic bag could be used to simulate a cell membrane in this activity.
- identify a particular indicator and explain how it is used to indicate whether or not a specific substance is present.
- explain why it was important to keep the onion skin material as flat as possible when making the wet-mount slide.
- describe the direction that particles move during the process of diffusion relative to the concentration of a substance or substances.

- describe how the size of a molecule can affect whether or not it can pass across (through) a membrane.
- provide several examples of cells being affected by the process of diffusion. The effects may be on the appearance of the cell, the contents of the cell, and/or the functioning of the cell.
- provide several specific examples of the process of diffusion occurring within the human body. For each example be able to identify the substance(s) diffusing and the effect of this process on body functioning.
- describe the effect of salt on the water content of cell cytoplasm.
- describe how distilled water can be used to counteract the effect of salt on living cells on a wet-mount microscope slide.
- predict the effect of an error in procedure by students doing this particular laboratory activity, such as putting a substance in the wrong place, using salt solution instead of water, using the wrong indicator, and so on.
- Understand that osmosis, the diffusion of water through a membrane, is a kind of diffusion and therefore follows the same general "rules" as for the diffusion of other substances.

- explain how the process of digestion is related to the process of diffusion—see question 6 on p. 9 (SLP).

Part D Review Questions: Lab 5

27. An investigation was set up to study the movement of water through a membrane. The results are shown in the diagram below.

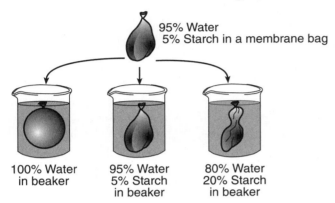

95% Water
5% Starch in a membrane bag

100% Water in beaker

95% Water 5% Starch in beaker

80% Water 20% Starch in beaker

Based on these results, which statement correctly predicts what will happen to red blood cells when they are placed in a beaker containing a water solution in which the salt concentration is much higher than the salt concentration in the red blood cells?

(1) The red blood cells will absorb water and increase in size.

(2) The red blood cells will lose water and decrease in size.

(3) The red blood cells will first absorb water, then lose water and maintain their normal size.

(4) The red blood cells will first lose water, then absorb water, and finally double in size.

28. Molecules A and B are both organic molecules found in many cells. When tested, it is found that molecule A cannot pass through a cell membrane, but molecule B easily passes through. State one way the two molecules could differ, that would account for the difference in the ability to pass through the cell membrane. [1]

29. Elodea is a plant that lives in freshwater. The diagram below represents one Elodea leaf cell in its normal freshwater environment.

Elodea cell in freshwater

Predict how the contents of the Elodea cell would change if the cell was placed in saltwater for several minutes by completing the diagram, "Elodea cell in saltwater" below. Label the location of the cell membrane. [2]

Elodea cell in saltwater

30. The photos below show two red onion cells viewed with the high power of a compound light microscope. Describe the steps that could be used to make cell A resemble cell B using a piece of paper towel and an eyedropper or a pipette without removing the coverslip. [3]

← Cell A   ← Cell B

31. An indicator for a protein is added to a solution that contains protein and to a solution that does not contain protein. State one way, other than the presence or absence of protein, that the two solutions may differ after the indicator has been added to both. [1]

Glossary

Glossary items with asterisk are required vocabulary for the Regents Examination.

*abiotic nonliving parts of the environment

acid/acidic a compound that releases hydrogen ions when dissolved in water; a substance, such as vinegar, with a sour taste. Any pH below 7 indicates an acid, the lower the pH, the stronger the acid. The lowest pH possible is pH 0. Strong acids are usually harmful to living cells.

acid rain rain that is more acidic than normal

*active transport the process by which cells use energy to transport molecules through the cell membrane from areas of low concentration to areas of high concentration

*adaptive value any trait that helps an organism survive and reproduce under a given set of environmental conditions

agarose a gel-like substance used in bacterial cultures

*AIDS (acquired immunodeficiency syndrome) the disease that results when the HIV virus attacks the human immune system

*allergy a condition in which a person's immune system is overly sensitive to environmental substances that are normally harmless

*amino acid any one of several building blocks of protein

animal a complex, multicellular organism with specialized tissues and organs, but no cell walls; a heterotroph that obtains energy by consuming other organisms

*antibiotic a medicine produced by microorganisms used to destroy pathogens in humans and domestic animals

*antibody (pl. **antibodies**) a protein, produced by the immune system, that either attacks invading pathogens or marks them for killing

*antigen a molecule found on the outer surfaces of cells that the immune system recognizes as either part of the body or an outside invader

antihistamine a substance that reduces the effects of histamines and the symptoms they cause

artificial selection the process of breeding two organisms with desirable characteristics to produce offspring that have the advantages of both parents

*asexual reproduction a method of reproduction in which all the genes passed on to the offspring come from a single individual or parent

*assumption something accepted as true that may or may not actually be true

*ATP (adenosine triphosphate) a compound that stores energy in cells

*autotroph an organism that produces its own food; the source of energy for all other living things on Earth

*bacterium (pl. **bacteria**) any one of many single-celled organisms without a distinct nucleus

*balance a tool that measures mass by comparing the unknown mass of an object with an object of known mass

base a compound that produces hydroxide ions when dissolved in water, raising the pH above 7; the higher the pH, the stronger the base; strong bases are usually harmful to living cells

*bias a tendency to favor something; prejudice

*biochemical process a chemical process that occurs in a living thing

*biodiversity the variety of species in an area

biome large groups of ecosystems with similar climates and organisms; examples include the tundra, taiga, temperate forest, chaparral, tropical rain forest, desert, temperate grassland, tropical savanna grassland, and polar and high-mountain ice

*biosphere all of Earth's ecosystems, collectively; the biologically inhabited portions of Earth, including all of the water, land, and air in which organisms survive

*biotechnology the combination of technology and biological sciences

*biotic the living parts of the environment

*body cells non-reproductive cells in an individual such as skin, liver, and muscle cells; body cells contain the full number of chromosomes typical of the species

*bond the chemical link between atoms that hold molecules together

calibrate to adjust the scale of a measurement tool

*carnivore an organism that survives by eating animals

*carrying capacity the largest population of any single species that an area can support

*catalyst a substance that can speed up the rate of a chemical reaction without being changed or used up during the reaction

*cell the basic unit of structure and function that makes up all organisms

*cell membrane the thin boundary between the cell and its environment

*cellular respiration the process in which nutrients are broken apart, releasing the chemical energy stored in them

Celsius a temperature scale based on 100 equal units, with 0 as the freezing point of water and 100 as the boiling point of water

*chloroplast the green organelle that contains chlorophyll; where photosynthesis takes place

chlorophyll the molecules in chloroplasts that help convert light energy to chemical bond energy

*chromatography a laboratory technique used to separate mixtures of molecules

*chromosome a thick, threadlike structure that contains genetic information in the form of DNA

*circulation the flow of materials within a cell as well as between parts of a multicellular organism

classify to group things based upon their similarities

climax community a relatively diverse and stable ecosystem that is the end result of succession

*clone an organism that is genetically identical to the organism from which it was produced

*cloning a technique used to make identical organisms

*community a combination of all the different populations that live and interact in the same environment

*competition the struggle between organisms for the same limited resources in a particular area

*compound light microscope a tool that uses more than one lens and a light source to magnify an object

*conclusion the decision made about the outcome of an experiment; usually based on how well the actual result matches the predicted result

*consumer an organism that obtains its energy from producers

*control that group in an experiment in which everything—except the variable to be tested—is identical; the standard of comparison in an experiment

*controlled experiment an experiment in which all variables—except for the one being tested—are exactly the same

coverslip a thin slice of glass that covers the specimen on a slide

*cytoplasm the jellylike substance that is between the cell membrane and the nucleus and that contains specialized structures

*data the results of specific trials or tests completed during experiments

*decomposer an organism, generally a bacterium or fungus, that consumes dead organisms and organic waste

decomposition the process whereby dead organisms, as well as the wastes produced by living organisms, are broken down into their raw materials and returned to the ecosystem

*deforestation forest destruction that results from human activity

*dependent variable the part of an experiment that is changed to test a hypothesis

depletion a serious decline or reduction

detrimental damaging; harmful

*development the changes that occur from the fertilized egg to a complete individual; occurs by mitosis and differentiation of cells

deviation a change from normal circumstances

*dichotomous key a guide that compares pairs of observable traits to help the user identify an organism

*differentiation the process that transforms developing cells into specialized cells with different structures and functions

*diffusion the movement of molecules from areas of high concentration to areas of low concentration

*digestion the process that breaks down large food molecules into simpler molecules that the organism can use

*direct harvesting the destruction of an organism, or the removal of an organism from its habitat

*disease a condition, other than injury, that prevents the body from working as it should

*dissection the act of cutting apart a dead organism to examine its internal structure

*DNA (<u>d</u>eoxyribo<u>n</u>ucleic <u>acid</u>) the material found in all cells that contains genetic information about that organism

*dynamic equilibrium the constant small corrections that normally occur to keep an organism's internal environment within the limits needed for survival

*ecological niche the specific role played by an organism or a population of organisms in the ecosystem

*ecological succession the process by which an existing community is replaced by another community

*ecology the study of how living things interact with one another and with their environment

*ecosystem all the living and nonliving things that interact in a specific area; a subdivision of the environment

*egg a sex cell produced by a female

*electronic balance a balance that measures mass automatically

*electrophoresis a tool that allows scientists to separate mixtures of molecules according to size

*element a substance consisting of only one kind of atom

*embryo an organism in the early stages of development (prior to birth)

endocrine glands various hormone-producing glands that secrete substances directly into the blood or lymph

endoplasmic reticulum an organelle that transports proteins and other materials from one part of the cell to another

*energy flow the movement of energy through an ecosystem

*energy pyramid a diagram showing how food energy moves through the ecosystem

*environment every living and nonliving thing that surrounds an organism

environmental impact statement a statement that includes an analysis of how a new project or technology might affect the environment

*enzymes proteins that speed up the rate of chemical reactions in living things

*equilibrium a state of balance and stability

estrogen a hormone (produced by the ovaries) that controls female sexual development and the reproductive process

*evidence support for the idea that something is true

*evolution the process by which species have changed over time

*excretion the removal of all the wastes produced by the cells of the body

*experiment a series of trials or tests that are done to support or refute a hypothesis

*expressed the way that an unseen gene is seen in an organism as an actual physical trait

*extinction the disappearance of all members of a species from Earth

Fallopian tubes that part of the female reproductive system where the egg cell is fertilized by the sperm cell; also called oviducts

*feedback mechanism a cycle in which the output of a system either modifies or reinforces the first action taken by the system

*fertilization the process that combines a sperm cell and an egg cell

*fetus the unborn, developing young of an animal during the later stages of development

*finite limited; able to be used up; opposite of infinite

flow of energy the movement of energy through an ecosystem

*food chain a representation that identifies the specific feeding relationships among organisms

*food web a representation of many interconnected food chains that shows the feeding relationships among producers, consumers, and decomposers

forceps a tool used mainly during dissection to lift out small parts, to move structures, and to pry parts open

*fossil the preserved remains of ancient organisms

*fossil fuel a fuel, such as coal and gas, that comes from the remains of organisms that lived millions of years ago

*fossil record a collection of fossils used to represent Earth's history

*fungus (pl. fungi) the kingdom of organisms that are mostly multicellular, have cell walls made of chitin, and are heterotrophic

*gamete an egg or sperm cell; a sex cell

*gas exchange the process of obtaining oxygen from the environment and releasing carbon dioxide

*gene (pl. genes) a segment of DNA (on a chromosome) that contains the code for a specific trait

*gene expression see *expressed*; the result of activated genes

*genetic engineering a set of technologies that humans use to alter the genetic instructions of an organism by substituting DNA molecules

*genetic recombination the formation of a new combination of genes during sexual reproduction

*genetic variation the normal differences found among offspring

*geologic time Earth's history as revealed by layers of rock

*global warming a increase in Earth's average surface temperature caused by an increase in greenhouse gases

*glucose a sugar that is a major source of energy for cells

*graduated cylinder a tool used to measure the volume of a liquid

greenhouse effect the trapping of heat by gases in the atmosphere

greenhouse gas an atmospheric gas that traps heat

growth an increase in the size or number of cells

*guard cells specialized cells that control the opening and closing of the pores on the surface of a leaf

*habitat the place where an animal or plant lives

*herbivore an organism that eats only plants

*heredity the passing of traits from parent to offspring

*heterotroph organism that cannot make its own food; a consumer

histamine a chemical that is released as the immune system's reaction to an allergy

*homeostasis the ability of an organism to maintain a stable internal environment even when the external environment changes

*hormone a chemical produced in the endocrine glands

*host the organism in a parasitic relationship that provides a home and/or food for the parasite

hot water bath in the science laboratory, usually a large beaker of water heated on a hot plate; used to heat test tubes that contain a flammable liquid, such as alcohol

humerus the long bone in the upper part of the arm

*hypothesis a statement that predicts a relationship between cause and effect in a way that can be tested

*immune system the body's primary defense against disease-causing pathogens

*immunity the body's ability to destroy pathogens before they cause disease

*independent variable a factor that might influence the dependent variable in an experiment

*indicator a substance that changes color when it encounters certain chemical conditions

*industrialization the process of converting an economy into one in which large-scale manufacturing is the primary economic base

*inference a conclusion or deduction based on observations

infinite without limits or bounds

*inorganic a type of molecule that does not contain both carbon and hydrogen but can contain any other combination of elements

*insulin a hormone that prompts glucose to move from the blood into body cells, resulting in a lower glucose level in the blood

*limiting factor any factor in the environment that limits the size of a population

lipid any one of a group of organic compounds that includes oils, fats, and waxes

*magnification the ability of a microscope to make an object appear larger

*mass a measure of the quantity of matter in an object

*meiosis the process that results in the production of sex cells (sperm and egg)

*meniscus the curved surface at the top of a column of liquid

*metabolism all the chemical reactions that occur within the cells of an organism

*metric ruler a tool used to measure the length of an object

*microbe any microscopic organism

micrometer a unit of length equal to one millionth of a meter

*microscope a tool that uses a lens or a combination of lenses to magnify an object

*mitochondria pod-shaped organelles that contain enzymes used to extract energy from nutrients

*mitosis the process that divides the cell's nucleus into two, each with a complete set of genetic material from the parent cell

*model a representation used to explain or demonstrate a process or structure; also used to predict what might occur in a new situation

molecule a particle in which two or more atoms combine to form a single unit; the smallest unit of a compound

muscular system a body system comprised of tissue that contracts when it is stimulated; the combination of muscles that enables the body to move

*mutation any alteration in the sequence of DNA

*natural selection the process by which the organisms that are best adapted to a specific environment survive and produce more offspring than organisms that are not as well adapted

neutral a solution with a pH of 7 that is neither acidic nor basic; the tissues of many living things maintain a pH within 1 or 2 units of this neutral point

*niche the specific role played by an organism in its ecosystem

nitrogen cycle the movement of nitrogen from the atmosphere to the soil and organisms and then back to the atmosphere

nitrogen fixation the process by which nitrogen forms compounds that can be used by living things

*nonrenewable resource any resource, such as fossil fuels and minerals, that cannot be replaced

*nuclear fuel an energy source that results from splitting atoms

*nucleus a large structure within a cell that controls the cell's metabolism and stores genetic information, including chromosomes and DNA

nucleic acids large, complex organic molecules that contain the instructions cells need to carry out their life processes

nutrient a substance that provides the body with the materials and energy needed to carry out the basic life of cells

objective one of the lenses of a microscope

*observation any information that is collected with any of the senses

ocular the eyepiece lens of a microscope

*opinion ideas people have that may or may not be based in fact

optimum the most favorable condition

*organ a body structure made of different kinds of tissues combined to perform a specific function

*organ system several organs that work together to perform a major function in the body

*organelle a structure within the cell that carries out a specific function

*organic term used to describe molecules that contain both hydrogen and carbon

*organic compound a compound that contains both hydrogen and carbon

*ovary (pl. **ovaries**) the organ of the human female reproductive system that produces an egg cell, the female gamete

*overproduction the potential for a species to increase its numbers beyond the area's carrying capacity

oviduct the part of the female reproductive system where the egg cell is fertilized by the sperm

oxygen-carbon dioxide cycle the movement of oxygen and carbon dioxide between living things and the environment

*ozone shield the layer of ozone gas in the upper atmosphere that protects Earth from some of the sun's radiation

*pancreas an endocrine organ that secretes insulin

*parasite an organism that survives by living and feeding on other organisms

parasitic relationship an arrangement in which one organism lives in or on a host organism, deriving some or all of its nourishment from the host, to the host's detriment

*pathogen an organism that invades the body, causing disease

*peer review the process by which scientists carefully examine the work of other scientists to look for possible flaws in their experimental design or their interpretation of results

*pH a measure of whether a substance is acidic, neutral, or basic

*photosynthesis the process by which some organisms are able to capture light energy and use it to make food from carbon dioxide and water

pioneer species the first organisms to become established in a new habitat

pipette a laboratory tool that looks like a slender tube but works something like an eyedropper

*placenta the organ that enables nutrients and oxygen to pass from the mother's blood to the fetus, and waste products to pass from the fetus to the mother's blood

plant any complex, multicellular organism that obtains energy through photosynthesis and consists of cell walls and specialized tissues and organs

poaching illegally capturing or killing an organism

*pollution a harmful change in the chemical makeup of the soil, water, or air

*population all the individuals of a single species that live in a specific area

*predator an animal that hunts and kills other animals for food

predator-prey relationship the connection between predators and prey that limits the growth of both populations

*prey an animal that is hunted and killed by predators

primary succession the first group of communities that moves into a previously lifeless habitat

*producer an organism that makes its own food from light energy and inorganic materials

*progesterone a hormone associated with sexual development and the reproductive system

proportion the relationship of one thing to another in terms of size, number, amount, or degree

protist a single-celled organism with both its genetic materials and its organelles enclosed in membranes

quarantine confined isolation

radius one of the two long bones of the lower forearm

*receptor molecule certain protein molecules in the cell membrane that can receive chemical messages from other cells

*recombination the additional mixing of genetic material from a sperm and egg which results in a unique combination of genes

refute to disprove

*replicate to copy

*renewable resource Earth's resources, such as our food supply and solar energy, which, given time, can be replaced

*research plan the initial stage of an experiment that involves finding background information, developing a hypothesis, and devising an experimental method for testing the hypothesis

*respiration the process by which the chemical bond energy stored in nutrients is released for use in cells

*reproduction the process by which organisms produce new organisms of the same type

*ribosome one of the tiny structures in the cell that is the site of protein production

rider one of the devices that is moved along the beam of a balance

*scavenger a carnivore that feeds on the bodies of dead organisms

science a way of learning about the natural world and the knowledge gained through that process

*scientific literacy a basic knowledge of the natural world combined with an understanding of the diverse ways that scientists gain knowledge

scientific theory a concept, which has been tested and confirmed in many different ways, that explains a wide variety of observations

secondary succession a type of change that occurs when a disturbance empties an existing habitat without destroying the soil

*selective breeding the process of choosing a few organisms with desirable traits to serve as the parents of the next generation

sensor a structure that reacts to stimuli by sending a nerve impulse to the brain

*sex cell an egg (female) or a sperm (male)

*sexual reproduction a method of reproduction that involves two parents to produce offspring that are genetically different from either parent

sibling a brother or sister

*simple sugar the result of the digestion of starches. Glucose is a simple sugar.

skeletal system the body system that contains the bones, provides shape and support, and protects internal organs

smog a kind of air pollution that results when certain pollutants react with sunlight

*species a group of organisms that share certain characteristics and can mate with one another, producing fertile offspring

sperm the male sex cell

splice to join two things together

*stain a chemical used to make cell structures more visible when viewed under a microscope

steady state the condition in which something remains relatively constant in spite of minor fluctuations

*stereoscope a microscope that uses two eyepieces; often used for dissections; also called a dissecting microscope

*stimulus (pl. **stimuli**) any change in the environment that causes an organism to react

stomata tiny pores found on the underside of most leaves

*subunit the section of a DNA molecule that contains a sugar, a phosphate, and a base

symbiotic a kind of long-term association between members of different species in which at least one species benefits and neither species is harmed

*synthesis a life process that involves combining simple substances into more complex substances

tare button a function on an electronic balance that returns the mass reading to zero

*technology all of the practical scientific knowledge that has been used to meet human needs

*template the pattern for a new molecule

*testes the male reproductive organ that produces sperm and the hormone testosterone

*testosterone a hormone associated with male sexual development and reproduction

*theory an explanation, supported by many observations and/or experiments, that can be used to accurately explain related occurrences

*thermal pollution a kind of water pollution in which the temperature of the water increases

*tissue a group of specialized cells that perform a specific function

toxic poisonous

*trade-off an exchange or agreement made to reach a compromise

*trait a characteristic that is passed from parent to offspring through the genes

transpiration the process whereby plants absorb water through their roots and eliminate it through tiny pores on the undersides of their leaves

*triple-beam balance a tool, with a single pan and three bars calibrated in grams, used to measure mass

tumor a clump of cells that develops when cancerous cells divide uncontrollably

ulna one of the two long bones in the lower forearm

*uterus the organ, in female animals, where the embryo develops into a fetus

*vaccine a substance made of weakened, killed, or partial pathogens and designed to protect the body from future invasions of that pathogen

*vacuole storage sacs within the cytoplasm of a cell that may contain either wastes or useful materials, such as water or food

vertebrate an animal with a backbone

*virus a nonliving particle of protein and genetic material that reproduces by invading the cell of a living organism

*volume the space occupied by something

*water cycle the process by which water continuously moves from Earth's surface to the atmosphere and back

*zygote the cell that results from the joining of the egg and sperm

Index

Acknowledgments

Photographs:
Every effort has been made to secure permission and provide appropriate credit for photographic material. The publisher deeply regrets any omission and pledges to correct errors called to its attention in subsequent editions.

Unless otherwise acknowledged, all photographs are the property of Pearson Education, Inc.

Photo locators denoted as follows: Top (T), Center (C), Bottom (B), Left (L), Right (R), Background (Bkgd)

Cover Betty Shelton/Shutterstock **i** Betty Shelton/Shutterstock; **66** Comstock Images/Thinkstock; **91** DK Images; **123** DK Images; **173** (B) Comstock Images/Thinkstock, (CR) Duncan Smith/Photodisc/Thinkstock; **178** (R) Comstock Images/Thinkstock, (L) Crestock.

Regents Exams: January 2015 3 Noah Strycker. **August 2014 5** Pearson Education. **June 2014 24** Annie Griffiths/National Geographic Creative; **24** Nicole Duplaix/National Geographic Creative; **24** Michael S. Quinton/National Geographic Creative; **24** Norbert Rosing/National Geographic Creative. **January 2014 3** Dan Guravich/Science Source. **June 2013 5** Andrew Evans/National Geographic Image Collection/Barcroft Media/Getty Images.

Text:
Grateful acknowledgment is made to the following for copyrighted material:

164 Excerpt from "Patients to Test Tumor Fighter" by The Associated Press. Used by permission of The Associated Press.

Regents Exams: January 2015 24 From Galapagos: A Natural History Guide, 7th ed by Pierre Constant. Copyright (c) 2007. Used by permission of the author. **August 2014 9** Wolf-Moose Interaction on Isle Royale: The End of Natural Regulation? from Ecological Applications, Vol 9, No 1 (Feb 1999), pp.10–16. Copyright © 1999 by Wolves and Moose of Isles Royale. Used by permission of Rolf Peterson; **20** Gaskell, G., Allum, N., Bauer, M. W., Jackson, J., Howard, S., & Lindsey, N. (2003). Ambivalent GM nation? Public attitudes to biotechnology in the UK, 1991–2002. Copyright © 2015 by London School of Economics and Political Science. Used by permission. **June 2014 20** "Female Shark Reproduced Without Male DNA, Scientists Say" by Henry Fountain from The New York Times, May 23, 2007. Copyright © The New York Times Company. Used by permission. **January 2014 21** From *Galapagos: A Natural History Guide, 7th ed* by Pierre Constant. Copyright © 2007. Used by permission of the author. **August 2013 22** From *Galapagos: A Natural History Guide, 7th ed* by Pierre Constant. Copyright © 2007. Used by permission of the author. **June 2013 15** Resisting Our Drugs from *Understanding Evolution.* Copyright © 2014 University of California Museum of Paleontology. Used by permission.

Note: Every effort has been made to locate the copyright owner of material reproduced in this component. Omissions brought to our attention will be corrected in subsequent editions.

New York Regents Examinations

The following examinations are actual Regents Examinations prepared by the New York State Education Department. They are provided here to give teachers and students a clear idea of the format and content of the Regents Examination for The Living Environment. The tests were given to students taking The Living Environment Course. The content of this book is designed to provide specifically what you need to review for The Living Environment Regents Examination.

Using the Regents Examinations

The best way to use these examinations is to take the entire test after you have reviewed the course content. Taking these tests as practice before your review may be both discouraging and of little value. Instead, use the tests to determine if you have reviewed enough to do well on the Regents Examination and to determine where further review will be most helpful.

Do not look up any information or answers while you take the examinations. Answer each question just as you would during a real test. As you take the Examination, use the margin of the paper to note any question where you are just guessing. Leave the more difficult questions for last, but be sure to answer each question. Every point counts so do not skip over a long question that is only worth a point or two. A long question could be easier than it looks and may make the difference between an A or a B or between passing or failing.

When you finish, have your teacher score your Examination and help you determine the areas where you need the most work. Also review the "guesses" you noted in the margin to find out what you need to study to ensure that you will be able to answer similar questions on the next test. Once you have determined your weaknesses, you can focus your review on those topics in this book.

Reviewing the areas where you know the least will give you the best chance of improving your final score. Spending time on areas where you are doing quite well will not produce much improvement in your total score, but it is still important if time permits.

Part A

Answer all questions in this part. [30]

Directions (1–30): For *each* statement or question, record on the separate answer sheet the *number* of the word or expression that, of those given, best completes the statement or answers the question.

1 Which observation could lead to the conclusion that an object is nonliving?

(1) It passes on hereditary information only through asexual reproduction.
(2) It carries out synthesis.
(3) It cannot perform metabolic processes.
(4) It is composed of a cell, but does not have tissues.

2 Decomposers are necessary in a food chain because they

(1) manufacture food by photosynthesis
(2) return nutrients to the ecosystem
(3) absorb energy from the Sun
(4) produce organic nutrients

3 In early spring, many wildflowers begin to grow, produce flowers, and release seeds. The leaves of the wildflowers make food before the leaves of the trees in the area begin to develop. The early growth pattern of the wildflowers would likely result in

(1) decreased competition for sunlight between the trees and the wildflowers
(2) decreased competition for suitable temperature between the trees and the wildflowers
(3) increased competition for space between the trees and the wildflowers
(4) increased competition for oxygen between the trees and the wildflowers

4 Which sequence best represents increasing complexity?

(1) tissues → cells → organelles → organs
(2) cells → organelles → organs → organism
(3) organelles → cells → tissues → organs
(4) organism → cells → tissues → organelles

5 The diagram below represents two processes that occur in organisms. A characteristic represented by X is common to both of these processes.

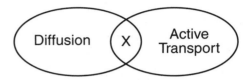

A characteristic that the two processes have in common is that each process

(1) uses ATP
(2) requires enzymes
(3) uses oxygen
(4) moves molecules

6 The molecules represented in the diagram below can interact to cause a biochemical process to occur.

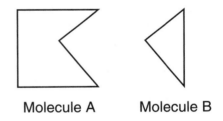

Molecule A   Molecule B

Molecule A and molecule B most likely represent

(1) a nerve signal and a gene
(2) a receptor and a hormone
(3) a chromosome and an antigen
(4) a starch and an amino acid

7 The cytoplasm in a single-celled organism and the circulatory system in a human both

(1) break down molecules into smaller components
(2) release energy to be used by the organism
(3) transport substances throughout the organism
(4) distribute blood to all of the parts of the organism

8 A hydrangea plant has blue flowers when grown in acidic soil, but has pink flowers when grown in basic soil. A clone of the pink-flowered plant is grown in acidic soil and produces blue flowers. This change in flower color is most likely due to

(1) sexual reproduction in the plants, resulting in variation
(2) asexual reproduction in the plants, resulting in variation
(3) genes being expressed in different ways due to environmental conditions
(4) a gene mutation that occurred after the clone was produced

9 The diagram below represents a microscopic structure observed during mitosis.

The region indicated by letter A is known as

(1) an enzyme   (3) a gene
(2) a gamete   (4) an amino acid

10 A significant difference between the effects of the genetic information passed on from asexually reproducing parents to their offspring and sexually reproducing parents to their offspring is the

(1) degree of modification of the size of chromosomes
(2) types of DNA subunits
(3) number of chromosomes in the body cells of the offspring
(4) amount of variation between the parents and the offspring

11 A normal sequence of DNA bases in a single human skin cell is CATGGC. If this sequence replicates in this cell and becomes GATGGC, this alteration will most likely be passed to

(1) every cell that develops from it
(2) all human body cells
(3) offspring of the human
(4) all skin cells of this person

12 Beta cells in the pancreas and human skin cells both contain the insulin gene. The beta cells can make insulin; however, skin cells cannot. Which process is responsible for this gene being expressed in one cell type and *not* in another cell type?

(1) mitosis   (3) differentiation
(2) replication   (4) meiosis

13 Information in segments of human DNA can be expressed by a bacterial cell as a result of

(1) sexual reproduction   (3) genetic variability
(2) random mutation   (4) genetic engineering

14 The photograph below shows a recently discovered all-black penguin chick and several typical black-and-white chicks.

The appearance of this penguin chick with all black feathers might

(1) increase the types of foods penguins can eat
(2) decrease the diversity of the penguin population
(3) decrease the number of variations present in the black penguin population
(4) result in an increase in black penguins over time if the trait provides a reproductive advantage

15 Natural selection and its evolutionary consequences provide a scientific explanation for

(1) the fossil record of ancient life-forms
(2) predictions about the rate of global warming
(3) the amount of precipitation in a rain forest
(4) the amount of soil used to grow certain crops

16 Some organs in the human body are represented in the diagram below.

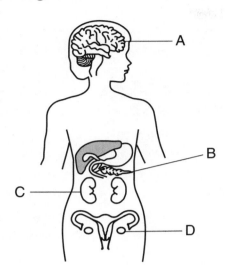

A sudden change in the DNA of cells developing in which organ could be passed to future generations?

(1) A   (3) C
(2) B   (4) D

17 Two cellular events that normally occur during two processes are represented below.

Cellular Event A   **Cellular Event B**

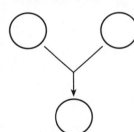

Which row in the chart below correctly identifies the processes in which these events occur?

Row	Cellular Event A	Cellular Event B
(1)	asexual reproduction	sexual reproduction
(2)	zygote formation	cloning
(3)	sexual reproduction	asexual reproduction
(4)	cloning	egg formation

18 Photosynthesis and respiration are alike in that they both

(1) require the Sun as a direct source of energy
(2) result in the production of glucose molecules
(3) require specific catalysts
(4) occur within mitochondria

19 The reproductive cycle in females is regulated primarily by

(1) estrogen and testosterone
(2) estrogen and progesterone
(3) progesterone and insulin
(4) progesterone and testosterone

20 One function of the male reproductive system in mammals is to

(1) produce insulin necessary for sexual reproduction
(2) transport eggs necessary for fertilization
(3) allow for delivery of gametes needed for reproduction
(4) provide protection for the developing zygote

21 A zygote develops into a multicellular organism through

(1) mitosis and specialization
(2) mitosis and meiosis
(3) recombination and communication
(4) genetic engineering and natural selection

22 *Pneumocystis* is an organism normally found in the human lungs that can cause pneumonia. It seldom causes problems in individuals with healthy immune systems. However, people with AIDS sometimes become seriously ill with pneumonia. This is most likely due to the fact that individuals with AIDS have

(1) inherited a tendency to contract pneumonia
(2) difficulty fighting off infections
(3) an allergy to this organism
(4) hormones that strengthen the infection

23 A technique used to alter cells is represented in the diagram below.

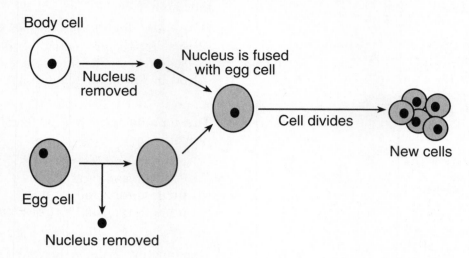

The genetic material contained in the nucleus of each of the new cells is most likely

(1) identical to that in the original body cell
(2) identical to that in the original egg cell
(3) 50% the same as the original egg cell and 50% the same as the original body cell
(4) 25% the same as the original egg cell and 75% the same as the original body cell

24 A graph is shown below.

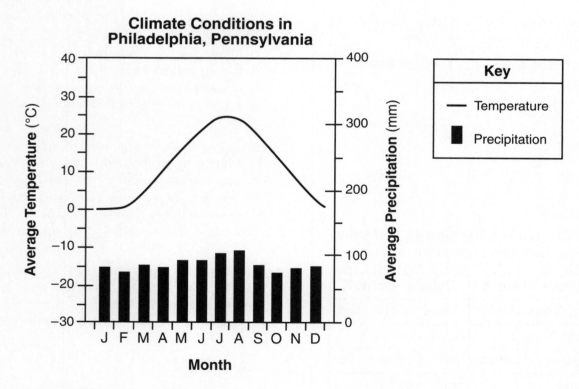

The graph contains information about

(1) finite resources
(2) limiting factors
(3) biotic factors
(4) mineral availability

January '15 Regents Examination

25 Nicotine is only one of the many toxic chemicals inhaled while smoking. What effect can such toxic chemicals have on the body?

(1) They stimulate an increase in height.
(2) They stimulate uncontrolled cell division.
(3) They eliminate carbon dioxide from cells.
(4) They eliminate chromosomes from many cells.

26 The diagram below represents different feeding levels in an energy pyramid.

The most likely explanation for showing fewer organisms at each feeding level going up the pyramid is that

(1) some energy is lost to the environment as heat
(2) the larger the organism, the less energy it requires
(3) some energy is recycled within each level and remains there
(4) decomposers convert most of the energy into inorganic compounds

27 Which process uses energy to combine inorganic molecules to synthesize organic molecules?

(1) respiration
(2) digestion
(3) photosynthesis
(4) decomposition

28 The Nature Conservancy is an organization that protects a variety of habitats around the world. A project this organization would probably support is one that

(1) uses endangered animals for medical research
(2) protects the biodiversity of areas for future generations
(3) alters habitats for industry and housing
(4) prevents animal species from migrating to other habitats

29 Certain animal species that are endangered or threatened have been cloned. Closely related species have been used to carry the embryos of the endangered species. This process of increasing the population size of a species in danger of becoming extinct is an example of a

(1) natural method to decrease ecosystem stability
(2) natural method of controlling the population of an endangered species
(3) technological fix to increase habitat destruction
(4) technological fix for the problem of endangered species

30 Car manufacturers have begun to explore the use of biofuels, such as biodiesel, ethanol, and cooking oils made from plant material. The desired outcome of using these biofuels would be

(1) a decrease in the use of fossil fuels
(2) a decrease in the release of oxygen gas
(3) an increase in abiotic resources
(4) an increase in global warming

Part B–1

Answer all questions in this part. [13]

Directions (31–43): For *each* statement or question, record on the separate answer sheet the *number* of the word or expression that, of those given, best completes the statement or answers the question.

31 In the 18th century, Carolus Linnaeus classified organisms based on their structural similarities. Modern classification determines relationships more accurately because it is based on genetic and other biochemical similarities. This change in classification method best illustrates that

(1) multiple trials are required to increase the validity of a scientific explanation
(2) scientific explanations are subject to the ethical view of the scientist proposing them
(3) peer review is required to validate the results of scientific investigations
(4) all scientific explanations are tentative and subject to change and improvement

32 Rabbits have evolved strategies that get them through periods of time when there is little food. The diagram below represents essential life functions that rabbits need to perform.

Energy Taken In with Food

Circulation
Respiration
Digestion
Coordination
Excretion
Reproduction
Growth

Which life function in the diagram could be eliminated without affecting an individual rabbit's ability to survive when food is scarce?

(1) digestion   (3) circulation
(2) excretion   (4) reproduction

33 The inability of an organism to produce certain proteins can occur when an organism is lacking an enzyme needed to combine

(1) oxygen molecules   (3) amino acids
(2) simple sugars   (4) biological catalysts

34 Bumblebees show some ability to control their own body temperature. During cold weather, bumblebees have been observed warming their flight muscles by shivering. The bees are able to maintain a body temperature several degrees above that of the surrounding air. Regulation of their internal body temperature is an example of

(1) diffusion   (3) respiration
(2) synthesis   (4) homeostasis

35 A cell begins to produce a new type of protein. This is most likely due to an alteration of the

(1) structure of the cell membrane
(2) sequence of bases in a section of a chromosome
(3) chemical makeup of the cytoplasm
(4) shape of the antibodies produced by the nucleus

36 Mother rattlesnakes care for and protect their young. Baby rattlesnakes find safety in the coils of their mothers. Female snakes stay together for the first few weeks after giving birth. This gathering of female rattlesnakes provides a safe environment for newborn rattlers. This is an example of which type of adaptation?

(1) structural   (3) molecular
(2) nutritional   (4) behavioral

January '15 Regents Examination

37 The diagram below represents one stage during the human reproductive process.

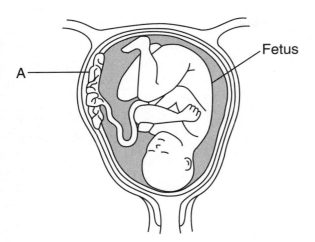

Fetus

A

A function of structure A is to

(1) remove nutrients from the fetus
(2) provide the fetus with metabolic wastes
(3) remove all toxins from the blood of the mother
(4) provide for the exchange of oxygen and carbon dioxide

38 Which statement is supported by the information in the graph below?

Enzyme Activity

Optimal temperature for typical human enzyme

Optimal temperature for enzyme of thermophilic (heat tolerant) bacteria

Rate of Reaction

Temperature (°C)

(1) The enzymes respond in a similar way to changes in temperature.
(2) The enzymes in bacteria function best at 40°C.
(3) The enzymes function best at the same temperature.
(4) The enzymes break down the same substances.

39 Farmland abandoned in 1899 was observed to have significant changes in plant species over a 50-year period. The changes are shown in the chart below.

Changes in Plant Species on Abandoned Farmland

Year Observed	Plant Species
1900	grasses
1910	shrubs and briars
1920	birch and cherry trees
1950	beech and maple trees

A forest fire burned all the trees on the land in 1955. Assuming no human interference, climate changes, or natural disasters, the plant species you would expect to see on this land in 2010 would most likely be

(1) grasses
(2) shrubs and briars
(3) birch and cherry trees
(4) beech and maple trees

40 A list of environmental issues is shown below.

• Rabbits transported from Europe overrun and deplete farmlands in Australia.
• Many areas in the southeastern United States are overgrown with the kudzu plant from Asia.
• In parts of New York State, bluebirds must compete with starlings originally brought here from England.

All of these issues are the result of

(1) introduction of nonnative species into stable ecosystems
(2) genetic engineering without using adequate safety precautions
(3) preservation of habitats due to human population growth
(4) use of foreign species to replace native predators

41 The diagram below represents a specimen in the low-power field of view of a compound light microscope.

If the slide is not moved, which view best represents the way the specimen will look when the high-power objective lens is switched into place?

(1)   (2)   (3)   (4)

42 Two methods of moving from place to place are represented below. The single-celled ameba moves by a process that involves the flow of cytoplasm.

Which statement is best supported by these diagrams?

(1) Both simple and complex organisms move directly by the movement of cytoplasm.
(2) Single-celled organisms, like complex organisms, are able to move; however, they differ in the way they carry out this activity.
(3) Cytoplasm is a fluid substance in simple cells and a solid substance in cells of complex organisms.
(4) Cells in complex organisms function in the exact same way as cells in simple organisms.

Base your answer to question 43 on the diagram below and on your knowledge of biology.

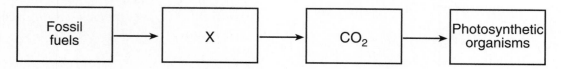

43 What information would be appropriate to add to box X in order to complete the diagram?

(1) cellular respiration by humans   (3) oxygen
(2) simple sugar   (4) burned by automobiles

Part B–2

Answer all questions in this part. [12]

Directions (44–55): For those questions that are multiple choice, record on the separate answer sheet the *number* of the choice that, of those given, best completes each statement or answers each question. For all other questions in this part, follow the directions given and record your answers in the spaces provided in this examination booklet.

Base your answers to questions 44 through 47 on the information and data table below and on your knowledge of biology.

Onondaga Lake is a small lake located near Syracuse, New York. Industrialized municipal wastes have been polluting the lake for decades. Eating fish from the lake has been banned due to mercury concentrations in the fish. The data table below indicates the mercury concentrations in smallmouth bass taken from Onondaga Lake. Smallmouth bass eat smaller fish, which feed on aquatic plants.

At each feeding level in the food chain, more mercury accumulates. The older and larger the fish, the greater the concentration of mercury.

Mercury in Onondaga Lake Smallmouth Bass

Year	Mercury Concentration (ppm – wet weight)
2000	1.5
2001	2.0
2002	1.75
2003	1.0
2004	2.5
2005	2.25

Directions (44–45): Using the information in the data table, construct a line graph on the grid below, following the directions below.

44 Mark an appropriate scale, without any breaks in the data, on each labeled axis. [1]

45 Plot the data on the grid. Surround each point with a small circle and connect the points. [1]

Example:

Mercury in Onondaga Lake Smallmouth Bass

Mercury Concentration
(ppm – wet weight)

Year

46 Explain how mercury dumped into the lake and taken up by plants reached the smallmouth bass population. [1]

_____

_____

Note: The answer to question 47 should be recorded on your separate answer sheet.

47 Which statement could be a possible explanation for the drop in mercury concentration in the fish of Onondaga Lake between the years 2002 and 2003?

(1) Between 2000 and 2005, a large number of fish were sampled.
(2) The dumping of industrial waste was prohibited in 2004.
(3) More young fish were tested in 2003, compared to the other years.
(4) The industrial waste contained more mercury in 2004.

Base your answers to questions 48 and 49 on the passage below and on your knowledge of biology.

Most animal fossils include hard body parts such as teeth and bones. Until recently, scientists had little hope that soft tissue could be preserved in the bones. A team of scientists has removed soft tissue containing a collagen protein from the leg bone of a 68-million-year-old fossil from a dinosaur, *Tyrannosaurus rex*. The technique of mass spectrometry was used to identify the sequences of certain molecules in several small fragments of the dinosaur collagen protein.

The molecular sequences were compared to those of modern animals. The scientist found that the collagen protein of the *Tyrannosaurus rex* more closely resembled the collagen protein found in modern chickens than that in some other modern animals.

48 State *one* kind of evidence that would support the conclusion that birds evolved from dinosaurs like *Tyrannosaurus rex*. [1]

_____

_____

Note: The answer to question 49 should be recorded on your separate answer sheet.

49 When the scientists compared the molecular sequences in the collagen proteins of the *Tyrannosaurus rex* to those of modern animals, they were most likely seeking information about

(1) patterns of behavior
(2) reproductive cycles

(3) common ancestry
(4) changing environmental conditions

Base your answers to questions 50 through 52 on the information below and on your knowledge of biology.

Found: A Plant-Eating Spider

Spiders are meat-eaters. Until recently, scientists thought that was true for the roughly 40,000 spider species in the world. Now, researchers have discovered a spider that eats mostly plants.

Bagheera kiplingi, a jumping spider, lives in Central America and Mexico. It nests in the leaves of acacia shrubs. Scientists have long known that ants live in these plants. The ants eat the plants' little yellow vegetables. But scientists had no idea that the spiders eat the vegetables too.

Christopher Meehan was a college student when he found the plant nibbling spiders. "I thought I was hallucinating," he told TFK (Time for Kids). "But by the end of the day, I had seen about 100 more spiders eating plants."

   Source: *Time for Kids World Report,* Edition 10/23/09 Vol. 15, #7 p.3

Note: The answer to question 50 should be recorded on your separate answer sheet.

50 Which row best characterizes *Bagheera kiplingi* and acacia shrubs?

Row	*Bagheera kiplingi*	Acacia
(1)	host	parasite
(2)	consumer	producer
(3)	autotroph	heterotroph
(4)	scavenger	herbivore

51 Identify *one* abiotic factor that most likely affects the size of the acacia shrub population. [1]

_____

52 Is competition likely to occur between the *Bagheera kiplingi* and ants living in acacia shrubs? Support your answer. [1]

_____

_____

_____

Base your answers to questions 53 through 55 on the passage below and on your knowledge of biology.

Inherited instructions control the color patterns of snakes. Some snakes that are not poisonous have colors that resemble the patterns on poisonous snakes. Predators avoid eating harmless snakes that have color patterns similar to those of the poisonous snakes. The results of a recent study indicate that predators in areas that have only harmless snakes do not avoid attacking snakes that have color patterns similar to poisonous snakes.

53 Identify the structure that contains the inherited instructions that determine the different color patterns in these snakes. [1]

_____

54 State *one* advantage for a nonpoisonous snake having coloration similar to that of a poisonous snake. [1]

_____

_____

55 State *one* reason why predators in some areas attack and eat harmless snakes, even though they have color patterns similar to those of poisonous snakes. [1]

_____

_____

_____

Part C

Answer all questions in this part. [17]

Directions (56–72): Record your answers in the spaces provided in this examination booklet.

56–59 Daphnia are freshwater organisms sometimes referred to as "water fleas." Design an experiment that could be used to test the effects of temperature on the size of a daphnia population. In your experimental design, be sure to:

- state a hypothesis to be tested [1]
- describe how the control group will be treated differently from the experimental group [1]
- identify the independent variable in the experiment [1]
- identify the type of data that will be collected [1]

_____

_____

_____

_____

_____

_____

_____

_____

January '15 Regents Examination

Base your answers to questions 60 through 62 on the passage below and on your knowledge of biology.

A Vaccine to Treat Addiction

A vaccine for cocaine addiction has been developed. This vaccine temporarily blocks the effects of cocaine. The vaccine consists of a cocaine molecule attached to the surface of an inactive, harmless cholera protein.

Since cocaine molecules alone are too small to stimulate the immune system to create antibodies, they are attached to the cholera protein. When people are injected with the vaccine, their bodies make antibodies against cholera. They also make antibodies against cocaine. When cocaine later enters the bloodstream, the antibodies bind to cocaine and prevent it from leaving the bloodstream, so it does not reach the brain. If the drug does not reach the brain, the user does not feel its effect. When antibodies were blocking the cocaine, people who took cocaine didn't get an effect from it, so the drug lost its appeal. Later, an enzyme breaks down the cocaine and it is flushed out of the body.

One problem revealed by the trial was that only 38 percent of vaccinated subjects developed high levels of antibodies against the drug. Additionally, the vaccine's protection seems to last for only about two months. Users need to receive booster shots every few months for approximately two years to make a complete recovery from the addiction.

60 Identify the *two* main substances contained in the vaccine. [1]

_____ and _____

61 Describe *one* effect the cocaine vaccine has on the immune system. [1]

_____

_____

62 How does this vaccine help to treat cocaine addiction? [1]

_____

_____

_____

Base your answers to questions 63 and 64 on the information below and on your knowledge of biology.

Mosquito Technologies of New York, Inc., has developed a Mosquito Killing System (MKS) to help control the mosquito population and reduce the transmission of West Nile Virus. The MKS works by taking advantage of the natural hunting strategies of mosquitoes, such as heat sensing and carbon dioxide detection. Beneficial insects do not use the same hunting strategies. The MKS unit produces heat and releases carbon dioxide in cycles, mimicking the breathing and body temperatures of humans, pets, and other warm-blooded animals. This attracts the mosquitoes to the device and, once inside, a vacuum pulls them in, where they pass through an electrocution grid, killing them. The mosquito remains are then returned to the environment through the bottom of the unit.

The unit contains a solar-powered photocell that turns the device on at dusk and turns it off at dawn.

63 State *one* positive effect the use of this MKS device has on the environment. [1]

_____

_____

64 A town wants to buy a number of MKS devices to solve their mosquito problem. One individual is concerned that this device could have a negative effect on insects that are beneficial to the environment. Based on the information given, is this a valid concern? Support your answer. [1]

_____

_____

Base your answers to questions 65 through 67 on the information and diagram below and on your knowledge of biology.

Blood Doping

Blood is a fluid tissue, which means that blood cells are suspended in a fluid called plasma. Blood tests are concerned with not only the number of blood cells present, but with the amount of plasma that surrounds the cells.

The diagram below represents tubes containing blood samples from an athlete before and after blood doping. Blood doping is an illegal practice reportedly used by some athletes a few weeks before an athletic event, and involves removing whole blood from an athlete, separating the oxygen-carrying red blood cells (RBCs), and then freezing them. These RBCs are thawed and returned to the athlete's body just before the athlete competes. Serious health risks are associated with this practice.

Blood Samples

65 Explain why athletes who practice blood doping would be expected to perform better at an athletic event. [1]

_____

_____

66 State *one* reason why the extra RBCs represented in sample 2 could be dangerous to the health of an athlete. [1]

_____

_____

67 More middle- and long-distance runners have tested positive for blood doping than short-distance runners, such as sprinters. State *one* reason why athletes participating in certain events might be more likely to practice blood doping than others. [1]

_____

_____

Base your answers to questions 68 and 69 on the information below and on your knowledge of biology.

A woman wanted to remove the dandelion plants from her lawn. She went to the store and bought an herbicide spray that was supposed to kill the dandelions. She sprayed it on her lawn according to the directions. Within two weeks, almost all of the dandelions had died; however, a few dandelions remained.

68 Explain how some dandelions were able to survive the spraying of the herbicide. [1]

_____

_____

69 Explain why this herbicide might *not* be effective for controlling future generations of dandelions in this lawn. [1]

_____

_____

Base your answers to questions 70 through 72 on the information below and on your knowledge of biology.

Types of Predators

When large predators, such as lions or wolves, are removed from a food web, smaller "mesopredators" step in to take their places, and the results may be severe. Mesopredators are usually smaller and more numerous than the larger "apex" predators that they replace. Some are also omnivores, eating plant and animal food sources, rather than eating the meat-only diet of the largest predators. Examples of mesopredators include coyotes, raccoons, and skunks.

In 1874, General George Custer noted that there was an abundance of wolves, but few coyotes, in South Dakota. Today, there is an abundance of coyotes, but no wolves. The wolves were removed to protect domestic sheep, but now the coyotes are often responsible for attacking sheep and other animals. The cost of controlling mesopredators by human intervention can be very high, as mesopredators are very numerous and quickly "bounce back" after control efforts. Meanwhile, the number of apex predators that are endangered continues to increase.

70 Describe how the wolf population is controlled naturally in the environment without human intervention. [1]

_____

_____

71 State how the mesopredator population was most likely controlled before the wolves were removed from the food web. [1]

_____

_____

72 If apex predators are so valuable to the ecological balance, state *one* possible reason why wolves were removed from the food web. [1]

_____

_____

Part D

Answer all questions in this part. [13]

Directions (73–85): For those questions that are multiple choice, record on the separate answer sheet the *number* of the choice that, of those given, best completes the statement or answers the question. For all other questions in this part, follow the directions given and record your answers in the spaces provided in this examination booklet.

Note: The answer to question 73 should be recorded on your separate answer sheet.

73 A laboratory setup that can be used to provide information about relationships between four plant species is represented below.

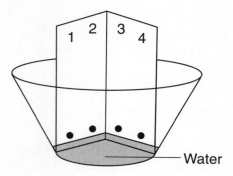

This setup is part of the technique known as

(1) electrophoresis

(2) biological staining

(3) dissection

(4) chromatography

Note: The answer to question 74 should be recorded on your separate answer sheet.

74 When people exercise, their body cells build up more waste quickly. Which two body systems work together to remove these wastes from their cells?

(1) immune and endocrine

(2) digestive and skeletal

(3) respiratory and circulatory

(4) circulatory and digestive

Note: The answer to question 75 should be recorded on your separate answer sheet.

75 Red onion cells undergo the change represented in the diagram below.

This change is most likely caused by the cell being transferred from

(1) distilled water to starch indicator

(2) distilled water to salt water

(3) salt water to tap water

(4) salt water to distilled water

Note: The answer to question 76 should be recorded on your separate answer sheet.

76 Which chemicals are used to cut DNA into fragments for a gel electrophoresis procedure?

(1) enzymes   (3) hormones

(2) molecular bases   (4) ATP molecules

77 The diagram below represents a laboratory setup used to demonstrate the movement of molecules across a selectively permeable membrane.

Selectively permeable membrane

In the diagram below, draw the 5 starch and the 12 glucose molecules to show where they would most likely be located after 15 minutes. [1]

Selectively permeable membrane

January '15 Regents Examination

Base your answers to question 78–79 on the Universal Genetic Code Chart below and on your knowledge of biology.

Universal Genetic Code Chart
Messenger RNA Codons and the Amino Acids for Which They Code

		SECOND BASE				
		U	**C**	**A**	**G**	
FIRST BASE	**U**	UUU UUC } PHE UUA UUG } LEU	UCU UCC UCA UCG } SER	UAU UAC } TYR UAA UAG } STOP	UGU UGC } CYS UGA } STOP UGG } TRP	U C A G
	C	CUU CUC CUA CUG } LEU	CCU CCC CCA CCG } PRO	CAU CAC } HIS CAA CAG } GLN	CGU CGC CGA CGG } ARG	U C A G
	A	AUU AUC ILE AUA AUG } MET or START	ACU ACC ACA ACG } THR	AAU AAC } ASN AAA AAG } LYS	AGU AGC } SER AGA AGG } ARG	U C A G
	G	GUU GUC GUA GUG } VAL	GCU GCC GCA GCG } ALA	GAU GAC } ASP GAA GAG } GLU	GGU GGC GGA GGG } GLY	U C A G

(right side label: **THIRD BASE**)

78–79 • In the table below, record the mRNA codons coded for by the DNA base sequences. [1]
• Then, using the Universal Genetic Code Chart, record the amino acid sequence that is coded for by the mRNA codons you placed in the table. [1]

DNA Base Sequence	AAG	CCA	TGA	ACA
mRNA codons	_____	_____	_____	_____
Amino acid sequence	_____	_____	_____	_____

80 A student hypothesized that drinking tea would cause an increase in pulse rate. He measured his pulse 20 minutes after drinking a glass of tea. It was 86 beats per minute. State *one* error in the experiment. [1]

_____

_____

Base your answers to questions 81 through 84 on the diagrams below and on your knowledge of biology. The diagrams represent the variations in the beaks of finches in the Galapagos Islands and the relative abundance of food sources on a certain island.

Variations in Beaks of Galapagos Islands Finches

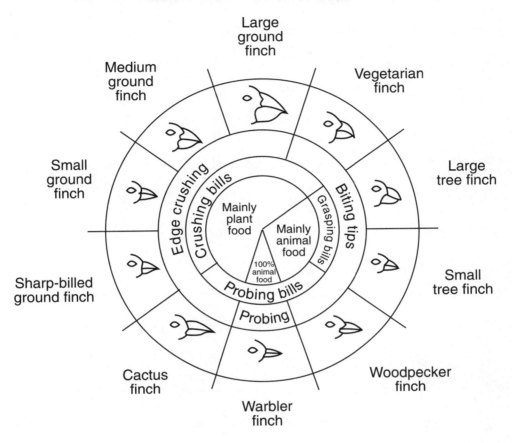

From: *Galapagos: A Natural History Guide*

Relative Abundance of Food Sources on a Certain Island

Key
✕ Large seeds
○ Small seeds
• Insects

Note: The answer to question 81 should be recorded on your separate answer sheet.

81 The diagram of the island suggests that in region *B* finches can feed on

(1) large seeds and insects

(2) small seeds, only

(3) a large variety of different-sized seeds

(4) insects and a limited number of small seeds

Note: The answer to question 82 should be recorded on your separate answer sheet.

82 Which histogram displays the relative abundance of small seeds in regions *A*, *B*, *C*, and *D*?

83 Explain why researchers would most likely observe the large ground finch in regions *A* and *D* on the island and *not* in regions *B* and *C*. [1]

_____

_____

84 A bird count was done on the island and the small tree finch was found in all regions. State *one* possible reason why the small tree finch is able to inhabit the entire island. [1]

_____

_____

_____

January '15 Regents Examination

85 Several days after a litter of three purebred puppies was born, a breeder noticed one extra puppy in the litter. The diagram below shows the results of electrophoresis of DNA fragments from all of the dogs. The puppies are labeled 1, 2, 5, and 6. The parent dogs are labeled 3 and 4.

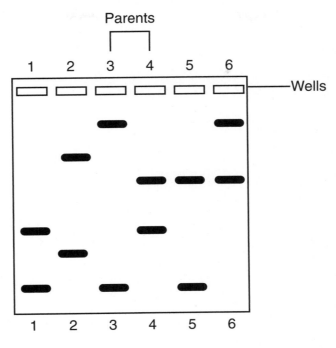

Identify which puppy might have been placed into this litter by mistake. Support your answer. [1]

Puppy: _____

_____

_____

_____

Part A

Answer all questions in this part. [30]

Directions (1–30): For *each* statement or question, record on the separate answer sheet the *number* of the word or expression that, of those given, best completes the statement or answers the question.

1 A function of cell membranes in humans is the

(1) synthesis of the amino acids
(2) production of energy
(3) replication of genetic material
(4) recognition of certain chemicals

2 Forests, mountains, rivers, and marshes are examples of the wide variety of ecosystems in New York State. The diversity of these ecosystems is most likely the result of

(1) the variety of abiotic conditions in these regions
(2) interactions between producers and decomposers
(3) increased efforts to protect endangered species
(4) a lack of competition between the heterotrophs living there

3 The diagram below represents two organisms.

Organism A
single-celled

Organism B
multicellular

Which statement concerning organism *A* and organism *B* is correct?

(1) Organism *A* contains organs, whereas organism *B* lacks organs.
(2) Organism *A* and organism *B* have the same organ systems.
(3) Organism *A* and organism *B* both have structures that perform life processes.
(4) Organism *A* lacks structures that help maintain dynamic equilibrium.

4 Which statement best describes the organelles in a cell?

(1) All organelles are involved directly with communication between cells.
(2) Organelles must work together and their activities must be coordinated.
(3) Organelles function only when there is a disruption in homeostasis.
(4) Each organelle must function independently of the others in order to maintain homeostasis.

5 A substance directly involved in cellular communication within the human body is

(1) an antibody   (3) a hormone
(2) an antibiotic   (4) a starch

6 The list below includes three organ systems that are directly used when a human runs.

circulatory system
muscular system
skeletal system

Which system should also be included in the list?

(1) immune system   (3) digestive system
(2) reproductive system (4) nervous system

7 In a pine forest, there are different species of birds known as warblers that are able to coexist on the same pine trees. The Cape May warblers feed on insects located on the tips of the highest pine branches. The yellow-rumped warblers feed on insects on lower branches of the same trees. The different feeding locations for these two species of warblers indicate that they have different

(1) niches
(2) ecosystems
(3) methods of asexual reproduction
(4) methods of selective breeding

8 The diagram below represents the locations of two mutations in a strand of a DNA molecule.

DNA   DNA with mutations

If this DNA is located in the nucleus of a skin cell, the cell will

(1) pass the mutations on to only half the cells that develop from it
(2) delete all of the DNA in the nucleus and synthesize new DNA
(3) correct the mutations after several generations
(4) pass the mutations on to the cells that develop from it

9 A human skin cell contains 46 chromosomes. A frog sperm cell contains 12 chromosomes. Which pair of numbers shows the chromosome number of a normal gamete from each of these species?

(1) human 46; frog 12   (3) human 23; frog 24
(2) human 46; frog 24   (4) human 23; frog 12

10 According to the theory of biological evolution, most present-day species of organisms

(1) developed from similar, smaller prehistoric organisms
(2) have always existed in the form they have today
(3) developed from fossils of the other organisms
(4) descended from earlier, different species of organisms

11 Corn seeds with identical genetic information were planted on two adjacent farms. The corn plants on one farm were well fertilized and grew large, while the plants on the other farm were not given fertilizer and did not grow as large. The best explanation for these observations is that

(1) crops grow differently in different climates
(2) the corn plants all contained mutated genes that made them grow
(3) environmental conditions affect gene expression
(4) the plants on one farm had different genes from the plants on the other farm

12 The male red-winged blackbird defends its territory and uses loud vocalizations to attract a mate. Such behavior directly benefits these birds because it results in

(1) increased competition for food
(2) greater reproductive success
(3) reduced biodiversity
(4) global stability

13 Extinction occurs when the environment changes and

(1) a species can reproduce successfully
(2) an individual has adaptive characteristics insufficient to allow survival
(3) all members of a species are no longer living
(4) one individual produces some offspring that evolve into a new species

14 All the information necessary for growth, development, and eventual reproduction of sexually reproducing organisms is present in

(1) sperm cells, only
(2) egg cells, only
(3) zygotes
(4) either sperm cells or egg cells

15 Which activity can occur without the use of energy?

(1) contraction of muscle tissue
(2) protein synthesis in a cell
(3) active transport of minerals
(4) movement of water across a membrane

August '14 Regents Examination

16 An alternative to the use of insecticides to combat the Mediterranean fruit fly is the Sterile Insect Technique (SIT). SIT involves the sterilization of male insects by radiation, which prevents the formation of functional male gametes. When these male insects mate with female insects of the same species, the result would be that

(1) only female offspring would be produced
(2) no offspring would be produced
(3) the offspring would have a reduced number of chromosomes
(4) the offspring would no longer be sterile

17 The diagrams below represent a human organ system.

The major function of the system is to

(1) provide immunity essential for the survival of each individual in a population
(2) provide cells that are necessary for the survival of the species
(3) produce chemical messages that are necessary for nerve cell development
(4) control the passage of nutrients into and out of a developing fetus

18 Sheep were the first species of mammals to be cloned. Which statement about cloned sheep is correct?

(1) Different kinds of body cells in a cloned sheep contain different DNA.
(2) Cloned sheep cannot produce offspring if they are mated with noncloned sheep.
(3) Two sheep cloned from the same parent cannot mate and have offspring.
(4) Many cells in cloned sheep have two identical nuclei, instead of a single nucleus.

19 In a sexually reproducing species, evolution could occur as a result of

(1) modification of genes in body cells
(2) modification of genes in sex cells
(3) increased reproduction among individuals with identical chromosomes
(4) recombination of genes in cells reproducing by mitosis

20 An increase in the level of hormone A causes an increase in the level of hormone B. The increase in the level of hormone B then causes a decrease in the level of hormone A. This process is an example of

(1) a failure to maintain homeostasis
(2) the breakdown of chemicals
(3) a disruption in cellular coordination
(4) a feedback mechanism

21 Human population growth has led to a reduction in the populations of predators throughout natural ecosystems across the United States. Scientists consider the loss of these predators to have a

(1) positive effect, because an increase in their prey helps to maintain stability in the ecosystem
(2) positive effect, because predators usually eliminate the species they prey on
(3) negative effect, since predators have always made up a large portion of our food supply
(4) negative effect, because predators have an important role in maintaining stable ecosystems

22 Which environmental change would cause the greatest reduction in the biodiversity of a large ecosystem?

(1) building a new home
(2) building a new store in a shopping mall
(3) widespread use of pesticides
(4) widespread recycling programs

23 The diagram below represents a variety of fossil types, which can be found in many rocks.

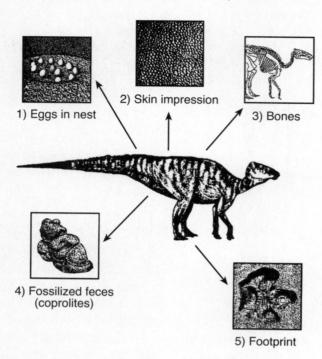

1) Eggs in nest

2) Skin impression

3) Bones

4) Fossilized feces (coprolites)

5) Footprint

Source: Audesirls, Audesirls, Byers,
Biology: Life on Earth, Prentice Hall, 2002

These fossils can be best used to provide information that could be used in a study of

(1) evolutionary relationships
(2) dynamic equilibrium
(3) selective breeding
(4) cell specialization

24 The bottom of Onondaga Lake in upstate New York contains large amounts of pollutants. One proposal to clean the lake bottom requires that the pollutants be removed and stored nearby. People who live near the proposed storage sites are opposed to this plan. The officials who must decide on the proposal will examine both the benefits and risks of the plan. The decision made by the officials will most likely involve

(1) increased industrialization
(2) direct harvesting
(3) an increase in finite resources
(4) consideration of trade-offs

25 The increased use of wind turbines and solar collectors to generate electric power will

(1) negatively affect ecosystems by increasing biodiversity
(2) negatively alter the chemical composition of soil and water
(3) reduce the amount of pollution that comes from the burning of fossil fuels
(4) increase oil consumption for business and industry

26 Antibiotics are substances used to help fight an infection of *Streptococcus*, a bacterium that causes strep throat. Overuse of these antibiotics can

(1) prevent future infections by these pathogens
(2) cause a decrease in the production of enzymes
(3) allow organic molecules to be synthesized
(4) select for resistant organisms

27 An allergic reaction to certain types of natural, unprocessed foods, such as peanuts, is caused by

(1) a lack of digestive enzymes
(2) a response to specific antigens
(3) microorganisms living within the food
(4) high levels of carbon dioxide in the air

28 A variety of pear tree, known as Bradford, was originally introduced into the eastern United States in the 1960s. Today, this tree is crowding out other plants in these states. This situation best illustrates

(1) an unintentional negative effect of altering an ecosystem
(2) how a foreign species is controlled in the eastern United States
(3) that the introduction of a foreign species does not affect food webs
(4) that serious environmental consequences can be avoided by importing a foreign species

29 The diagram below represents a process that occurs in nature.

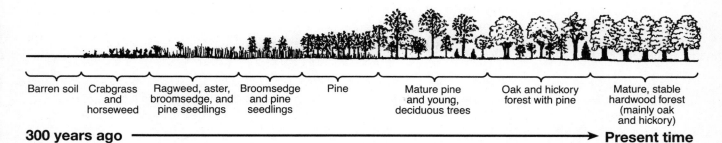

Barren soil   Crabgrass   Ragweed, aster,   Broomsedge   Pine   Mature pine   Oak and hickory   Mature, stable
              and   broomsedge, and   and pine   and young,   forest with pine   hardwood forest
              horseweed   pine seedlings   seedlings   deciduous trees   (mainly oak
                                                                                                           and hickory)

300 years ago ⎯⎯⎯⎯⎯⎯⎯⎯⎯⎯⎯⎯⎯⎯⎯⎯⎯⎯⎯⎯⎯⎯⎯⎯⎯⎯→ **Present time**

If the oak and hickory trees were burned in a forest fire, leaving bare soil, which group of plants would most likely be the first to grow back?

(1) crabgrass and horseweed
(2) oak and hickory trees

(3) broomsedge and pine seedlings
(4) mature pine and young deciduous trees

30 A growing mass of plastic garbage is collecting in an area of the Pacific Ocean. This is caused by plastic garbage that is discarded by people, and it ends up in rivers that carry it to the ocean. Over time, ocean currents cause it to accumulate in this area of the Pacific. Currently, the mass is estimated to cover an area of ocean twice the size of Texas. As these plastics slowly break down, chemicals enter the water, and can enter ocean organisms that we might eventually use for food. This sequence of events illustrates that

(1) humans modify ecosystems as a result of population growth, consumption, and technology
(2) human activities that degrade ecosystems result in an increase in diversity of ecosystems
(3) when humans alter ecosystems by adding specific organisms, serious consequences could result
(4) industrialization brings a reduced demand for fossil and nuclear fuels

Directions (31–43): For *each* statement or question, record on the separate answer sheet the *number* of the word or expression that, of those given, best completes the statement or answers the question.

31 Which organic compounds would be the best to analyze in order to determine if two species are closely related?

(1) fats   (3) sugars
(2) starches   (4) proteins

32 The diagram below represents some structures observed in a drop of human blood.

Red blood cells

Platelets

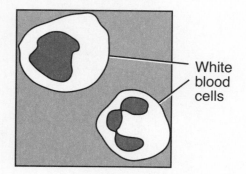

White blood cells

Which statement correctly describes all of these structures in human blood?

(1) They produce antibiotics that fight disease.
(2) They are useful in the digestion of oxygen.
(3) They use all of the DNA present in the cells of the body.
(4) They perform specific functions that aid in maintaining homeostasis.

Base your answer to question 33 on the energy pyramid below and on your knowledge of biology.

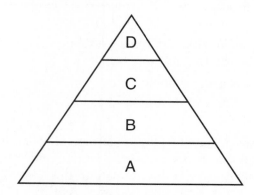

33 Letter *A* in the pyramid represents

(1) scavengers   (3) carnivores
(2) producers   (4) herbivores

34 The graph below shows changes in the level of glucose in the blood of a person over a period of time.

Change in Blood Glucose Level

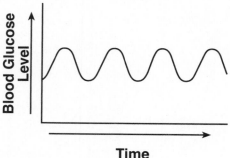

Time

The graph represents the

(1) maintenance of dynamic equilibrium
(2) failure of homeostasis
(3) reaction of white blood cells to a pathogen
(4) oxygen carrying capacity of the blood

Base your answer to question 35 on the information and data table below and on your knowledge of biology.

The Thousand Islands region in upstate New York has many isolated islands. On one island, a fire burned most of the trees. The data table below indicates the percentages of tan beetles and dark-brown beetles present before and after the fire.

Changes in Beetles Population

Time	Tan Beetles (%)	Dark-Brown Beetles (%)
before fire	88	12
8 months after fire	80	20
16 months after fire	70	30
24 months after fire	65	35
48 months after fire	60	40
60 months after fire	56	44

35 The increase in the percentage of dark-brown beetles over time was most likely due to the fact that the

(1) dark-brown beetles could not find food as well as the tan beetles
(2) dark-brown beetles were harder for predators to locate
(3) tan beetles turned dark brown to blend in with the darker, ash-covered ground
(4) exposure to ash from the fire changed the DNA of some of the tan beetles

36 The graph below represents the growth in length and mass of a fetus up to week 32. The length is measured in millimeters (mm) and the mass in grams (g).

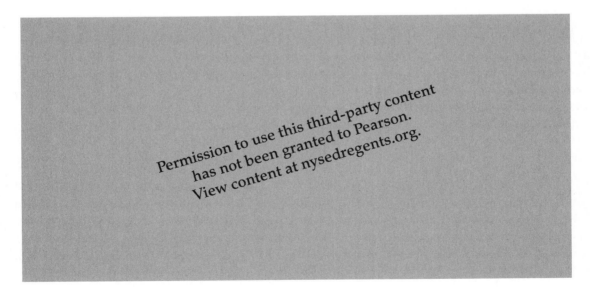

Permission to use this third-party content has not been granted to Pearson. View content at nysedregents.org.

Which statement best describes human fetal growth between weeks 26 and 32?

(1) There is a faster rate of increase in mass than in length.
(2) The rate of increase in mass levels off, while the increase in length constantly increases.
(3) The fetal mass increases by 750 g and the fetal length increases by about 100 mm.
(4) There are slight decreases in both length and mass.

Base your answers to questions 37 and 38 on the diagram below and on your knowledge of biology.

Wolf and Moose Populations, 1960 to 1999

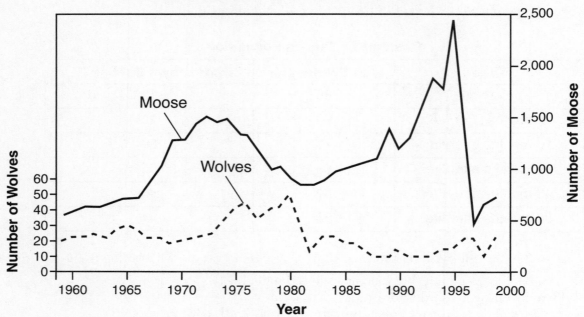

Source: Ecological Studies of Wolves on Isle Royale, Rolf O. Peterson,
School of Forestry and Wood Products, Michigan Technological University

37 The population of wolves in 1980 was close to
(1) 20
(2) 50
(3) 800
(4) 1000

38 An observable trend in the wolf and moose data between 1980 and 1995 is
(1) as the wolf population decreases, the moose population increases
(2) as the wolf population decreases, the moose population decreases
(3) the numbers of wolves and moose are relatively constant
(4) the numbers of wolves and moose appear to be unrelated

39 A student wants to test the hypothesis that an acidic environment will decrease enzyme activity. In the experiment, the student used an enzyme that breaks down hydrogen peroxide into water and bubbles of oxygen. To test the hypothesis, the student should collect data on the number of oxygen bubbles produced at different

(1) temperatures
(2) pH levels
(3) enzyme concentrations
(4) concentrations of hydrogen peroxide

Base your answers to questions 40 and 41 on the diagram below and on your knowledge of biology. The diagram represents events that occur during embryonic development. Letters A through E represent structures.

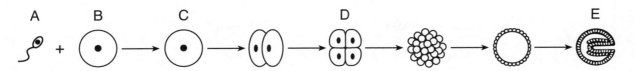

40 Between which two letters does mitosis occur?

(1) A and B
(2) B and C

(3) A and C
(4) C and D

41 Between which two letters does differentiation occur?

(1) A and B
(2) B and C

(3) C and D
(4) D and E

42 The graph below represents a change in event A that leads to changes in events B and C.

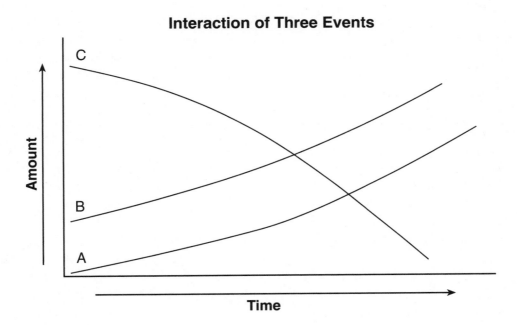

Interaction of Three Events

Which row in the chart best identifies each event in the graph?

Row	A	B	C
(1)	deforestation	amount of biodiversity	atmospheric concentration of carbon dioxide
(2)	industrialization	energy consumption	global temperature
(3)	loss of ozone layer	global warming	rate of skin cancer
(4)	human population	consumption of resources	habitat preservation

43 Which graph best shows changes in a population of yeast that develops in a test tube and completely consumes a limited supply of food?

Time

(1)

Time

(3)

Time

(2)

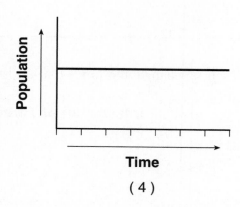

Time

(4)

Answer all questions in this part. [12]

Directions (44–55): For those questions that are multiple choice, record on the separate answer sheet the *number* of the choice that, of those given, best completes each statement or answers each question. For all other questions in this part, follow the directions given and record your answers in the spaces provided in this examination booklet.

Base your answers to questions 44 through 48 on the information below and on your knowledge of biology.

Five groups of corn seeds, each containing 275 seeds, were soaked for 1 hour in different concentrations of gibberellic acid, a plant growth hormone. After 1 hour, the seeds were rinsed in tap water and drained of all excess water. The seeds were then placed on paper towels and kept moist for 7 days. After 7 days, the growing stems were cut and weighed to determine the increase in growth. Then, the percent increase in growth compared to the growth of a group of untreated seeds was calculated. The results were recorded and are shown in the data table below.

Growth Rate in Corn Plants Treated with Gibberellic Acid

Concentration of Gibberellic Acid in Parts per Million (ppm)	Increase in Growth * (%)
225	15
300	30
400	23
500	15
600	6

* percent increase in growth compared to the growth of untreated seeds

Source: Adaped from www.super-grow.biz/GibberellicAcid.jsp

Directions (44 and 45): Using the information given in the data table, construct a line graph on the grid, following the directions below.

44 Mark an appropriate scale, without any breaks, on each labeled axis on the grid on the next page. [1]

45 Plot the data from the table on the grid on the next page. Surround each point with a small circle and connect the points. [1]

Example:

**Growth Rate in Corn Plants
Treated with Gibberellic Acid**

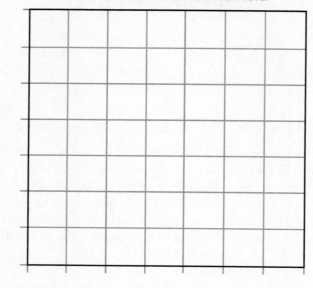

Increase in Growth (%)

**Concentration of Gibberellic
Acid** (ppm)

46 Identify the control group in this experiment. [1]

_____

_____

Note: The answer to question 47 should be recorded on your separate answer sheet.

47 Which conclusion is supported by the data from this investigation?
   (1) A concentration of gibberellic acid under 300 ppm inhibits the growth of corn plants.
   (2) Plants from untreated corn seeds grow better than those treated with gibberellic acid at a concentration of 600 ppm.
   (3) A concentration of gibberellic acid over 300 ppm makes corn seeds germinate best.
   (4) Corn seedlings treated with gibberellic acid at concentrations between 225 and 600 ppm grow better than untreated seedlings.

48 State how farmers should use gibberellic acid to grow the largest plants. Support your answer with data from this experiment. [1]

_____

_____

_____

August '14   Regents Examination

Base your answers to questions 49 and 50 on the graph below and on your knowledge of biology.

**The Influence of Temperature
on the Growth Rate of Fish**

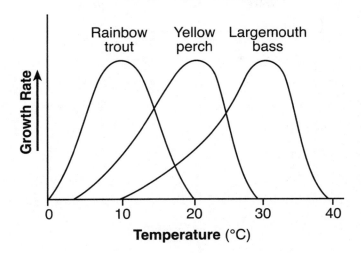

Note: The answer to questions 49 and 50 should be recorded on your separate answer sheet.

49 The temperature range in a pond in which all three fish species could grow and survive is most likely

(1) 2°C to 8°C   (3) 22°C to 28°C
(2) 12°C to 18°C   (4) 32°C to 38°C

50 In the pond where these fish live, temperature is both a

(1) source of energy and biotic factor   (3) limiting factor and biotic factor
(2) source of nutrition and abiotic factor   (4) limiting factor and abiotic factor

51–52 The work of a cell is carried out by the many different types of molecules it assembles. Most of these molecules are proteins. Explain how the cell is able to make the many different proteins it needs. In your answer, be sure to:

• identify where in the cell the information necessary to construct a particular protein is located and the specific molecule that contains this information   [1]

• identify *both* the cellular structure that assembles these proteins and the kinds of molecules that are used as the building blocks of the proteins   [1]

_____

_____

_____

_____

_____

Base your answers to questions 53 through 55 on the diagram below and on your knowledge of biology. The diagram represents a food web.

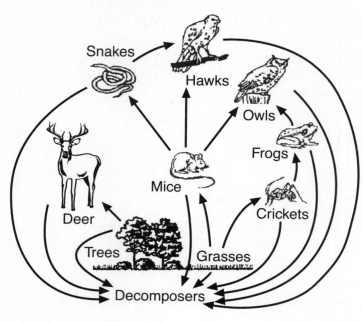

53 Identify *two* herbivores that compete for food in the food web above. [1]

Herbivores: _____ and _____

54 Even though both hawks and owls have two sources of food, explain why hawks would be *less* likely to survive if a disease wiped out the mice. [1]

_____

_____

55 State the role of the decomposers in this food web. [1]

_____

_____

_____

August '14 Regents Examination

Part C

Answer all questions in this part. [17]

Directions (56–72): Record your answers in the spaces provided in this examination booklet.

Base your answers to questions 56 through 59 on the information below and on your knowledge of biology.

     There has been an increase in the number of dead birds found on the beaches of the Great Lakes. These birds were poisoned by a bacterial toxin in the lake water. The birds do not ingest enough water to become sick directly from the toxin found in the lake water. Scientists think that the cause of the increasing bird deaths lies with an invasive species— the zebra mussel. This freshwater organism was introduced into the Great Lakes accidentally by humans, and has become well established in the Great Lakes. Zebra mussels filter out microscopic organisms, as well as the toxins found in the lake water. The toxins become concentrated in the zebra mussels, which are eaten by small fish called gobies, and the gobies are eaten by the birds. The concentration increases in each level of the food chain. It appears that the introduction of the zebra muscles into the Great Lakes has resulted in a new food chain that increases the concentration of the naturally occurring toxins and passes dangerous levels on to these top-level predators. This process is known as bioaccumulation.

56 Why are the accidentally introduced zebra mussels referred to as an invasive species? [1]

_____

_____

57 On the diagram below, complete the food chain by filling in the correct organisms from the passage. [1]

_____

↑

_____

↑

_____

↑

microscopic organisms

58 How has bioaccumulation resulted in the deaths of large numbers of birds even though the toxin level in the lake water is not high enough to make them sick? [1]

_____

_____

_____

59 Describe *one* possible effect that the increased deaths of the birds could have on the rest of the ecosystem. [1]

_____

_____

_____

60–63 The immune system protects against foreign substances and even some cancers. Explain how the immune system functions. In your answer, be sure to:

• identify *one* way the immune system fights pathogens [1]
• identify the substance in a vaccine that stimulates the immune system [1]
• describe the response of the immune system to the vaccine [1]
• identify *one* disease that damages the immune system and state how it affects this system [1]

_____

_____

_____

_____

_____

_____

_____

_____

August '14 Regents Examination

Base your answer to question 64–68 on the information below and on your knowledge of biology.

Some poinsettia plants have green leaves that turn red. A garden club decided to study the color change of poinsettia plants. Knowing that poinsettias change color during the short daylight periods of winter, they decided to investigate the effect of different daylight lengths on color change.

64–68 Design a controlled experiment using three experimental groups that could be used to determine if the number of hours of daylight has an effect on the color change of poinsettias. In your experimental design, be sure to:

- state *one* hypothesis the experiment would test   [1]
- state *one* way the three experimental groups would differ   [1]
- identify *two* factors that must be kept the same in all three groups   [1]
- identify the dependent variable in the experiment   [1]
- describe experimental results that would support your hypothesis   [1]

_____

_____

_____

_____

_____

_____

_____

_____

_____

_____

_____

69 An accident resulted in a man's hand being cut off from his arm. Paramedics arriving first on the scene placed the cut-off hand in ice. The man and his hand were flown to a hospital, where doctors successfully reattached the hand to his arm. Explain, using *one* biological reason, why placing the hand in ice improved the chances of saving it. [1]

_____

_____

Base your answer to question 70 on the information below and on your knowledge of biology.

Researchers monitoring the atmosphere of Earth report that the ozone shield has stopped shrinking and will most likely be on the mend over the next several decades. These findings were based on analyses of satellite records and instruments monitoring the surface of Earth. Scientists credit an international agreement to phase out the production of ozone-depleting chemicals for this turnabout.

70 State *one* reason why the ozone shield is important. [1]

_____

_____

Base your answers to questions 71 and 72 on the information below and on your knowledge of biology.

Climate Change for Biotechnology

Many people were surveyed in 2002 and asked their opinion of some procedures that involved biotechnology. These procedures are listed below.

- Genetic testing to detect inheritable diseases, such as cystic fibrosis
- Cloning human cells to replace diseased cells in an individual with Parkinson's disease, diabetes, or heart disease
- Using xenotransplants introducing human genes into pigs to produce hearts for human transplants
- Genetically modifying crops (GM crops) to make crop plants insect resistant
- Genetically modifying foods (GM foods) to make them higher in protein

These people were asked whether the technology should be used, if the technology was risky, if the technology is morally acceptable, and if they would encourage the technology. Those surveyed rated each technology as "definitely agree," "tend to agree," "no opinion," "tend to disagree," and "definitely disagree." The responses were given a numerical score and then averaged together. The results of the survey are shown below.

Adapted from: Gaskell, et. al., *AgBioForum*, 2003, Volume 6, Article 12

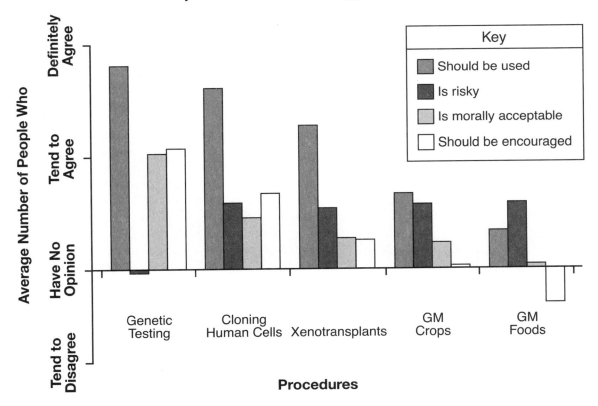

Opinion of Biotechnology Procedures

71 Which biotechnology procedure did most people feel was the safest? Support your answer. [1]

Procedure: _____

_____

_____

72 State *one* possible advantage of xenotransplants. [1]

_____

_____

Part D

Answer all questions in this part. [13]

Directions (73–85): For those questions that are multiple choice, record on the separate answer sheet the *number* of the choice that, of those given, best completes the statement or answers the question. For all other questions in this part, follow the directions given and record your answers in the spaces provided in this examination booklet.

Note: The answer to question 73 should be recorded on your separate answer sheet.

73 Which branching tree diagram shows that species W and Z are most closely related?

(1)

(2)

(3)

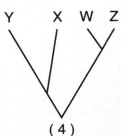
(4)

Note: The answer to question 74 should be recorded on your separate answer sheet.

74 Students noticed that some of their classmates have a hard time concentrating during class. They thought it may have some connection with the fact that these students consume energy drinks just before class. An experiment was proposed to find out if there is a connection between energy drinks and the lack of ability to concentrate in class. A properly designed experiment to determine this would include having

(1) the whole class drink energy drinks and no water at all, for the entire time of the experiment
(2) the whole class drink water and no energy drinks at all, for the entire time of the experiment
(3) the students drink both water and an energy drink just before class
(4) half the students drink water and the other half drink an energy drink just before class

Note: The answer to question 75 should be recorded on your separate answer sheet.

75 Which technique could be used to separate pigments from a mixture?

(1) preparing a wet-mount slide
(2) staining

(3) paper chromatography
(4) dissection

Base your answers to questions 76 and 77 on the information below and on your knowledge of biology.

Permission to use this third-party content has not been granted to Pearson. View content at nysedregents.org.

Note: The answer to question 76 should be recorded on your separate answer sheet.

76 The differences seen in the beaks of the four species of finches are most likely the result of

(1) gene expression and asexual reproduction
(2) variation and natural selection
(3) migration and the need to adapt
(4) heredity and a diet of seeds

77 A person expressed concern that the vegetarian finch may face greater competition when other finch populations increase. State whether the vegetarian finch will face competition if the populations of warbler finches, woodpecker finches, and mangrove finches increase. Support your answer. [1]

_____

_____

_____

Base your answers to questions 78 through 80 on the information below and on your knowledge of biology.

A laboratory procedure involving a microscope slide is represented in the diagram below.

78 State *one* purpose for this procedure. [1]

_____

_____

79 Identify *one* specific substance represented by the liquid in *A*. [1]

_____

_____

80 State the purpose of the paper towel labeled *B*. [1]

_____

_____

Base your answers to questions 81 and 82 on the diagram below and on your knowledge of biology. The diagram represents two solutions, A and B, separated by a selectively permeable membrane.

Note: The answer to questions 81 and 82 should be recorded on your separate answer sheet.

81 A sample from solution A and solution B were each tested with blue-colored glucose indicator solution before the solutions were placed in the beaker. Which row represents the results?

Row	Solution A	Solution B
(1)	red or orange	blue
(2)	blue black	amber
(3)	blue	red or orange
(4)	amber	blue black

82 Which statement best describes the outcome after 20 minutes?

(1) Solution A will contain approximately the same number of glucose molecules as solution B.
(2) Solution A will contain all of the water molecules.
(3) Solution B will remain unchanged.
(4) Solution B will lose all of the glucose molecules to solution A.

Base your answers to questions 83 through 85 on the information below and on your knowledge of biology.

The relationship between lung capacity and gender was studied in a laboratory investigation. Relative lung capacity was measured by having each student fill a balloon with a deep breath and then measuring the circumference of the balloon. Each student was given three trials and the average balloon circumference was recorded in the data table below.

Lung Capacity of Lab Group Members

Gender (male/female)	Average Balloon Circumference (cm)
female	51.6
female	52.7
female	53.3
female	55.0
male	54.6
male	56.0
male	56.3
male	62.3

83 A student calculated the group average to be 441.8. State the specific error made in this calculation. [1]

_____

_____

84 A student concluded that "all females have a smaller lung capacity than males." Is this a valid conclusion? Support your answer. [1]

_____

_____

85 Identify *one* biological condition or personal activity that could make it difficult for a person to perform well on a test of lung capacity. [1]

_____

_____

_____

Part A

Answer all questions in this part. [30]

Directions (1–30): For *each* statement or question, record on the separate answer sheet the *number* of the word or expression that, of those given, best completes the statement or answers the question.

1 How do cells in the ovary detect a hormone from the brain?

(1) The brain sends a nerve impulse to the ovary.
(2) White blood cells bring the hormone to the ovary.
(3) Receptor molecules on the cells of the ovary bind with the hormone.
(4) Vacuoles within the ovary bind with the hormone.

2 Single-celled organisms are able to maintain internal stability because they

(1) have multiple organ systems
(2) work with other cells
(3) contain structures that perform life functions
(4) carry out photosynthesis to produce food

3 A similarity between humans and many other multicellular animals is that they

(1) occupy the same niche in most food webs
(2) are composed of organ systems
(3) have the same DNA sequences
(4) carry out autotrophic nutrition

4 In order to enter cells and be useful to the body, starch must be

(1) absorbed through the skin
(2) broken down into fats and water
(3) digested into simple sugars
(4) converted to carbon dioxide and ATP

5 The increase of certain types of gases in the atmosphere has contributed to the problem of global warming. All these gases are

(1) biotic factors
(2) abiotic factors
(3) organic factors
(4) endangered factors

6 Several goldfish were kept in a small aquarium for several years. The fish grew to be approximately 6 centimeters long in the first year, and after that, growth in length stopped. These fish were later transferred to a large pond. In the pond, the goldfish grew much larger, reaching lengths of around 25 centimeters. Which statement provides the best explanation for the increased growth of the fish in the pond?

(1) Chemicals present in the pond increased the amount of DNA in the fish, causing the growth increase.
(2) The expression of genetic information in the fish was influenced by their surroundings.
(3) The fish expressed and passed on only those characteristics that enabled them to survive in the new environment.
(4) The size of the fish depended only on their food supply and not on their DNA.

7 Autotrophs might survive when heterotrophs cannot, because autotrophs are able to

(1) reproduce asexually
(2) become dormant
(3) exist without respiration
(4) make their own food

8 The inability of sperm cells to move normally could prevent the production of offspring by interfering with

(1) meiosis   (3) fertilization
(2) mitosis   (4) differentiation

9 Which type of pathogenic microbe causes AIDS?

(1) a bacterium
(2) a virus
(3) a multicellular fungus
(4) a single-celled algae

10 The diagram below represents a technique used to produce carrots.

Which reproductive process determines the traits present in the cluster of cells?
(1) meiosis   (3) fertilization
(2) mitosis   (4) differentiation

11 The diagram below represents a scientific technique in use today.

Scientists have used this technique to

(1) produce hormones for human use at a lower cost than other methods
(2) produce pathogens that are able to live in humans
(3) clone human cells with desired characteristics
(4) eliminate the need for laboratory production of medicines for humans

June '14 Regents Examination

12 DNA is able to control cellular activities most directly by regulating the process of
   (1) meiotic division   (3) active transport
   (2) protein synthesis   (4) selective breeding

13 Which statement describes an effect of natural selection on a species?
   (1) It favors the survival of certain members of the species and results in a change in the proportion of individuals with highly adaptive traits.
   (2) It provides feedback mechanisms for members of a species and results in a change in the proportion of individuals with homeostatic controls.
   (3) It leads to reproduction with other species, increasing the number of different adaptations.
   (4) It increases competition between populations that occupy different niches, increasing the chance of extinction of the less-adapted species.

14 Maple leaf beetles and willow leaf beetles are named for the type of tree where they live and reproduce. They look identical to each other when observed, but experiments have shown that willow beetles would starve before eating maple leaves. This is an example of specialization that would directly reduce
   (1) variation   (3) adaptation
   (2) competition   (4) replication

15 Which event would most likely cause a change in a genetic sequence in an organism?
   (1) eating certain foods high in saturated fats
   (2) strenuous physical activity
   (3) exposure to radiation
   (4) a sudden exposure to cooler temperatures

16 During the process of cellular respiration, energy is released from
   (1) carbon dioxide   (3) water molecules
   (2) oxygen atoms   (4) chemical bonds

17 A new vaccine was developed and then tested on a large sample of individuals. This new vaccine will be considered effective if it helps prepare the body to fight future invasion by
   (1) inhibiting the response of red blood cells
   (2) stimulating the reproduction of microbes
   (3) inhibiting the action of immune cells
   (4) stimulating the production of antibodies

18 Which expression correctly represents a reproductive process that usually occurs in humans where $2n$ is equal to the number of chromosomes in each body cell?
   (1) $n + n \rightarrow n$ (3) $n + 2n \rightarrow 2n$
   (2) $n + n \rightarrow 2n$ (4) $2n + 2n \rightarrow 4n$

19 One effect of uncontrolled diabetes is that the blood might develop an acidic pH. As a result, cells may not be able to regulate their internal pH. Within these cells, this could cause a disruption of the function of biological catalysts known as
   (1) enzymes   (3) antibodies
   (2) toxins   (4) antigens

20 A Native American saying states that, "We do not inherit the land we live on from our grandparents, we borrow it from our grandchildren." This saying is an attempt to make us understand that
   (1) the impact we have on the environment lasts for many generations
   (2) we must pay a lot of money to buy land from our parents
   (3) what we do today to the environment has little impact on our children
   (4) human actions only affect other humans

21 Cells of the immune system are able to respond to the presence of invading organisms because they recognize the
   (1) antigens present on the invaders
   (2) antibodies present in invading pathogens
   (3) DNA pattern in the nuclei of viruses
   (4) antibiotics released from microbes

22 Typhoid fever, a disease that causes headaches, digestive upset, and a high fever, is caused by the bacterium *Salmonella typhi*. Typhoid can be spread from person to person by contaminated water or food or by a lack of cleanliness. Since the 19th century, the number of individuals infected with this disease has decreased. Which statement best explains why the number of people with this disease and other bacterial diseases has decreased over the last 100 years?

(1) Scientists have corrected the damaged genes that cause typhoid fever and other infectious diseases.
(2) Public health officials have placed better controls on the use of the toxic substances that cause these diseases.
(3) Typhoid fever, like most other bacterial diseases, is often caused by a lack of proper nutrition.
(4) Personal habits, such as hand washing, have greatly reduced contamination from bacteria.

23 Deforestation most directly results in

(1) an increase in oxygen in the atmosphere
(2) a decrease in soil erosion
(3) a decrease in biodiversity in the area
(4) an increase in the absorption of carbon dioxide

24 In the California Mojave Desert, an energy company is building a large solar-power facility. It is expected to produce enough power for 140,000 homes and also cut carbon dioxide emissions by 500,000 tons a year. The facility will be built on 4,050 acres of wildlife habitat, which is near a protected refuge for a species of desert tortoise. The decision to build this power plant is most likely based on

(1) proving that positive atmospheric changes are less important than preserving wildlife
(2) a trade-off, weighing the need for a cleaner energy source versus the protection of a natural resource
(3) the fact that building these solar-power energy plants disrupts wildlife habitats
(4) providing evidence that technological advances always produce positive environmental impacts

25 As a result of human activity, a significant percentage of the coral reefs in the oceans have been damaged. One-third of marine fish species depend on coral reefs for survival. Many of these fish might die. The most direct cause of the death of these fish would be

(1) habitat destruction
(2) direct harvesting
(3) recycling of nutrients
(4) use of nuclear fuels

26 Which statement best describes the role of decomposers?

(1) They convert carbon dioxide and water to glucose.
(2) They break down organic compounds into products used by other organisms.
(3) They release oxygen to the atmosphere.
(4) They provide energy for the synthesis of proteins.

27 Many scientists are worried about some of Earth's finite resources because humans are

(1) using carbon dioxide faster than it is being produced
(2) placing industrial wastes in landfills
(3) interfering with energy flow from consumers to producers
(4) using large amounts of some materials that cannot be renewed

28 Many communities have started programs to dispose of evergreen trees after the holiday season. These programs allow individuals to bring these trees to be shredded, and the resulting chips are spread around parks and recreational areas as mulch. These programs benefit the environment by

(1) increasing pollution in parks
(2) taking up more space in landfills
(3) returning materials to the environment
(4) increasing carbon dioxide in the atmosphere

29 Modern dogs are direct descendants of the gray wolf. They first appeared about 130,000 years ago. Today, there are about 150 different breeds of domestic dog, a few of which are shown below.

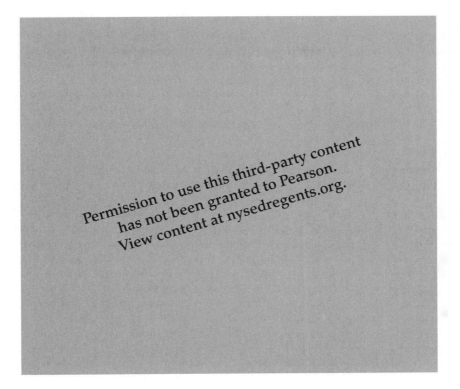

Permission to use this third-party content has not been granted to Pearson. View content at nysedregents.org.

The great variety of modern dogs can best be explained by

(1) selective breeding of dogs over many years
(2) the cloning of domestic dogs
(3) genetic alterations in gray wolves alive today
(4) natural selection favoring wolves over dogs

30 The diagram below shows an alteration that occurred during the replication process of a portion of a gene. The numbers identify the locations of specific bases in the sequence.

$$\underline{\text{A T C C G C A T C T T A T}} \xrightarrow{\text{Replication}} \underline{\text{A T C G C A T C T T A T}}$$

1 2 3 4 5 6 7 8 9 10 11 12 13

This alteration is most likely the result of

(1) a substitution at base 2
(2) a deletion of base 2
(3) an insertion of base 3
(4) a deletion of base 4

Part B–1

Answer all questions in this part. [13]

Directions (31–43): For *each* statement or question, record on the separate answer sheet the *number* of the word or expression that, of those given, best completes the statement or answers the question.

Base your answers to questions 31 and 32 on the diagram below and on your knowledge of biology. The diagram represents a food web.

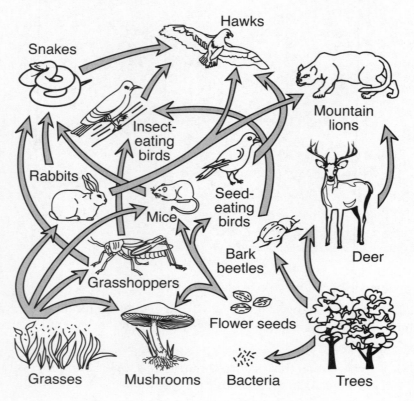

31 What do the arrows in the diagram represent?

(1) an increase in population   (3) the flow of energy
(2) the evolution of organisms   (4) ecological succession

32 Which statement correctly describes interactions between organisms in this ecosystem?

(1) Hawks are predators of insect-eating birds, but not of seed-eating birds.
(2) Hawks and snakes prey on both rabbits and grasshoppers.
(3) Rabbits and mice compete for both grasses and flower seeds.
(4) Grasshoppers and mice compete for grasses, but not flower seeds.

33 Humans have altered ecosystems by activities that are sometimes deliberate and sometimes accidental. In the United States, humans have altered ecosystems by introducing invasive species that outcompete native species. Which activity resulted in the accidental introduction of an invasive species?

(1) importing Japanese knotweed because it has an attractive flower
(2) transporting zebra mussels to the Great Lakes by discharging water taken on in European ports to stabilize large ships
(3) releasing Chinese mitten crabs in the Hudson River to establish them as a food source
(4) planting purple loosestrife that was brought here from Europe as a source of medicine

34 The diagram below represents a specialized cell located in the root of a plant. The arrows in the diagram indicate the movement of molecules of oxygen and water into the cell.

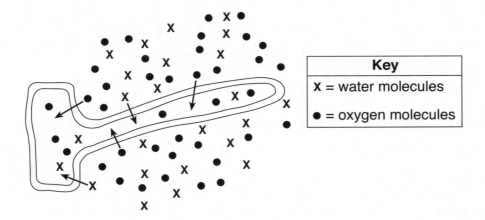

Key
X = water molecules
● = oxygen molecules

Which row in the chart below correctly identifies the process responsible for the movement of each type of molecule represented in the diagram?

Row	Water	Oxygen
(1)	diffusion	active transport
(2)	diffusion	diffusion
(3)	active transport	diffusion
(4)	active transport	active transport

Base your answer to question 35 on the graph below and on your knowledge of biology. The graph shows the level of gene expression of five different genes in normal and cancerous cells.

35 Which statement is a valid inference that can be made based on the data in this graph?

(1) The change in the level of gene expression in gene 4 could indicate it plays a major role in the development of cancer.
(2) Slight decreases in gene expression will always result in the formation of cancer cells.
(3) Cells will develop cancer if the gene expression of these five genes remains below four peptides per second.
(4) An increase in the level of gene expression in these five genes is necessary for cancer to develop in cells.

36 The cells of some organisms contain both chloroplasts and mitochondria. Which statement describes what would happen in these cells if they were moved from a light environment to a dark one?

(1) The amount of oxygen present would decrease and the amount of carbon dioxide would increase.
(2) The amount of glucose present would increase and ATP would no longer be available.
(3) The amount of carbon dioxide present would decrease and ATP would continue to be synthesized.
(4) The amount of oxygen present would increase and the amount of glucose available would decrease.

June '14   Regents Examination

37 In the spring of 2010, there was a catastrophic explosion on an ocean oil drilling rig, causing millions of gallons of oil to be released into the Gulf of Mexico. Many organisms died due to the thick sludge in their habitat. However, in some organisms, such as shellfish, the oil stuck to tissues inside their shells. Which statement expresses a major concern of environmentalists about the accumulation of the oil in certain organisms in the Gulf of Mexico ecosystem?

(1) Larger organisms eat the shellfish and more chemicals will build up in their tissues.
(2) The shellfish will prevent other organisms from obtaining oil.
(3) Smaller organisms will be unaffected by the chemicals.
(4) Larger organisms will be less affected by the oil, because they can eat other organisms.

Base your answers to questions 38 and 39 on the information and data table below and on your knowledge of biology.

Fertilized eggs containing embryos from the same species of alligator were incubated at different temperatures. The sex of the hatched offspring is shown in the table below.

Sex of Offspring Incubated at Different Temperatures

	Temperature of Egg Incubation					
	26°C	28°C	30°C	32°C	34°C	36°C
Number of Eggs Used	100	100	100	100	100	100
Number of Embryos that Died	80	4	3	2	6	86
Number of Females Hatched	20	96	97	85	0	0
Number of Males Hatched	0	0	0	13	94	14

38 A review of this data could lead to the conclusion that

(1) the most alligator eggs hatched if incubated at 26°C
(2) the sex of the offspring depends on the incubation temperature
(3) female alligators develop at higher temperatures
(4) temperature doesn't affect the survival of alligator embryos

39 The percent of surviving females at 32°C from the original number of eggs incubated was

(1) 13%   (3) 85%
(2) 2%   (4) 98%

Base your answers to questions 40 and 41 on the graph below and on your knowledge of biology. The graph shows the growth of a population of rabbits in a specific ecosystem.

Rabbit Population in a Specific Ecosystem

40 Which environmental factor could have caused the change indicated at *A*?

(1) increased predation by herbivores

(2) increased availability of food

(3) increased number of decomposers

(4) increased competition among carnivores

41 Over a period of time, the location of the dashed line would move from location *B* to location *C* on this graph if

(1) the birthrate of the rabbit population was equal to the death rate of the rabbit population

(2) there was a decrease in the number of rabbit predators and an increase in the availability of plants

(3) there was a decrease in the availability of minerals, water, and shelter

(4) the entire rabbit population migrated to a new ecosystem containing more autotrophs

Base your answers to questions 42 and 43 on the diagram below and on your knowledge of biology. The diagram represents the effect of two chemical substances, *A* and *B*, in maintaining the level of glucose in the blood in humans.

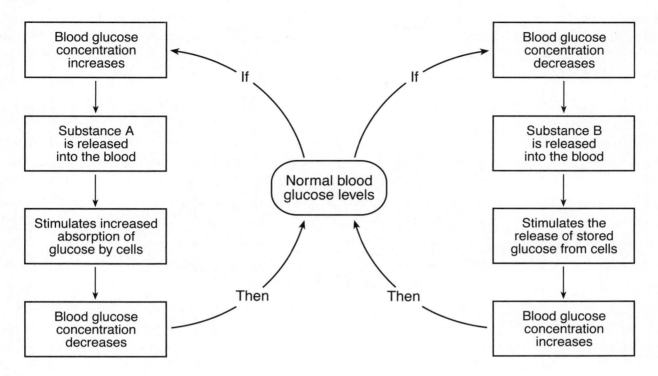

42 The interaction of substances *A* and *B* is an example of

(1) a genetic mutation   (3) an immune response

(2) homeostatic feedback   (4) active transport

43 Which statement is correct regarding the substances involved in these interactions?

(1) Substance *A* is insulin, which is released by cells in the pancreas.

(2) Substance *B* is a chemical receptor molecule produced by blood cells.

(3) Both substances *A* and *B* are classified as biological catalysts.

(4) Substance *A* is a chemical that is produced by specialized blood cells.

Answer all questions in this part. [12]

Directions (44–55): For those questions that are multiple choice, record on the separate answer sheet the *number* of the choice that, of those given, best completes each statement or answers each question. For all other questions in this part, follow the directions given and record your answers in the spaces provided in this examination booklet.

44 Two views through a compound light microscope of a wet-mount slide preparation of cells are shown in the photographs below.

Which procedure was most likely followed to obtain view *B*? [1]

_____

GO ON TO THE NEXT PAGE ⟹

Base your answers to questions 45 through 47 on the data table below and on your knowledge of biology. The data table shows the concentration of estrogen in picograms per milliliter (pg/mL) in the blood of a woman over the course of 28 days.

Estrogen Concentration in Blood

Day	Concentration of Estrogen (pg/mL)
1	30
5	80
10	200
15	180
20	30
28	25

Directions (45–46): Using the information given in the data table, construct a line graph on the grid following the directions below.

45 Mark an appropriate scale, without any breaks, on the axis labeled "Concentration of Estrogen." [1]

46 Plot the data for concentration of estrogen on the grid. Surround each point with a small circle and connect the points. [1]

Example:

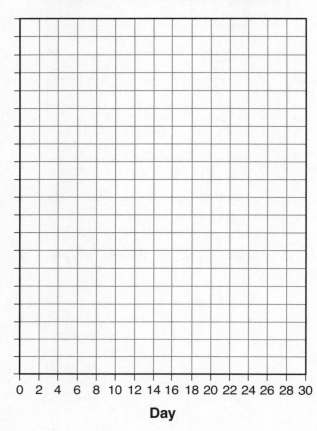

Estrogen Concentration in Blood

Concentration of Estrogen (pg/mL)

Day

Note: The answer to question 47 should be recorded on your separate answer sheet.

47 The concentration of estrogen at day 8 is closest to

(1) 28 pg/mL

(2) 80 pg/mL

(3) 150 pg/mL

(4) 200 pg/mL

June '14 Regents Examination

Base your answers to questions 48 and 49 on the word equations below and on your knowledge of biology. The equations represent two biochemical processes that occur in living organisms. The letter X represents a molecule produced from process 1.

Process 1: oxygen + glucose → carbon dioxide + water + X

Process 2: carbon dioxide + water → oxygen + glucose

48 Identify the molecule represented by letter X in process 1.   [1]

_____

Note: The answer to question 49 should be recorded on your separate answer sheet.

49 Which process occurs in the cells of a green plant leaf?

(1) process 1, only
(2) process 2, only

(3) neither process 1 nor process 2
(4) both process 1 and process 2

Base your answers to questions 50 through 53 on the graph below and on your knowledge of biology. The graph shows some events associated with the reproductive cycle of human females.

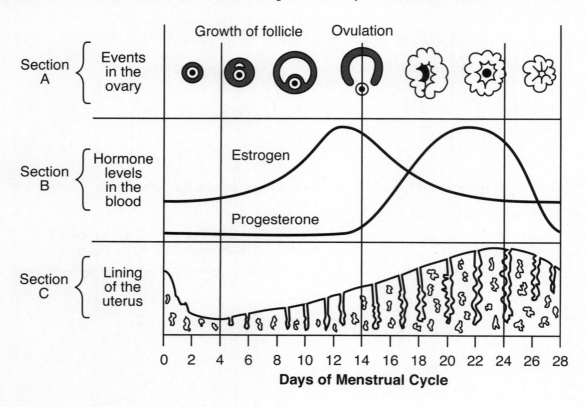

Note: The answer to question 50 should be recorded on your separate answer sheet.

50 Which sections of the graph represent structures affected directly by the hormones shown?

(1) section *A* and section *B*, only

(2) section *B* and section *C*, only

(3) section *A* and section *C*, only

(4) section *A*, section *B*, and section *C*

51 According to the graph, on which day is the egg released from the ovary? [1]

Day:_____

52 Which section of the graph shows the location where the zygote would most likely become implanted and develop? [1]

Section:_____

53 Identify another human reproductive hormone that is *not* shown on this graph. [1]

_____

_____

Base your answers to questions 54 and 55 on the information below and on your knowledge of biology.

Different plant species require different amounts of direct sunlight in order to flower. A student designed an experiment to determine the length of exposure to direct sunlight necessary for a specific plant species to produce flowers. The student collected the data below.

0 hours, 0% with flowers; 9 hours, 0% with flowers

1 hour, 0% with flowers; 5 hours, 90% with flowers

3 hours, 80% with flowers; 7 hours, 10% with flowers

54 Organize the data collected, from shortest to longest length of exposure, in the data table below. [1]

Relationship of Sunlight Exposure to Flower Production

Hours of Exposure to Direct Sunlight	Percent of Plants with Flowers

55 At the end of the experiment, the student stated that if plants are exposed to more hours of daylight, they will always produce a greater percentage of flowers. Is this a valid conclusion? Support your answer. [1]

_____

_____

_____

Part C

Answer all questions in this part.   [17]

Directions (56–72): Record your answers in the spaces provided in this examination booklet.

Base your answers to questions 56 and 57 on the information below and on your knowledge of biology.

Decline in the Amphibians

Declines in amphibian species, such as frogs, toads and salamanders, might affect the ways in which ecosystems function. Amphibians prey on many types of small organisms that survive by consuming leaf litter (leaf material on the ground of ecosystems). These small organisms include animals such as earthworms, centipedes, millipedes, pill bugs, and many species of insects. In turn, amphibians are preyed on by fish, herons, chipmunks, turkeys, foxes, coyotes, and other animals.

Human activities often cause a reduction in the size of amphibian populations. As amphibian populations are reduced, the organisms that are preyed on by amphibians increase in number. As the populations of small forest organisms increase, the amount of leaf litter decreases. The decrease in the amount of leaf litter on the forest floor may have negative effects on the forest ecosystem.

56 Identify *one* human activity and describe how that activity could directly or indirectly lead to a reduction in amphibian populations.   [1]

_____

_____

57 State *one* possible effect an increase in the amount of leaf litter on the forest floor would have on the amphibian population. Support your answer.   [1]

_____

_____

_____

Base your answers to questions 58 and 59 on the information below and on your knowledge of biology.

Female Shark Reproduced Without Male DNA, Scientists Say

A hammerhead shark that gave birth in a Nebraska aquarium reproduced without mating, a genetic analysis shows.

This form of asexual reproduction, called parthenogenesis, has been found in other vertebrate species, including some snakes and lizards. But this is the first time it has been documented in a shark....

Instead, the female shark's own genetic material combined during this process of cell division that produces an egg. A cell called the secondary oocyte, which contains half the female chromosomes and normally becomes the egg, fused with another cell called the secondary polar body, which contains the identical [amount of] genetic material....

Robert E. Hueter, director of the Center for Shark Research at the Mote Marine Laboratory in Sarasota, Fla., said the finding helped fill a gap in understanding parthenogenesis, which has been found to occur in most vertebrate lines except mammals, and until now, cartilaginous fishes like sharks....

"It's a last-resort tactic that animals use when they absolutely can't find another mate," Dr. Hueter said.

Source: Henry Fountain, *The New York Times*, May 23, 2007

58 State why parthenogenesis is considered a form of asexual reproduction. [1]

_____

_____

59 Explain why parthenogenesis could prove to be harmful to the survival of this species if it were the only method of shark reproduction. [1]

_____

_____

Base your answers to questions 60 through 62 on the information below and on your knowledge of biology.

Ticks, such as deer ticks and dog ticks, feed on the blood of humans and other animals. Part of the feeding process involves the tick injecting its saliva to help make blood flow. In the process, they sometimes spread disease organisms to their host. Sometimes ticks get on clothing, and can remain there for a few days before actually biting their host.

A scientist found that ticks might be able to survive even when exposed to hot water and detergent in a washing machine.

Students designed the experiment below to test how well ticks survive a hot-water washing machine cycle with detergent. Note that some details of the design are incorrect.

Hypothesis: Can ticks survive a hot water and detergent wash cycle in a washing machine?	
Data to be Collected:	Number of ticks surviving the cold-water wash cycle

	Control Group	Experimental Group
Test Subjects:	deer tick	dog tick
Experimental Setup:	ticks in washing cycle with cold water and detergent	ticks in washing cycle with hot water and detergent
Number Used:	10	100

60 Identify *one* error with the hypothesis. [1]

_____

_____

61 Explain why the students' proposed data to be collected would not likely test what the students intended. [1]

_____

_____

62 Identify *one* error in the students' design in the shaded area of the table and explain how the students should change the experiment to correct the error. [1]

Error:_____

Correction:_____

_____

Base your answers to questions 63 through 66 on the passage below and on your knowledge of biology.

The Return of the Large Blue Butterfly

In 1979, the Large Blue Butterfly was declared extinct in the United Kingdom, despite the efforts to protect the grasslands where it lived.

Research into the butterfly life cycle discovered the following facts. The butterflies lay their eggs on flowering thyme plants, and the caterpillars fall to the ground after they hatch. The young butterfly caterpillars have a "honey gland" on their posterior end, which, when stimulated by red ants, makes the caterpillars smell and wiggle like red ants. The red ants treat the butterfly caterpillars as ant grubs and carry them to their underground homes. The red ants keep looking after them and guard them, even though the caterpillars eat ant grubs for 10 months before flying away as adult butterflies in the spring.

The red ants live in fields of short grass. The grass is short enough to let the sun warm the soil. This is where the ants find and eat insects and plants. Rabbits had kept the grass short until the mid-1950s, when the rabbit populations were suddenly devastated by a viral disease. Additionally, farmers allowed pastures to get overgrown by not letting cattle graze on the grass. The red ants vanished when the taller grass increased the shade and cooled the soil.

A program was introduced to protect the pastures where the red ants nested. Their numbers came back. Populations of Large Blue Butterflies from Sweden were brought into the area, and now the Large Blue Butterfly is thriving again.

63 Describe *one* way humans have *negatively* influenced the ecosystem of the red ant. [1]

_____

_____

64 Describe *one* adaptation present in the butterfly caterpillars that enables the Large Blue Butterfly to survive. [1]

_____

_____

_____

65 In the space below, construct a food chain consisting of *at least three* organisms, including a producer, that would be present in the ant ecosystem.   [1]

66 Select *one* organism from the food chain you constructed and write it on the line below. State *one* way the removal of the organism you selected would affect another organism in the food chain. Support your answer.   [1]

Organism: _____

_____

_____

_____

June '14   Regents Examination

Base your answer to question 67–69 on the information and photographs below and on your knowledge of biology.

In addition to their use for hearing, ears contain many blood vessels that allow heat to escape into the air. Animals that live in warm climates tend to have ears with large areas exposed to the environment. Animals in cold climates have a more compact ear that keeps exposure to the environment to a minimum. The photographs below show a jackrabbit from desert regions of the southwestern United States and a fennec fox from northern Africa with large ears, and a snowshoe hare and an arctic fox with small ears.

| Jackrabbit | Fennec Fox | Snowshoe Hare | Arctic Fox |

67–69 Discuss how differences in ear size in these organisms might have occurred. In your answer, be sure to:

- explain how the size of these animals' ears can help the animals survive in their environment [1]
- identify *one* process that most likely resulted in the animals in warm climates having large ears, while animals in cold climates have small ears [1]
- state how the overproduction of offspring in each species for many generations contributed to the presence of different ear sizes [1]

_____

_____

_____

_____

_____

_____

_____

_____

_____

Base your answers to questions 70 and 71 on the information below and on your knowledge of biology.

Plasmodium, the world's most lethal parasite, causes malaria. The parasite enters the bloodstream through a mosquito bite, hiding in the human liver before invading red blood cells. Ultimately, millions of infected blood cells explode at once, causing fever and death in 3 million people a year worldwide.

Source: Zimmer, February 12, 2001, "Animal Parasites – As Gross As It Gets,"
"Science World," pg 11.

70 State *one* reason why *Plasmodium* is considered a parasite of humans. [1]

_____

_____

71 State *one negative* impact on humans when the use of pesticides for mosquitoes is decreased. [1]

_____

_____

72 If a large quantity of herbicide, a chemical that is designed to kill weeds, were accidentally spilled into a large lake, it could endanger all the organisms living in the lake. State *one* way the effects of killing the weeds in the lake could be destructive to populations of fish and other animals. [1]

_____

_____

Part D

Answer all questions in this part. [13]

Directions (73–85): For those questions that are multiple choice, record on the separate answer sheet the *number* of the choice that, of those given, best completes the statement or answers the question. For all other questions in this part, follow the directions given and record your answers in the spaces provided in this examination booklet.

Base your answers to questions 73 and 74 on the diagram below and on your knowledge of biology. The diagram represents evolutionary relationships among some primates.

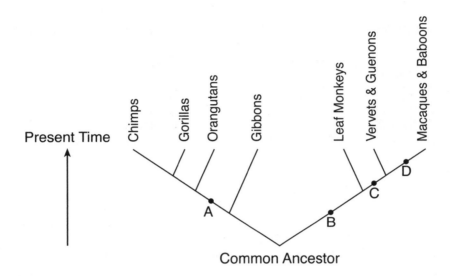

Note: The answers to questions 73 and 74 should be recorded on your separate answer sheet.

73 Which statement best describes a relationship between the common ancestor and the other organisms in the diagram?

(1) The common ancestor most likely has segments of its DNA that will match each of the other organisms'.
(2) The common ancestor is more closely related to macaques than to gibbons.
(3) Orangutans and gorillas have exactly the same DNA as the common ancestor.
(4) Chimps and baboons were the first organisms to evolve from the common ancestor.

74 A line representing an organism that is closely related to leaf monkeys and that evolved at about the same time as the gibbons would be drawn beginning at point

(1) A
(2) B

(3) C
(4) D

75 The parents of a new baby believe they brought the wrong child home from the hospital. Gel electrophoresis was performed using DNA samples from the parents and the child. A section of the gel electrophoresis results is shown below.

Note: The answer to question 75 should be recorded on your separate answer sheet.

Which conclusion is valid based on the gel electrophoresis results?

(1) They have the correct child, because her genetic information is identical to that of the father.
(2) They have the wrong child, because her genetic information does not match that of either parent.
(3) They have the correct child, because her genetic information came from both parents.
(4) They have the wrong child, because her genetic information matches only that of the mother.

Note: The answer to question 76 should be recorded on your separate answer sheet.

76 The extremes of dry and wet weather of the Galapagos Islands cause the food supply to constantly change. During dry years, the food is mainly large, hard seeds, and finches with large beaks are found in greater numbers.

Which statement best explains this observation?

(1) Dry environments cause mutations in finches.
(2) Finches grow larger when they have more water.
(3) Small finches become smaller during dry seasons.
(4) Large beak size is an adaptation to dry conditions.

June '14 Regents Examination

Base your answers to questions 77 and 78 on the information below and on your knowledge of biology.

Three students took their pulse rates in beats per minute (bpm) while sitting in class. The results are shown in the data table below.

Pulse Rates of Three Students

Student	Pulse Rate (bpm)
1	73
2	85
3	67

77 State *one* reason why the pulse rates were *not* the same for all three students, even though they were all resting at the time. [1]

_____

_____

78 What is the average pulse rate, in bpm, for this group of students? [1]

_____ **bpm**

_____

Base your answers to questions 79 and 80 on the information and data table below and on your knowledge of biology.

In an experiment, three plants of the same species were grown in each of six identical pots. The heights of the plants were measured when growth began. Each of the pots was watered every day with salt solutions of different concentrations. The data for the experiment are shown in the table below.

Effect of Salt Solution on the Height of Plants

Plant Group	Percent Salt Solution Used for Watering the Plants	Average Initial Height (centimeters)	Average Final Height (centimeters)
A	0	2	30
B	1	2	28
C	2	3	15
D	3	2	10
E	4	3	(died)
F	5	3	(died)

79 State the effect of increasing the percent of salt in the solution used to water the plants on the average final height of the plants in groups *A* through *D*. [1]

_____

_____

80 State *one* way diffusion was involved in the cause of death of the plants in groups *E* and *F*. [1]

_____

_____

_____

81 In an experiment to determine the effect of exercise on pulse rate, a student checks his pulse rate before and after exercising for several minutes. The purpose of checking his pulse rate before exercising is that it

(1) serves as the conclusion for the experiment
(2) is needed to justify the sample size
(3) serves as a control for the experiment
(4) is needed to formulate a hypothesis

82 What is an advantage of a change in pulse rate after exercising?

(1) The heart needs to produce more energy to supply the active muscle cells and maintain homeostasis.
(2) An increased blood flow carries excess waste products away from the active muscle cells.
(3) The blood is removing oxygen from muscle cells that were not active and carrying it to muscle cells that are active.
(4) The blood is supplying the active muscle cells with carbon dioxide to neutralize wastes in those cells.

83 The diagrams below represent seeds taken from a carrot plant and seeds taken from plant species 1, 2, and 3.

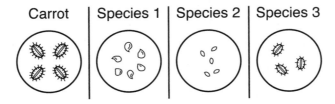

Which species would be expected to be most similar to the carrot? Support your answer. [1]

_____

_____

84 Other than having a variation in beak characteristics, describe another variation in a finch species that could promote survival of an individual bird. Support your answer. [1]

_____

_____

85 Identify or describe *one* tool used in "The Beaks of Finches" lab, and explain why the special features of this beak represented *either* an advantage or a disadvantage in the competition. [1]

Tool: _____

Advantage or disadvantage: _____

Explanation: _____

_____

Part A

Answer all questions in this part. [30]

Directions (1–30): For *each* statement or question, record on the separate answer sheet the *number* of the word or expression that, of those given, best completes the statement or answers the question.

1 The concentration of potassium is higher in red blood cells than in the surrounding blood plasma. This higher concentration is maintained by the process of

(1) circulation   (3) excretion
(2) diffusion   (4) active transport

2 Human genetic material is represented in the diagram below.

The region labeled *A* is made up of a section of

(1) a protein that becomes an enzyme
(2) DNA that may direct protein synthesis
(3) a carbohydrate made from amino acids
(4) glucose that may be copied to make DNA

3 Brothers and sisters often have similar facial characteristics, such as nose shape or eye color, because they

(1) are raised in similar environments
(2) eat similar types of foods
(3) have similar types of proteins
(4) use similar types of facial care products

4 Compared to a normal body cell, a normal egg cell contains

(1) the same number of chromosomes
(2) half the number of chromosomes
(3) twice the number of chromosomes
(4) four times the number of chromosomes

5 The variations that exist in a population of wild giraffes are usually a result of events that occur during

(1) mitotic division
(2) genetic engineering
(3) asexual reproduction
(4) sexual reproduction

6 Evidence that best supports the theory of biological evolution was obtained from the

(1) investigation of environmental niches
(2) study of fossil records
(3) comparison of the number of cells in organisms
(4) analysis of food chains and food webs

7 The human immune system fights infection by releasing

(1) ATPs   (3) antibodies
(2) antibiotics   (4) antigens

8 The function of a specific enzyme is most directly influenced by its

(1) molecular size   (3) carrying capacity
(2) physical shape   (4) stored energy

9 A vaccine for the viral disease known as chicken pox would contain

(1) a large amount of live virus
(2) a dead or weakened form of the pathogen
(3) several different antibiotics
(4) a small number of white blood cells

10 Which process will result in a gain of energy in an ecosystem?

(1) photosynthesis in algae cells
(2) digestion in hummingbirds
(3) ATP synthesis in fungi
(4) respiration in maple tree cells

11 A photograph of a polar bear in its environment is shown below.

One possible reason why polar bears might not be able to survive if the environment they live in changes is because

(1) the species will experience decreased competition for mates
(2) the new environment will cause greater variation in the species
(3) there will be a larger variety of food sources available
(4) they are adapted to the specific environment in which they now live

12 An ecological process is represented below.

Time (years)

Which statement describes an event in this process?

(1) Community B modifies the environment, making it suitable for community C.
(2) Community D modifies the environment, making it suitable for community C.
(3) Community E will develop into community A, if the environment remains stable.
(4) Community A organisms will develop directly into community D organisms.

13 An infection in the body might result in a sudden

(1) decrease in the activity of antigens produced by the mitochondria
(2) decrease in the amount of DNA present in the nuclei of cells
(3) increase in the activity of white blood cells
(4) increase in the number of red blood cells

14 Which disorder could develop in the human body when the immune system attacks a usually harmless environmental substance?

(1) cancer
(2) AIDS
(3) an allergy
(4) an infection

15 In the human body, carbon monoxide reduces the amount of oxygen that can be transported to cells. Breathing in too much carbon monoxide will most likely result in the production of

(1) less ATP
(2) less glucose
(3) more DNA
(4) more protein

16 Which human activity would interfere most directly with the production of oxygen in the environment?

(1) using fertilizer for agriculture
(2) using nuclear fuels
(3) accelerating deforestation
(4) preserving wetlands

17 Tissues of oleander plants contain chemicals that are poisonous to many mammals. The production of these poisonous chemicals most likely benefits oleanders by preventing leaf loss caused by

(1) lack of rain
(2) scavengers
(3) mineral absorption
(4) herbivores

18 Sugar maples and white pines are two different tree species that often grow side by side in the Adirondack Mountains. Which statement concerning these trees is correct?

(1) Since they are both trees, they can interbreed.
(2) Since they are not closely related, they do not compete with one another.
(3) Even though they are both trees, each plays a different role in the ecosystem.
(4) They utilize totally different abiotic resources.

19 People living in and around the Amazon rain forest have used parts of the gaviola tree to prepare medicines. Research is being conducted to determine if this tree can provide cures for many types of cancer. Continued destruction of rain forests might

(1) reduce biodiversity and remove organisms with the potential to help humans
(2) increase biodiversity and remove damaged and diseased trees
(3) reduce biodiversity and increase the reproductive rates of all organisms
(4) increase biodiversity and ecosystem stability where humans plant crops

20 A fundamental concept of ecology is that living organisms

(1) are independent and do not interact with each other or with the physical environment
(2) do not interact with other living organisms, but do interact with the physical environment
(3) interact with each other, but do not interact with the physical environment
(4) interact with other living organisms and interact with the physical environment

21 Many families now use compost to make the soil in their gardens more fertile. They collect vegetable scraps and yard trimmings, place them in a compost pile or special container, and let them decompose. The organisms primarily responsible for decomposing the vegetable scraps and yard trimmings are

(1) plant parasites
(2) autotrophs
(3) bacteria and fungi
(4) scavengers and viruses

22 In 2003, the city of Rochester, New York, began killing weeds with steam. A machine heats water to 280°F then sprays it on the weeds with great pressure. The extreme heat destroys the cellular structure of the plants. What is a possible *disadvantage* of this method of weed control?

(1) It can be used safely in areas where children play.
(2) It reduces the number of mutations in the ecosystem.
(3) It destroys weeds without chemicals.
(4) It alters the habitats of some beneficial insects.

23 A food chain is represented below.

grass → rabbit → hawk

Structures within the rabbit are formed using

(1) solar energy from the grass
(2) heat energy lost to the environment
(3) chemical energy from the hawk
(4) chemical energy from the grass

24 The graduating class of a high school would like to give the school a gift that would have a positive impact on the environment. Which plan would be the best choice?

(1) making wooden benches by harvesting trees from school property
(2) planting native trees along the border of the school property
(3) introducing a new population of foxes, the school mascot, to school grounds
(4) clearing an area to make room for additional student parking

25 Which graph best illustrates the change in the human population over the past 2000 years?

26 Which processes lead to the greatest variety of genetic combinations?

(1) asexual reproduction and cloning
(2) meiosis and fertilization
(3) meiosis and mitosis
(4) cloning and mitosis

27 One possible explanation for the fact that some simple, one-celled organisms did *not* evolve into complex, multicellular organisms is that

(1) energy flow in an ecosystem requires simple autotrophic organisms
(2) the reproductive rate of single-celled organisms is too fast for change to occur
(3) these organisms possessed traits that enabled them to survive in a changing environment
(4) stability within an ecosystem requires the presence of a variety of different species

28 In New York State, cars are inspected to be sure they are not releasing excessive amounts of several gases into the atmosphere. This is done in an effort to

(1) recycle more nutrients
(2) reduce biodiversity
(3) reduce global warming
(4) increase the growth rates of forests

29 Damage to the ozone shield over the United States is likely to cause

(1) increased warming of local ecosystems
(2) increased exposure to ultraviolet light
(3) reduction in the pH of acid precipitation
(4) reduction in the frequency of floods and droughts

30 Researchers recently discovered that when hammerhead sharks were moved to shallower water, resulting in exposure to increased light intensity, their backs turned a deep brownish black. Which statement best supports this observation?

(1) Genes are inherited, but their expression can be modified by interactions with the environment.
(2) The cells of hammerhead sharks contain many thousands of different genes in their nuclei.
(3) An inherited trait of an individual can be determined by one or by many genes.
(4) Asexually produced offspring are normally genetically identical to the parent.

Part B–1

Answer all questions in this part. [13]

Directions (31–43): For *each* statement or question, record on the separate answer sheet the *number* of the word or expression that, of those given, best completes the statement or answers the question.

Base your answers to questions 31 through 33 on the information below and on your knowledge of biology.

An experiment was carried out to answer the question "Does the pH of water affect the growth of radish plants?" Two groups of ten radish plants were set up. One group was watered with water having a pH of 3.0, and the other group was watered with water having a pH of 7.0. Both groups of plants received the same amount and intensity of light, the same amount of water, and they were grown in the same type of soil. The heights of the radish plants were measured every 2 days for a period of 2 weeks.

31 Which sentence is a possible hypothesis that was tested in this experiment?
(1) Does the pH of water affect the growth of radish plants?
(2) Will the amount of water alter the heights of the radish plants?
(3) The temperature of the water will affect the heights of the radish plants.
(4) The pH of the water will affect the heights of the radish plants.

32 What was the dependent variable in this experiment?
(1) heights of the plants   (3) temperature of the water
(2) pH of the water   (4) type of soil

33 Which activity might help to increase the validity of this experiment?
(1) repeating the experiment several times
(2) using two different types of radish seeds in each group
(3) using the same pH for both groups of plants
(4) placing one set of plants in sunlight and one in darkness

Base your answers to questions 34 and 35 on the information below and on your knowledge of biology.

Female mosquitoes spread diseases when they bite humans to obtain blood. It is only the females that do the biting. Research is being conducted to alter the DNA of male mosquitoes. These altered males could then mate with normal female mosquitoes. All of the resulting female offspring would have wing defects that prevent them from flying.

34 One assumption from this research is that the
(1) altered males would begin to bite humans and spread the diseases
(2) female offspring would be unable to bite humans, since they cannot fly
(3) altered males would not be able to reproduce
(4) female offspring would become larger in size

35 The method used to alter the male mosquitoes is an example of an application of
(1) a feedback mechanism
(2) selective breeding
(3) biotechnology
(4) physiology

36 Scientists have successfully cloned animals, including large mammals such as sheep. Which statement provides the most likely reason that a human has *not* yet been cloned?
(1) Humans have DNA that is structurally very different from other mammals.
(2) Cloning can only be performed on animals that normally reproduce asexually.
(3) Human genes are made of too many different types of simple sugars.
(4) Some people consider human genetic experiments unethical.

37 Some evolutionary pathways are represented in the diagram below.

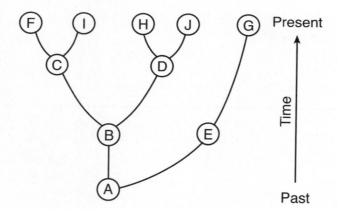

An inference that can be made from information in the diagram is that
(1) species *E* evolved from species *G*
(2) species *A* was probably much larger than all the other species
(3) species *C* is a direct descendant of species *I*
(4) species *J* is adapted to the existing environment

38 The diagram below represents a technique used in some molecular biology laboratories.

Portion of human DNA

Cut bacterial DNA

Inserted into bacterial cell

Which phrase best describes a possible result of this process?

(1) the production of gametes having both human and bacterial DNA
(2) the production of a human hormone by the bacterial cell
(3) the introduction of a pathogen into a human cell
(4) the separation of DNA fingerprints in the bacterial cell

39 The diagram below represents a portion of a molecule found in cells of the human body.

Sequences represented by the letters in this molecule enable human cells to

(1) alter the method of absorption of material
(2) carry out asexual reproduction by meiosis
(3) synthesize enzymes from organic molecules
(4) modify genetic recombination during mitosis

40 Potatoes were the main crop in Ireland in the 1800s. Almost the entire population of Ireland was dependent on a single variety of potato, the "lumper." These potatoes were reproduced by a method of asexual reproduction known as vegetative propagation. In the middle of the 1800s, a disease caused by a fungus killed almost the entire lumper crop within two years. As a result, millions of people in Ireland died of starvation. The most likely reason the potato disease was able to destroy the potato crop in such a short time is that the

(1) potato population lacked variations
(2) lumper variety had a long reproductive cycle
(3) lumper had several variations caused by vegetative propagation
(4) potato population in Ireland utilized all of the finite resources

41 The chart below shows examples from two groups of organisms, multicellular and one-celled.

Group A – Multicellular Organisms		Group B – One-celled Organisms	
Cow	Cat	*Paramecium*	*Vorticella*

The tissues and organs in group *A* perform functions that are

(1) similar to those performed by the tissues and organs in group *B*
(2) similar to those performed by the cell organelles in group *B*
(3) different from those performed by the tissues and organs in group *B*
(4) identical to those performed by the cell organelles in group *B*

42 The graph below shows changes in the concentrations of glucose and insulin in the blood of a human over a period of time.

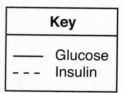

Changes in Glucose and Insulin Levels Over Time

Key
——— Glucose
- - - Insulin

Which statement correctly explains these changes?

(1) High glucose levels cause more insulin to be released.
(2) High insulin levels cause more glucose to be released.
(3) Low glucose levels cause more insulin to be released.
(4) Low insulin levels cause more glucose to be released.

43 The diagram below represents an incomplete sequence of levels of organization.

organelles → tissues → organs → organ systems → organism

This sequence can be completed correctly by inserting

(1) "cells →" between organelles and tissues
(2) "proteins →" between tissues and organs
(3) "populations →" between organs and organ systems
(4) "molecules →" between organ systems and organisms

Answer all questions in this part. [12]

Directions (44–55): For those questions that are multiple choice, record on the separate answer sheet the *number* of the choice that, of those given, best completes each statement or answers each question. For all other questions in this part, follow the directions given and record your answers in the spaces provided in this examination booklet.

Base your answers to questions 44 through 48 on the data table below, which shows the estimated population of wolves in Minnesota from 1995 through 2002.

Minnesota Wolf Population

Year	Estimated Population
1995	2000
1996	2200
1997	2300
1998	2450
1999	2500
2000	2600
2001	2600
2002	2600

Directions (44–46): Using the information in the data table, construct a line graph on the grid, following the directions below.

44 Label the *y*-axis on the line provided. [1]

45 Mark an appropriate scale, without any breaks, on each labeled axis. [1]

46 Plot the data on the grid. Surround each point with a small circle and connect the points. [1]

Example:

January '14 Regents Examination

Minnesota Wolf Population

Year

Note: The answer to question 47 should be recorded on your separate answer sheet.

47 The most likely explanation for the size of the wolf population for the 2000–2002 period is that the population

(1) reached the carrying capacity of the environment
(3) began reproducing at a faster rate

(2) stabilized due to global warming
(4) was affected by a new pathogen

48 Wolves prey on animals such as deer. Identify *one* adaptation of deer that would help them to survive in an area populated by wolves.   [1]

_____

_____

_____

January '14 Regents Examination

Base your answers to questions 49 through 51 on the passage below and on your knowledge of biology.

Tracking the Big Horn

Bighorn sheep, *Ovis canadensis*, are a majestic symbol of the mountainous West. They browse at high altitudes and in steep, rocky areas from Texas to British Columbia. Rams' horns curl around their eyes and grow up to 45 inches long. Males butt horns to establish dominance during the fall rut [mating season]. Ewes [females] sport shorter, spiked horns similar to a mountain goat's. From their first days of life, bighorns are surefooted enough to scale cliffs too steep for most predators to follow....

Two centuries ago, an estimated 1.5 million to 2 million bighorn sheep lived in North America; today, a mere 28,000 remain. Diseases caught from domestic sheep, competition from livestock for forage, and trophy hunting for their horns caused populations to plummet [drop rapidly]. Bighorns graze in mountain meadows, habitat that is being lost to expanding forests, which are growing beyond their historic boundaries in part because the wildfires that are used to hold them in check have been suppressed. Glacier National Park, home to 400 to 600 bighorn sheep, lists the animals as a "species of concern," that is, at risk of becoming endangered....

Source: Becky Lomax, *Smithsonian Magazine,* March, 2008
"Tracking the Big Horn"

Note: The answers to questions 49 and 50 should be recorded on your separate answer sheet.

49 The feeding activity of the bighorn sheep is best described as

(1) consumers feeding on autotrophs
(2) decomposers feeding on consumers
(3) autotrophs feeding on decomposers
(4) autotrophs feeding on heterotrophs

50 Which statement best accounts for the decline in bighorn sheep populations?

(1) Predators of the sheep decreased in number.
(2) Sheep ewes that have shorter, spiked horns increased in number.
(3) Human activities directly and indirectly affected the sheep.
(4) The sheep were listed as a "species of concern" by Glacier National Park.

51 State *one* way that young bighorn sheep are able to avoid predators. [1]

_____

_____

_____

Base your answer to question 52 on the information below and on your knowledge of biology.

For many years, scientists hypothesized the existence of a single tomato gene that increases the sweetness and production of tomatoes. After years of research, a team of scientists identified the gene and observed greater sweetness and tomato production in plants that contain this gene.

52 Identify a process that could be used to insert this gene into other plant species to increase fruit production. [1]

_____

_____

Base your answer to question 53 on the information below and on your knowledge of biology.

Bisphenol-A (BPA), is an industrial chemical commonly added to disposable, plastic water bottles to make them sturdier. BPA has been shown to inhibit the development of tadpoles into frogs. Some tadpoles exposed to high levels of BPA develop into frogs without legs. Others, when exposed to the chemical as tadpoles, fail to reabsorb their tails and thus grow into frogs with significantly long tails.

53 State *one* specific way humans can help decrease the exposure of animals to bisphenol-A. [1]

_____

_____

54 Organ systems of the human body interact to maintain a balanced internal environment. As blood flows through certain organs of the body, the composition of the blood changes because of interactions with those organs. State *one* change in the composition of the blood as it flows through the respiratory system. [1]

_____

55 State *one* possible *negative* impact of importing a natural predator to control a pest. [1]

_____

_____

Part C

Answer all questions in this part.   [17]

Directions (56–72): Record your answers in the spaces provided in this examination booklet.

Base your answer to question 56–60 on the information below and on your knowledge of biology.

A student has a sandwich for lunch. The bread contains starch molecules and various other molecules. After chewing and swallowing some of the sandwich, the starch moves along the digestive system and is digested. The sequence below represents what takes place next.

digested starch → bloodstream → cell → cell structure → ATP

56–60 Explain what occurs, beginning with the digestion of starch and ending with ATP production. In your answer, be sure to:
- identify the molecules that are used to digest the starch   [1]
- identify the molecules produced when starch is digested   [1]
- explain why starch must be digested before its building block molecules can enter the bloodstream   [1]
- identify the structure in the cell that will produce ATP from the starch building blocks   [1]
- state why ATP is important to cells   [1]

_____

_____

_____

_____

_____

_____

_____

_____

_____

_____

Base your answers to questions 61 through 63 on the information below and on your knowledge of biology.

A Study of Antibacterial Cleansers

An experiment was designed to test the effectiveness of three antibacterial hand-cleansing solutions against bacteria present on hands. Swabs were used to take one sample each from the unwashed hands of ten test subjects. Each swab was then rubbed across the surface of bacterial growth medium in a separate petri dish. The dishes were placed in an incubator to allow bacterial colonies to develop.

Ten other test subjects treated their hands with an antibacterial hand-cleansing solution, then had their hands swabbed, and ten more petri dishes were set up and incubated in the same way as the first set of dishes.

The process was repeated again with ten more test subjects for a second hand cleanser, and again for a third group with a third hand cleanser.

The results from the incubated petri dishes were averaged. The averages are shown in the data table below.

Effectiveness of Antibacterial Cleansers

Treatment Before Swabbing	Average Number of Bacterial Colonies
none	30
antibacterial hand-cleansing solution 1	12
antibacterial hand-cleansing solution 2	13
antibacterial hand-cleansing solution 3	11

61 What was the purpose of testing unwashed hands? [1]

_____

_____

62 Explain why the researchers used data from ten trials and averaged them, rather than data from a single trial. [1]

_____

_____

63 Based on the data provided, what could the researchers conclude regarding the effectiveness of the antibacterial hand-cleansing solutions tested? [1]

_____

_____

Base your answer to question 64–66 on the information below and on your knowledge of biology.

The Critical Role of the Placenta

The proper functioning of the placenta is critical to the growth and development of a healthy fetus. For example, the placenta appears to act as a nutrient sensor. It regulates the amounts and types of nutrients that are transported from the mother to the fetus.

Improper functioning of the placenta can alter the structure and function of specific cells and organ systems in the developing fetus, putting it at risk for health problems as an adult. For example, in some pregnancies, the placenta develops a resistance to blood flow. This resistance appears to force the heart of the fetus to work harder. This could result in an increased chance of the individual developing heart disease as an adult. A group of hormones known as glucocorticoids affects the development of all the tissues and organ systems. One of the things this group of hormones does is to alter cell function by changing the structure of cell membrane receptors.

64–66 Discuss the importance of the placenta in the development of a healthy fetus. In your answer, be sure to:
- identify *two* factors that could influence the nutrients that can pass from the mother to the fetus   [1]
- identify the group of hormones that alter cell membrane receptors and explain how this alteration can affect cell function   [1]
- state the role of the uterus in the development of the fetus and the placenta   [1]

_____

_____

_____

_____

_____

_____

67 A farmer planted two corn varieties, one of which was very tasty but had small ears, and the other one had large ears but did not taste nearly as good. The pollen from one variety was used to fertilize the other variety of corn. State *one* biological advantage this method of reproduction has over cloning.   [1]

_____

_____

Base your answer to question 68–70 on the information below and on your knowledge of biology.

68–70 Feedback mechanisms have evolved that maintain homeostasis. Describe how homeostasis is maintained through feedback. In your answer, be sure to:

- identify *one* feedback mechanism in the human body   [1]
- identify, other than death, *one* specific result if homeostasis fails in the human body   [1]
- describe how a plant regulates water loss through a feedback mechanism that involves guard cells   [1]

_____

_____

_____

_____

_____

_____

Base your answers to questions 71 and 72 on the information below and on your knowledge of biology.

New York State relies on natural gas for 24% of its energy supply. It is estimated that large deposits of natural gas are located in New York State. It is possible to extract the gas via high-volume hydraulic fracturing (hydrofracking). Hydrofracking involves freeing the natural gas by using a large amount of water treated with chemicals, which produces large quantities of waste products. Some people are in favor of hydrofracking, while others are against it. One side is concerned about the negative effect it will have on the environment. The other side points out the potential benefits it might provide.

71 Describe a trade-off that must be considered in the decision whether to move forward with hydrofracking.   [1]

_____

_____

72 Identify *one* renewable alternative to natural gas as an energy source that New York State could use and describe the advantage of using this source, other than it is renewable.   [1]

_____

_____

Part D

Answer all questions in this part. [13]

Directions (73–85): For those questions that are multiple choice, record on the separate answer sheet the *number* of the choice that, of those given, best completes the statement or answers the question. For all other questions in this part, follow the directions given and record your answers in the spaces provided in this examination booklet.

Note: The answer to question 73 should be recorded on your separate answer sheet.

73 A class is recording pulse rates of the students in a data table like the one shown below.

Class Pulse Rates

Row	Pulse Rate (beats per minute)	Number of Students
A	< 51	
B	51–70	
C	71–90	
D	>90	

One student checks his pulse and counts 23 beats over a time interval of 20 seconds. In which row in the data table should the pulse rate of this student be recorded?

(1) A

(2) B

(3) C

(4) D

Note: The answer to question 74 should be recorded on your separate answer sheet.

74 The diagram below represents a compound light microscope. Several parts have been labeled.

In order to make an image brighter, which labeled part of the microscope would most likely be adjusted?

(1) A

(2) B

(3) C

(4) D

75 Cell membranes are said to be selectively permeable. Which statement best explains what selectively permeable means?

(1) The cell membrane prevents any harmful substance from entering the cell.
(2) The cell membrane lets certain substances enter the cell and keeps certain substances out of the cell.
(3) The cell membrane allows only large molecules to diffuse into the cell.
(4) The cell membrane has pores that let only water and glucose into the cell and carbon dioxide out.

Base your answers to questions 76 and 77 on the information below and on your knowledge of biology.

One of the effects of Hurricane Katrina, which devastated New Orleans in 2005, was the death of almost all of the plants in flooded areas. Initially, toxic chemicals and bacteria were suspected as a possible cause. Scientists later determined that the salt concentration in the floodwater caused the plants to die.

Note: The answer to question 76 should be recorded on your separate answer sheet.

76 The death of the plants was most likely due to

(1) water moving into plant cells from the surrounding environment
(2) water moving out of plant cells into the surrounding environment
(3) both water and salt moving from plant cells into the surrounding environment
(4) both water and salt moving into plant cells from the surrounding environment

77 Identify the process responsible for the effect that the salt water had on the plants. [1]

_____

_____

January '14   Regents Examination

Base your answers to questions 78 and 79 on the information and data table below and on your knowledge of biology.

An investigation was carried out on four different plant species to determine which of three species was most closely related to an unknown plant species. The results of the investigation are shown in the data table below.

Comparison of Four Plant Species

Plant Species	Test for Enzyme M	Differences in Amino Acid Sequences	Gel Electrophoresis Banding Pattern
unknown	+		11, 8, 6, 2
1	−	4	24, 8, 5
2	+	1	11, 8, 6, 2
3	+	3	13, 7, 5, 2

78 Which plant species appears to be most closely related to the unknown species? Support your answer. [1]

Species: _____

_____

_____

79 Identify *two* pieces of evidence, other than those shown in the chart, that can be used to determine if two plant species are related. [1]

(1) _____

(2) _____

_____

Base your answer to question 80 on the diagram below and on your knowledge of biology.

Variations in Beaks of Galapagos Islands Finches

From: *Galapagos: A Natural History Guide*

80 There are a number of islands in the Galapagos that these finches could possibly inhabit. Explain why each island would *not* be expected to have all of the species shown. [1]

_____

_____

_____

January '14   Regents Examination

Base your answers to questions 81 through 83 on the information and chart below and on your knowledge of biology.

The Galapagos Islands are home to many different species of finches. Three finch species, their relative beak sizes, and their food preferences are represented below. All three species live on the same island.

Three Galapagos Finches and Their Sources of Nutrition

Name	Foods
Vegetarian finch *Platyspiza crassirostris*	Buds, leaves, fruit of trees
Warbler finch *Certhidea olivacea*	Flying and ground-dwelling insects
Cactus finch *Geospiza scandens*	Cactus flowers and nectar

Note: The answers to questions 81 and 82 should be recorded on your separate answer sheet.

81 Which statement is correct concerning the nutritional preferences of these finches?

(1) The three species do not compete for food because they eat different types of foods.
(2) The vegetarian and cactus finches compete for food because they both feed on producers.
(3) The vegetarian and warbler finches compete for food because they both live in trees.
(4) The three species of finches compete for food because their beaks are similar in shape and size.

82 Which process allows for the evolution of finches over time?

(1) natural selection
(2) selective breeding
(3) asexual reproduction
(4) ecological succession

83 Complete the food web below by placing the names of the finches in the correct locations. [1]

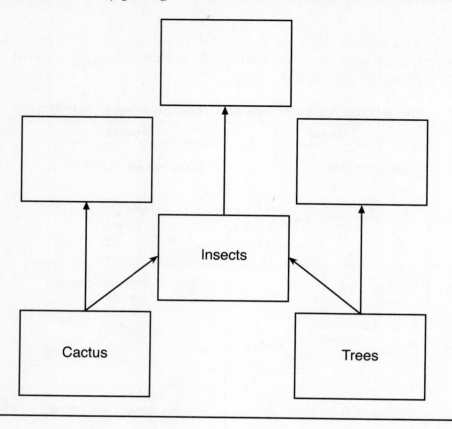

84 Identify *one* trait, other than a beak characteristic, that could affect the survival of a finch. Support your answer. [1]

_____

_____

85 Identify *one* specific substance necessary for muscle activity that is delivered to muscles more effectively as a result of increased heart rate. [1]

_____

_____

January '14   Regents Examination

Part A

Answer all questions in this part. [30]

Directions (1–30): For *each* statement or question, record on the separate answer sheet the *number* of the word or expression that, of those given, best completes the statement or answers the question.

1 The organisms in a pond and the physical factors influencing them best describe

(1) a population
(2) an ecosystem
(3) a biosphere
(4) a food chain

2 Which row in the chart below best describes decomposers?

Row	Method of Nutrition	Recycles
(1)	autotrophic	nutrients
(2)	heterotrophic	nutrients
(3)	autotrophic	energy
(4)	heterotrophic	energy

3 Some processes that occur in a cell are listed below.

    A. utilize energy
    B. detect changes in the environment
    C. rearrange and synthesize chemical compounds

Which processes will all living organisms use to maintain homeostasis?

(1) *A* and *B*, only
(2) *B* and *C*, only
(3) *C* and *A*, only
(4) *A*, *B*, and *C*

4 Which cell structures are correctly paired with their functions?

(1) The mitochondria produce enzymes, and ribosomes transport them.
(2) The ribosomes make proteins, and the nucleus stores genetic information.
(3) The cell membrane makes enzymes, and cytoplasm transports them.
(4) The vacuole stores genetic information, and chloroplasts make proteins.

5 The diagram below represents the region between two nerve cells. Cell *A* releases a chemical that travels to and binds with structure *X* on cell *B*.

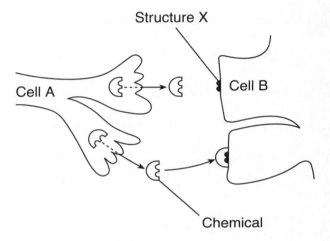

Structure *X* most likely represents

(1) a receptor molecule
(2) an inorganic substance
(3) a ribosome
(4) an antibody

6 Over the past few thousand years, humans have helped to bring about changes in many plant and animal species in order to make them more useful. Examples include strong workhorses, hunting dogs, large-eared corn, and beautiful flower varieties. These changes were primarily brought about by humans, using the process of

(1) mitosis
(2) selective breeding
(3) cloning
(4) natural selection

7 Certain antibacterial soaps kill 99% of the bacteria present on hands. Constant use of these soaps could be harmful over time because

(1) more pathogens may be resistant to the soap
(2) microbes prevent viral diseases
(3) large populations of pathogens are beneficial to the hands
(4) the soap stimulates skin cell division

8 Which factor would cause two specialized tissues that contain identical chromosomes to function differently?

(1) Specific sections of DNA molecules in the chromosomes are activated.
(2) All of the sections of DNA molecules in the chromosomes are activated.
(3) Specific sections of the amino acid molecules in the cytoplasm are activated.
(4) All of the amino acid molecules in the cytoplasm are activated.

9 Some variation must be present in a population in order for natural selection to take place. These variations arise from mutations in the DNA and

(1) sorting of chromosomes during sexual reproduction
(2) combining of chromosomes during organ development
(3) changing of chromosomes during cloning
(4) removal of chromosomes during selective breeding

10 The diagram below represents a segment of a gene on two chromosomes.

Normal gene	A	T	A	C	C	T
Mutated gene	A	T	G	C	C	T

The change in the gene sequence is an example of

(1) an insertion   (3) a substitution
(2) a deletion   (4) a replication

11 In a certain species of insect, some individuals have flattened white disks on their bodies that protrude and interlock, resembling an orchid flower. This adaptation provides the insect with a better opportunity to capture its prey. If environmental conditions remain unchanged, it is most likely that, in future generations, the proportion of the population with this adaptation will

(1) increase, only
(2) decrease, only
(3) increase, then decrease
(4) decrease, then increase

12 Which structure is correctly paired with its function?

(1) ovary — provides milk for newborns
(2) testis — development of sperm
(3) placenta — storage of released eggs
(4) uterus — produces estrogen

13 The fruit fly represented in the diagram below has unusual, curled wings that formed after exposure to radiation.

In order for the fly to pass this trait on to its offspring, a change had to occur in

(1) the blood cells of the fly
(2) the gametes of the fly
(3) all the body cells of the fly
(4) the muscles of the fly

14 In a population of birds, the percentage of individuals having a certain gene changes from 20% to 60% over the span of several hundred years. This situation will most likely affect the rate of

(1) biological evolution
(2) asexual reproduction
(3) gene mutation
(4) ecological succession

15 The finite resources of Earth are often affected by increasing human consumption. These finite resources are

(1) not renewable over a short period of time
(2) the products of rapid human population growth
(3) the result of deforestation
(4) needed to degrade ecosystems

16 A student made the drawing shown below of a single-celled organism as he observed it with a compound light microscope under the high-power objective.

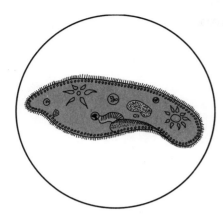

Several minutes later, he drew the diagram shown below of the same organism, using the same magnification.

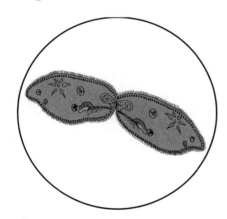

These drawings show that the organism is carrying out the process of

(1) asexual reproduction
(2) sexual reproduction
(3) embryo formation
(4) genetic alteration

17 Which statement best describes why pathogens are harmful?

(1) All of the cells of an organism infected by pathogens become pathogens.
(2) Pathogens cannot be controlled once they enter the cells of an organism.
(3) Pathogens produce antibodies that will kill the host organism.
(4) Pathogens can interfere with normal life functions.

18 In 1996, scientists cloned the first mammal, a sheep. This technique involved the removal of the nucleus from an egg cell. The nucleus from a cell of another adult sheep was then inserted into this egg cell. Once this cell began to develop into an embryo, it was implanted into a third female sheep that later gave birth to a healthy lamb, Dolly. Which statement concerning Dolly is correct?

(1) Her offspring would be genetically identical.
(2) Dolly and her DNA donor are genetically identical.
(3) Two different gametes were manipulated to produce Dolly.
(4) Dolly was produced by the recombination of genetic material.

19 Which activity would most likely increase the mutation rate in a culture of bacteria being grown in a laboratory experiment?

(1) adding more distilled water to the culture
(2) adding excess nutrients to the culture
(3) exposing the culture to a higher concentration of CO_2
(4) exposing the culture to ultraviolet radiation

20 Which two processes are responsible for keeping the percentage of atmospheric oxygen at relatively constant levels?

(1) circulation and coordination
(2) respiration and coordination
(3) respiration and photosynthesis
(4) photosynthesis and circulation

21 Chemicals that help chemical reactions occur at faster rates in living organisms are known as

(1) biotic resources
(2) simple sugars
(3) oxygen molecules
(4) organic catalysts

22 The action of insulin on sugar levels in the blood helps to

(1) interfere with homeostasis
(2) maintain dynamic equilibrium
(3) coordinate enzyme production
(4) regulate digestion of protein

23 An individual recovers from the common cold, which is caused by rhinovirus *A*. The person then becomes infected with the avian influenza virus, which causes the bird flu. Which statement best describes what will most likely happen to this person?

(1) He will have the symptoms of the bird flu because he is not immune to the avian influenza virus.

(2) He will have the symptoms of the common cold because he is not immune to the avian influenza virus.

(3) He will not have the symptoms of the bird flu because he is immune to rhinovirus *A*.

(4) He will not have the symptoms of the common cold because the avian influenza virus causes it.

24 The wetland plant purple loosestrife was imported to North America from Europe. Since its introduction, the loosestrife has spread, which has resulted in a dramatic decline in the biological diversity of native wetland plants. A likely reason for the spread of the purple loosestrife is that it can

(1) successfully compete with native herbivores for food

(2) serve as an excellent food source for native herbivores

(3) successfully compete with native plants for space

(4) prevent the migration of native plants

25 Deer ticks are responsible for spreading Lyme disease. This organism, which feeds on the blood of warm-blooded organisms like mice, deer, and humans, is best described as a

(1) predator   (3) parasite
(2) scavenger   (4) host

26 Years ago, an article was written titled "Medicine Chest in the Jungle." This article most likely described the

(1) potential for ecosystems to be a source for new drugs

(2) dangers of poisonous jungle plants and animals

(3) deforestation of jungles for the development of large pharmacies

(4) use of antibiotics to treat certain disorders in trees

27 After a building was torn down and the area was cleared, grasses began to grow in the area. Several years later, small bushes replaced the grasses. This pattern of plant growth is known as ecological

(1) stability   (3) succession
(2) cultivation   (4) coordination

28 A human activity that could significantly *decrease* the amount of carbon dioxide in the air is

(1) increasing the use of fossil fuel

(2) controlling insect pests that eat stored grain

(3) burning garbage and trash to generate electricity

(4) preserving and expanding forest habitats that shelter wildlife

29 Ethanol-fueled vehicles have increased in popularity as people try to be more environmentally responsible. Ethanol can be made from corn. Some farmers are clearing forests and planting large expanses of corn to meet the rising demand. Which statement describes a likely result of this increased corn production?

(1) There will be a reduction in the biodiversity of areas that are converted to grow corn.

(2) The corn will produce more carbon dioxide than it uses, contributing to global warming.

(3) Insect biodiversity in the area will increase.

(4) Growing more corn will increase the nutrient content of the soil.

30 Windmills that generate electricity are being built in coastal areas. The main benefit of these windmills is that they

(1) produce finite resources

(2) reduce dependency on fuels that cause air pollution

(3) absorb the noise of passing boats

(4) maintain the salt concentration in the ocean

August '13   Regents Examination

Directions (31–43): For *each* statement or question, record on the separate answer sheet the *number* of the word or expression that, of those given, best completes the statement or answers the question.

31 The dichotomous key below provides a way to classify some animals into groups according to their physical characteristics.

Dichotomous Key		
I	wings....................	go to II
	no wings...............	group A
II	feathers................	group B
	no feathers...........	go to III
III	two legs................	group C
	six legs.................	group D

The key can be used to classify each of the four animals represented below.

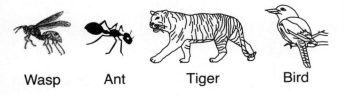

Wasp   Ant   Tiger   Bird

Which row in the chart shows the correct classification group for each animal?

Row	Wasp	Ant	Tiger	Bird
(1)	group D	group D	group A	group B
(2)	group B	group A	group D	group C
(3)	group B	group D	group A	group C
(4)	group D	group A	group A	group B

32 Part of a process necessary for reproduction in complex organisms is represented below.

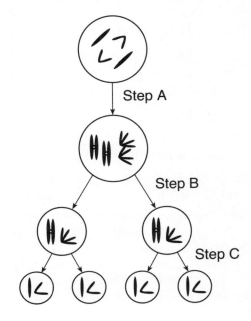

Step *C* results in the production of

(1) four zygotes that will develop into embryos
(2) embryonic cells that could unite and develop into an organism
(3) four cells that will recombine to form two offspring
(4) gametes that could be involved in the formation of a zygote

33 The diagram below represents an evolutionary tree.

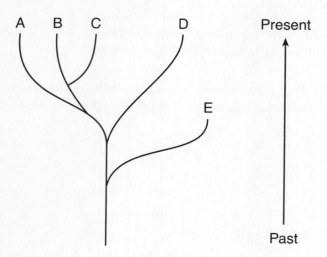

Which statement best describes species *E*?

(1) Species *D* is an ancestor of species *E*.
(2) Through natural selection, species *E* produced increased survival mechanisms.
(3) Species *E* had greater success due to patterns of behavior.
(4) Species *E* had insufficient adaptive characteristics for survival in a changing environment.

34 The diagram below represents one type of white blood cell. This type of white blood cell ingests microbes.

A function of another type of white blood cell is to

(1) prevent the loss of blood from a wound
(2) produce specialized molecules that mark invaders
(3) increase the number of red blood cells in the blood
(4) cause gene mutations that will increase immune responses

35 The table below indicates a reproductive pattern in some sea turtles when eggs develop in areas with differing temperatures.

Sex Determination in Sea Turtles

Temperature (°C)	Offspring Produced
below 23	usually none
23–27	mostly males
28–30	50/50 males: females
31–33	mostly females
above 33	usually none

The sex of turtle offspring is most probably

(1) determined only by genes inherited from the parent turtles
(2) controlled entirely by the location where the young are raised
(3) a result of genetic information being influenced by environmental conditions
(4) an identical pattern to the reproductive pattern found in humans

36 The diagram below represents a food web.

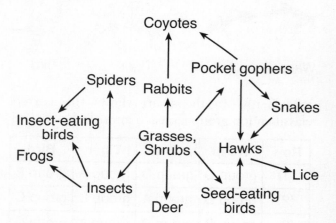

Which statement regarding organisms in this food web is correct?

(1) There would be more snakes than pocket gophers.
(2) There would be more coyotes than rabbits.
(3) There would be more insects than insect-eating birds.
(4) There would be more hawks than seed-eating birds.

Base your answers to questions 37 through 39 on the information and graph below and on your knowledge of biology.

The pH of the internal environment of lysosomes (organelles that contain digestive enzymes) is approximately 4.5, while the pH of the surrounding cytoplasm is approximately 7. The average pH of the human stomach during digestion is approximately 2.5, while the average pH of the small intestine during digestion is about 8.

The graph below shows how pH affects the enzyme activity of four different enzymes, A, B, C, and D.

The Effect of pH on Enzyme Activity

37 What will most likely happen to the action of an enzyme from the small intestine if it is placed in an environment similar to the environment in which enzyme C functions best?

(1) It would no longer be able to function because the environment is too acidic.
(2) It would adapt to the new environment and start carrying out the same function as enzyme C.
(3) It would continue to function because it is able to modify the pH of the environment.
(4) It would be able to function because the pH of the environment is similar to that of the intestine.

38 Lysosomes break open during the process of digestion, releasing enzymes into the cytoplasm. Which statement may explain why the entire cell may not be digested?

(1) The acidic environment of the cytoplasm destroys the enzymes.
(2) Antibodies in the cytoplasm break down foreign enzymes.
(3) The pH of the cytoplasm causes the enzymes to function less effectively.
(4) Enzymes can function only in the location where they are synthesized.

39 Which enzyme functions best in a pH environment most similar to that of human stomach enzymes?

(1) A   (3) C
(2) B   (4) D

40 The blood glucose range for a healthy adult is 65–104 mg/dL. Which graph best illustrates normal blood glucose levels in a healthy adult over the course of a day?

Base your answers to questions 41 through 43 on the information below and on your knowledge of biology.

…Unless actions are taken to slow the decline of domesticated honeybees and augment [increase] their populations with wild bees, many fruits and vegetables may disappear from the food supply, said Claire Kremen, a conservation biologist at Princeton University in New Jersey.…

The honeybee decline, which is affecting domesticated and wild bee populations around the world, is mostly the result of diseases spread as a result of mites and other parasites as well as the spraying of crops with pesticides, scientists say.…

Source: "Bee Declines May Spell End of Some Fruits, Vegetables," *National Geographic News*, October 5, 2005

41 The decrease in the honeybee population is partly due to
   (1) the use of pesticides
   (2) a decrease in prey
   (3) the use of fertilizers
   (4) a decrease in fruits and vegetables

42 A decrease in honeybee populations will
   (1) eliminate the need to spray crops
   (2) increase the number of bee parasites
   (3) reduce the occurrence of natural disasters
   (4) disrupt the stability of an ecosystem

43 Some honeybees have been able to survive the changes in their environment and reproduce. This is most likely due to
   (1) the aggressive behavior of wild bees
   (2) an abundance of food sources for the bees
   (3) genetic diversity in the bees
   (4) lack of mutations in the bees

Part B–2

Answer all questions in this part. [12]

Directions (44–55): For those questions that are multiple choice, record on the separate answer sheet the *number* of the choice that, of those given, best completes each statement or answers each question. For all other questions in this part, follow the directions given and record your answers in the spaces provided in this examination booklet.

Base your answers to questions 44 through 48 on the information and data table below and on your knowledge of biology.

Yellowstone Park Wolf Update

For the first time in nearly 70 years, the howl of the wolf is being echoed throughout Yellowstone National Park. *Canis lupus*, the gray wolf, one of the largest and most complex of the canine species, has been successfully reintroduced into the Yellowstone ecosystem.
In mid-January 1995, 14 wolves from many separate packs were captured in Canada and then transported into Yellowstone Park and placed into three one acre pens....

Source: http://www.yellowstone-bearman.com/w-update.html

After the wolves were given time to establish a new pack structure, the packs were released into the wild. The number of wolf pups was counted each year for four years. The data are shown in the table below.

Number of Wolf Pups Observed

Year	Number of Pups
1996	11
1997	64
1998	42
1999	61

Directions (44–45): Using the information in the data table, construct a bar graph on the grid, following the directions below.

44 Mark an appropriate scale, without any breaks, on the axis labeled "Number of Pups." [1]

45 Construct vertical bars to represent the data. Shade in *each* bar. [1]

Number of Wolf Pups Observed

Number of Pups (y-axis)

Year (x-axis): 1996, 1997, 1998, 1999

46 State *one* positive result of reintroducing wolves into Yellowstone Park. [1]

_____

_____

Note: The answer to question 47 should be recorded on your separate answer sheet.

47 The number of wolves that can be supported in this environment for a long period of time is known as

(1) ecosystem stability

(2) carrying capacity

(3) ecological succession

(4) biological evolution

48 State *one* possible reason why the wolf population showed a decline from 1997 to 1998. [1]

_____

_____

Note: The answer to question 49 should be recorded on your separate answer sheet.

49 Some levels of organization in a multicellular organism are shown in the sequence below.

$$A \rightarrow \text{cells} \rightarrow \text{tissues} \rightarrow B \rightarrow \text{organ systems} \rightarrow \text{organism}$$

Which terms represented by letters A and B would complete the sequence?

(1) A–gametes; B–zygote

(2) A–zygote; B–gametes

(3) A–organs; B–organelles

(4) A–organelles; B–organs

Base your answers to questions 50 through 53 on the information and chart below and on your knowledge of biology.

Excess body weight is considered to be a risk factor for diseases such as diabetes and high blood pressure. The Body Mass Index (BMI) chart below can be used as a guide to determine if a person's body weight puts that person at risk for such diseases.

Body Mass Index (BMI)

BMI	Healthy		Overweight					Obese			
	19	24	25	26	27	28	29	30	35	40	45
Height	Weight in Pounds										
5'0"	97	123	128	133	138	143	148	153	179	204	230
5'1"	100	127	132	137	143	148	153	158	185	211	238
5'2"	104	131	136	142	147	153	158	164	191	218	246
5'3"	107	135	141	146	152	158	163	169	197	225	254
5'4"	110	140	145	151	157	163	169	174	204	232	262
5'5"	114	144	150	156	162	168	174	180	210	240	270
5'6"	118	148	155	161	167	173	179	186	216	247	278
5'7"	121	153	159	166	172	178	185	191	223	255	287
5'8"	125	158	164	171	177	184	190	197	230	262	295
5'9"	128	162	169	176	182	189	196	203	236	270	304
5'10"	132	167	174	181	188	195	202	209	243	278	313
5'11"	136	172	179	186	193	200	208	215	250	286	322
6'0"	140	177	184	191	199	206	213	221	258	294	331
6'1"	144	182	189	197	204	212	219	227	265	302	340
6'2"	148	186	194	202	210	218	225	233	272	311	350
6'3"	152	192	200	208	216	224	232	240	279	319	359

Note: The answer to question 50 should be recorded on your separate answer sheet.

50 The BMI for a person who is 5 feet 9 inches tall and weighs 170 pounds is between

(1) 24 and 25   (3) 27 and 28

(2) 25 and 26   (4) 29 and 30

51 Is a person with a BMI of 27 at risk for diseases such as diabetes or high blood pressure? Support your answer. [1]

_____

_____

52 State whether an individual who is 5 feet 3 inches tall and weighs 146 pounds needs to gain or lose weight in order to be classified as healthy. [1]

_____

53 Calculate the minimum number of pounds that an individual who is 6 feet 3 inches tall and weighs 232 pounds would have to gain or lose to be classified as a healthy individual with a BMI of 24. [1]

_____ **pounds**

_____

Base your answers to questions 54 and 55 on the information below and on your knowledge of biology.

The Arctic National Wildlife Refuge in Alaska is over 19 million acres of land. This unique habitat supports many species of land and marine animals, including 36 species of fish and 180 species of birds. Some people want to drill for oil in parts of the refuge. Scientists estimate that the total amount of recoverable oil in the refuge is between 5 and 16 billion barrels.

54 State *one* benefit of drilling for oil in the refuge in Alaska. [1]

_____

_____

55 Describe *one* environmental problem that could be caused by drilling for oil in the refuge in Alaska. [1]

_____

_____

Part C

Answer all questions in this part. [17]

Directions (56–72): Record your answers in the spaces provided in this examination booklet.

Base your answer to question 56–58 on the information below and on your knowledge of biology.

Fish Farming

Fish farming has risen in popularity to the point that, in 2009, it was estimated that 30% of all fish consumed by humans came from fish farms. Fish farms tend to specialize in one or two species of fish, which are produced in great numbers. Fish farms are conveniently located along shorelines, where the fish are contained in pens. Deep-sea vessels are not necessary to harvest the fish, as they are when fish are caught in the wild. The farms provide a relatively inexpensive way to provide protein for a growing world population.

As the technique gains in popularity, however, scientists and coastal residents have become concerned that the concentrated mass of fish in fish farms is producing large quantities of wastes. These wastes may be carried by ocean currents to public beaches and recreational boating areas, making them unusable. Others are concerned that uneaten fish food will decay, produce strong odors, and pollute marine environments miles away. If the wastes are not flushed out of the pens, they accumulate on the ocean floor and create a toxic "dead zone" beneath the fish.

56–58 Describe some aspects of fish farming that are examples of humans interacting with the environment. In your answer, be sure to:

- state *one* specific benefit humans gain from fish farming [1]
- state how biodiversity may be reduced by fish farming and support your answer [1]
- describe the impact, other than a reduction in biodiversity, fish farming may have on the natural ecosystems of coastal water if no changes are made [1]

_____

_____

_____

_____

_____

_____

Base your answers to questions 59 through 62 on the data table and information below and on your knowledge of biology. The data table describes various pH levels.

pH Levels

pH	pH Description
1	very acidic
5	slightly acidic
7	neutral
9	slightly basic
13	very basic

A scientist is concerned about the effects of acid rain on newly fertilized fish eggs in lakes in the Adirondack Mountains of New York State. The scientist would like to investigate the hatching rates of these fish eggs in water at different acidic pH levels. The scientist designed an experiment that could show the effect of an acid pH on the hatching of these fish eggs.

59 State how the control group would be treated differently from the experimental groups. [1]

_____

_____

60 State *two* factors that must be kept the same in both the experimental groups and the control group. [1]

_____

_____

61 Describe the type of data to be collected. [1]

_____

_____

62 State *one* example of experimental results that would show that the increasing acidity of lake water has a *negative* effect on the hatching rate of fish eggs. [1]

_____

_____

_____

August '13 Regents Examination

Base your answers to questions 63 and 64 on the passage below and on your knowledge of biology.

The Protein Shredder

In every cell, thousands of important processes are occurring around the clock. One of the ways a cell manages to coordinate all of these processes is by sending protein messages. After the protein messages are delivered and read, they need to be destroyed to prepare for the arrival of the next message.

The task of destroying these proteins falls on cell structures known as proteasomes. Think of a proteasome as a tubelike protein shredder. Protein molecules that have served their purpose are transported to the proteasome, unfolded, fed through the tube, and cut into smaller molecules that can then be used to synthesize new protein molecules. Proteasomes can shred any type of protein.

Individuals with a neurological disorder known as hereditary ataxia have been found to have an excess of protein in the cells of their brains and spinal cords. The abnormal level somehow leads to the death of cells in portions of the cerebellum. These areas of cell loss can be seen on a brain scan.

There are several forms of hereditary ataxia but all of them result in poor coordination. The symptoms progress over a period of years. In the beginning, the individuals experience only minor coordination problems. As time passes, the symptoms become worse. The affected individuals will have poor balance when walking. They will be clumsy and have difficulty talking and swallowing.

63 Based on the symptoms shown by individuals with hereditary ataxia, state *two* functions regulated by the cerebellum and spinal cord. [1]

Functions:_____ and _____

64 Explain why researchers could think that proteasomes might *not* be working correctly in nerve cells of individuals with hereditary ataxia. [1]

_____

_____

Base your answer to question 65–68 on the diagram below and on your knowledge of biology. The diagram represents three groups of organisms that are part of an ecosystem.

Groups of Organisms

Plants	Animals	Fungi
A	B	C

65–68 Explain the role of these groups of organisms in the cycling of materials and the transfer of energy in an ecosystem. In your answer, be sure to:
- explain why an ecosystem requires a constant input of energy [1]
- explain how organisms in group *B* obtain energy [1]
- explain the role of organisms in group *C* in the ecosystem [1]
- identify the process used by *all three* groups of organisms to make energy available to their cells to carry out life functions [1]

_____

_____

_____

_____

_____

_____

_____

_____

69–72 Discuss the process used by scientists to insert a gene from one organism into the DNA of another. In your answer, be sure to:
- identify the scientific technique used to insert a gene from one organism into another [1]
- describe the function of a gene [1]
- identify the type of molecule used to cut the gene from the DNA of an organism [1]
- state *one* benefit of this technique to humans [1]

_____

_____

_____

_____

_____

_____

_____

_____

Part D

Answer all questions in this part. [13]

Directions (73–85): For those questions that are multiple choice, record on the separate answer sheet the *number* of the choice that, of those given, best completes the statement or answers the question. For all other questions in this part, follow the directions given and record your answers in the spaces provided in this examination booklet.

Base your answers to questions 73 through 75 on the information and graph below and on your knowledge of biology.

Students were asked to design a lab that investigated the relationship between exercise and heart rate. Heart rate was determined by recording the pulse rate in beats per minute. The students hypothesized that increased exercise results in an increased heart rate. The class results for the experiment are shown in the graph below.

Note: The answers to questions 73 through 75 should be recorded on your separate answer sheet.

73 Which statement is best supported by the graph?

(1) Before exercising, the average pulse rate was 65; four minutes after exercising, the average pulse rate was 65.
(2) After four minutes of exercising, the average pulse rate was 120; two minutes after exercising, the average pulse rate was 120.
(3) While exercising, the highest average pulse rate was 150; before exercising, the average pulse rate was 65.
(4) Two minutes before exercising, the average pulse rate was 80; after two minutes of exercise, the average pulse rate was 140.

74 Students in a different science class carried out the same experiment. The data they obtained did *not* support the hypothesis that increased exercise results in increased heart rate. The most scientifically sound way to deal with this situation is to

(1) write a new hypothesis
(2) read about pulse rate in a biology textbook
(3) have the students in both classes vote to decide which hypothesis is correct
(4) ask students in a third class to do the experiment and see if their results support the hypothesis

August '13 Regents Examination

75 The change in heart rate that occurs between 1 and 5 minutes of exercise is an adaptation that

   (1) reduces the rate at which oxygen is carried to the muscle cells
   (2) increases the rate at which carbon dioxide is carried to the muscle cells
   (3) results in the production of more ATP in muscle cells
   (4) slows the destruction of enzymes involved in respiration of muscle cells

---

Note: The answer to question 76 should be recorded on your separate answer sheet.

76 A student hypothesized that watching sports on television would cause viewers' pulse rates to increase. She designed an experiment to determine the effect of watching sports on pulse rate. A group of 200 volunteers took their pulse rates and then watched their favorite sports on television. After the games, they immediately took their pulse rates again. The data collected showed that the pulse rates of some people increased, but the pulse rates of an equal number of people did not change. Although the hypothesis was not supported by the data, the hypothesis is still valuable because it

   (1) may lead to further investigation
   (2) can be changed to fit the data

   (3) is the opinion of the experimenter
   (4) is based on beliefs of the volunteers

Base your answers to questions 77 and 78 on the Universal Genetic Code Chart below and on your knowledge of biology.

Universal Genetic Code Chart
Messenger RNA Codons and the Amino Acids for Which They Code

		SECOND BASE				
		U	**C**	**A**	**G**	
F I R S T B A S E	**U**	UUU } PHE UUC } UUA } LEU UUG }	UCU } UCC } UCA } SER UCG }	UAU } TYR UAC } UAA } STOP UAG }	UGU } CYS UGC } UGA } STOP UGG } TRP	U C A G	**T H I R D B A S E**
	C	CUU } CUC } LEU CUA } CUG }	CCU } CCC } PRO CCA } CCG }	CAU } HIS CAC } CAA } GLN CAG }	CGU } CGC } ARG CGA } CGG }	U C A G	
	A	AUU } AUC } ILE AUA } AUG } MET or START	ACU } ACC } THR ACA } ACG }	AAU } ASN AAC } AAA } LYS AAG }	AGU } SER AGC } AGA } ARG AGG }	U C A G	
	G	GUU } GUC } VAL GUA } GUG }	GCU } GCC } ALA GCA } GCG }	GAU } ASP GAC } GAA } GLU GAG }	GGU } GGC } GLY GGA } GGG }	U C A G	

77 The table below shows the DNA, mRNA, and amino acid sequences from two similar plant species. Using the information given, fill in the missing mRNA base sequences for species A on the table below. [1]

78 Using the Universal Genetic Code Chart, fill in the missing amino acids for species B on the table below. [1]

Species A	DNA base sequence	CCG	TGC	ATA	CAG	GTA
	mRNA base sequence	_____	_____	UAU	_____	_____
	amino acid sequence	GLY	THR	TYR	VAL	HIS
Species B	DNA base sequence	CCG	TGC	ATA	CAG	GTT
	mRNA base sequence	GGC	ACG	UAU	GUC	CAA
	amino acid sequence	GLY	_____	_____	VAL	_____

Base your answers to questions 79 and 80 on the information and diagram below and on your knowledge of biology.

Two models of a cell were made with dialysis tubing and placed in two beakers of fluid, A and B, each containing starch indicator solution, as represented in the diagram below. Enzyme Z was added to the artificial cell in beaker B. The solution outside each cell was tested for the presence of sugar. Initially, no sugar was present in the solution outside each cell. The results after one hour are represented below.

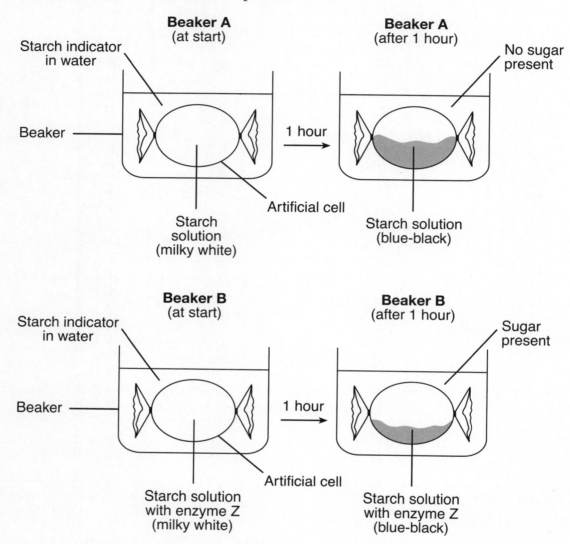

79 State *one* reason for the color change in beaker A after one hour. [1]

_____

_____

80 How would the results have been different in beaker B if an enzyme that digests protein was used instead of enzyme Z? [1]

_____

_____

Base your answers to questions 81 and 82 on the chart below and on your knowledge of biology.

Evolutionary Chart of Galapagos Finches

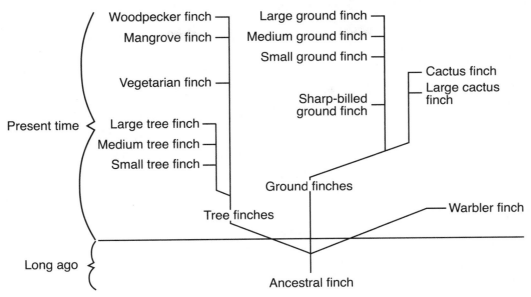

adapted from: *Galapagos: A Natural History Guide*

Note: The answers to questions 81 and 82 should be recorded on your separate answer sheet.

81 Which finches would be most like the ancestral finch?
(1) large ground finches   (3) warbler finches
(2) cactus finches   (4) large tree finches

82 Present-day cactus finches are a type of
(1) tree finch   (3) warbler finch
(2) ground finch   (4) ancestral finch

Base your answers to questions 83 through 85 on the information below and on your knowledge of biology.

As part of a laboratory technique, DNA samples taken from four plants were separated. The results are represented in the diagram below.

83 Circle the band in the diagram below in the results for plant *X* that would contain the smallest DNA fragments. Support your answer. [1]

_____

_____

84 Which plant is most closely related to plant *X*? Support your answer using information from the diagram. [1]

Plant number: _____

_____

_____

85 Identify the technique used to obtain the results represented in the diagram. [1]

_____

_____

Part A

Answer all questions in this part. [30]

Directions (1–30): For *each* statement or question, record on the separate answer sheet the *number* of the word or expression that, of those given, best completes the statement or answers the question.

1 Fish absorb oxygen through the gills, earthworms absorb oxygen through the skin, amebas take in oxygen through the cell membranes, and cows inhale oxygen through the nasal passages into their lungs. This statement demonstrates that living things

(1) rely on similar or the same processes, but accomplish them in different ways
(2) rely on different processes and accomplish them in different ways
(3) rely on different processes, but perform them in the same or related ways
(4) have no relationship to one another, and are all independent individuals

2 In New York State, small farms that were abandoned many years ago have become hardwood forests. This is an example of

(1) local deforestation
(2) biotechnology
(3) ecological succession
(4) habitat loss

3 Goats have been genetically modified to produce an anticlotting protein in their milk. The protein is extracted from the milk and given to people who have inherited a disorder that causes their bodies to produce blood clots, which can be fatal. A benefit of the technology used to produce this protein is that it

(1) can be used to overcome the effects of a harmful mutation
(2) can provide people with a new kind of nutrient-rich milk
(3) will result in healthier goats with more nutritious milk for their offspring
(4) will reduce blood clots in other farm animals that are modified in this way

4 The diagram below represents factors that affect New York State ecosystems.

An increase in human activity at X would most likely result in

(1) a decrease in rainfall in the area
(2) a decrease in available carbon dioxide
(3) an increase in air pollution in the area
(4) an increase in the supply of fossil fuels

5 Which graph correctly represents the pattern of human population growth over the past 5000 years?

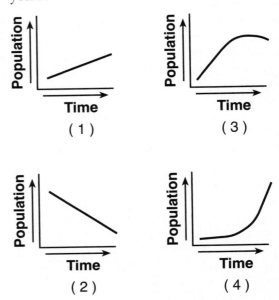

6 The fossil record of ancient life forms provides scientific evidence of

(1) direct harvesting
(2) selective breeding
(3) gene manipulation
(4) evolutionary changes

7 Spider plants can reproduce both sexually and asexually. The diagram below represents a spider plant reproducing asexually by a method known as vegetative propagation.

Parent plant

Offspring

Which statement best describes the relationship between the parent plant and the offspring in the diagram?

(1) The cells of the offspring contain half the amount of DNA as the cells of the parent plant.
(2) The parent plant provides genetic material to the offspring through its gametes.
(3) The cells of the offspring have the same genetic content as the cells of the parent plant.
(4) The cells of the parent plant have more genetic diversity, compared to the cells of the offspring.

8 The processes of deletion, insertion, and substitution can alter genes in a skin cell. The altered genes will most likely be passed on to

(1) sperm cells
(2) egg cells
(3) every cell that develops from that skin cell
(4) only a few of the cells that develop from that skin cell

9 Before starch can enter a cell, it must be

(1) absorbed by simple sugars
(2) diffused into simple sugars
(3) digested to form simple sugars
(4) actively transported by simple sugars

10 In a cell, protein synthesis is the primary function of

(1) ribosomes   (3) chloroplasts
(2) mitochondria   (4) vacuoles

11 In a multicellular organism, organs carry out a variety of life functions. In a single-celled organism, these functions are performed by

(1) tissues   (3) organ systems
(2) organelles   (4) organs

12 Chlorophyll gives plants their green color. Chlorophyll is produced only when plants are exposed to light, so plants kept in darkness have no chlorophyll and appear white. The best explanation for this is that

(1) chlorophyll is not needed by green plants at night
(2) darkness mutates the chlorophyll genes, causing them to produce a white color
(3) light is required for chlorophyll genes to be expressed
(4) genetic information in cells is not influenced by the outside environment

13 In order for the human body to maintain homeostasis, the breakdown of glucose to release energy must be followed by the

(1) production of oxygen
(2) division of the cell
(3) removal of wastes
(4) production of receptor molecules

14 In the past, humans developed varieties of dogs, such as the German shepherd and the bearded collie, using

(1) selective breeding for particular traits
(2) recombination of genes during mitosis
(3) mutations present only in body cells
(4) natural selection of favorable traits

15 In an organism, a muscle cell has the same DNA as a nerve cell, yet the cells perform different functions. This is possible because

(1) different mutations occur in each cell type, changing the genetic instructions
(2) temperature variations within the body alter DNA
(3) proteins in each cell type change the structure of DNA
(4) different parts of the genetic instructions are used in each type of cell

16 Which sequence best represents sexual reproduction?

(1) mitosis → gametes → zygote → fertilization
(2) gametes → meiosis → mitosis → fertilization
(3) fertilization → gametes → meiosis → zygote
(4) meiosis → gametes → fertilization → zygote

17 The reproductive system of a male mammal provides

(1) support for the internal development of the embryo
(2) materials through the placenta
(3) a means for the delivery of gametes
(4) the ovaries for gamete production

18 The energy used to obtain, transfer, and transport materials within an organism comes directly from

(1) ATP   (3) sunlight
(2) DNA   (4) starch

19 The failure of the human body to effectively maintain dynamic equilibrium can result in

(1) reproductive success
(2) gene manipulation
(3) differentiation
(4) disease

20 Melanoma is a type of cancer in which abnormal skin cells divide uncontrollably. Some chemotherapy drugs, which stop the growth of the cancer, directly interfere with the process of

(1) meiosis   (3) mitosis
(2) coordination   (4) recombination

21 Riding a bicycle requires balance and constant adjustment and monitoring by the rider in order to continue cycling. Successfully riding a bicycle most directly results from the ability to

(1) sexually reproduce
(2) grow and develop
(3) detect and respond to change
(4) metabolize food for energy

22 The first successful transplant of insulin-producing cells from a living donor pancreas was completed in April 2000 in Japan. This enabled the body of the recipient to

(1) regulate fat concentration by a feedback mechanism
(2) provide protection against an infectious disease
(3) slow down the heart rate after a period of activity ends
(4) maintain blood sugar levels throughout the day

23 A study was done on three different fish species living in a pond in New York State. The influence of temperature on the growth rates of the fish populations is shown in the graph below.

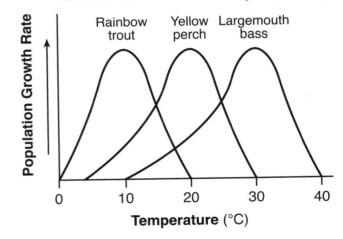

The Influence of Temperature on Growth Rates of Fish Populations

In this pond where these fish live, temperature is a

(1) limiting factor
(2) hereditary factor
(3) source of ATP
(4) source of solar energy

24 A 6-year-old child ate a peanut butter sandwich at snack time in school. Five minutes later, her throat became swollen and she collapsed. This allergic reaction occurred because her body

(1) recognized an antigen in peanut butter and produced antibiotics against it
(2) digested the white blood cells that can recognize an antigen in peanut butter
(3) did not recognize an antigen in peanut butter and could not produce antibodies against it
(4) recognized an antigen in peanut butter and produced an immune response

25 Which type of organism helps to reduce atmospheric carbon dioxide?

(1) carnivores   (3) decomposers
(2) producers   (4) herbivores

26 Which statement best describes an ecosystem maintaining a state of approximate equilibrium?

(1) Nutrients from decayed organisms are recycled in a forest ecosystem.
(2) All the frog species in a South American rain forest become extinct.
(3) A mutation spreads through a species of bacterium, making them unable to decompose wastes.
(4) Mice are released into a field ecosystem as food for a declining predator population.

27 In some parts of the world, forests are being cut down and burned to clear land for new homes and new farmland. A *negative* effect of these activities might be

(1) an increase in global warming
(2) destruction of the ozone shield
(3) a decrease in the average temperature of the atmosphere
(4) an increase in biodiversity of the deforested areas

28 The photograph below shows two penguins of the same species displaying different feather color patterns.

Source: http://green.yahoo.com/blog/guest_bloggers/24/all-black-penguin-discovered.html

The newly discovered all-black penguin had only black feathers since emerging from the egg. The sudden appearance of this characteristic was most likely due to

(1) a change in environmental conditions
(2) deposition of oil on the feathers due to pollution
(3) a random change in the sequences of bases in DNA
(4) a change in the diet of the penguin chick

June '13   Regents Examination

29 The diagram below represents different stages of an ecosystem over a period of time.

Which stage of the ecosystem has the greatest long-term stability?

(1) A

(2) B

(3) C

(4) D

30 The diagram below represents the same field of mice hunted by a hawk over a period of three months.

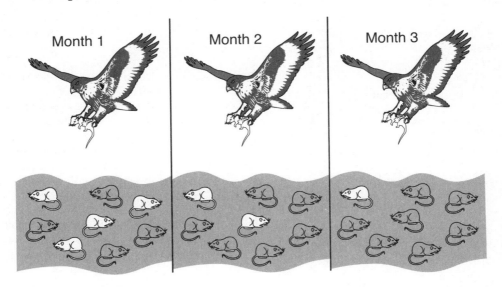

The overall changes in the population of mice can be explained best by

(1) natural selection

(2) succession

(3) reproduction

(4) mouse extinction

Directions (31–43): For *each* statement or question, record on the separate answer sheet the *number* of the word or expression that, of those given, best completes the statement or answers the question.

31 Testosterone directly affects the
- (1) formation of a zygote
- (2) changes within an ovary
- (3) production of sperm cells
- (4) development of a placenta

Base your answers to questions 32 through 34 on the diagram below and on your knowledge of biology. The diagram represents a food web in an ecosystem.

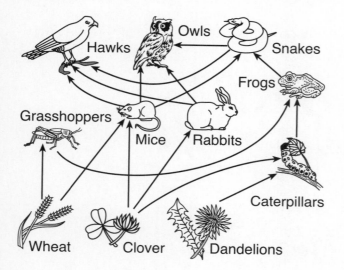

32 If the population of hawks in this area increases, their prey populations might decrease. Later, with fewer prey, the hawk population might decrease. The prey populations might then increase. This is an example of
- (1) an ecosystem that is completely out of balance
- (2) how ecosystems maintain stability over time
- (3) interaction between biotic and abiotic factors within an ecosystem
- (4) ecological succession in an ecosystem

33 Missing from the diagram of this ecosystem are the
- (1) biotic factors and decomposers
- (2) abiotic factors and decomposers
- (3) autotrophs, only
- (4) heterotrophs, only

34 Which row in the chart below best identifies the relationship between the mice and the wheat?

Row	Role of Mice	Role of Wheat
(1)	producer	consumer
(2)	predator	host
(3)	host	predator
(4)	consumer	producer

35 The diagram below represents a sequence of events that occurs in living things.

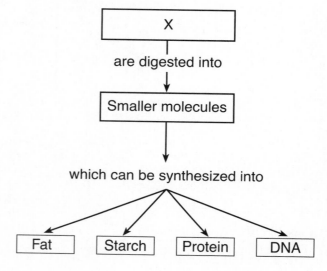

Letter *X* represents
- (1) inorganic molecules
- (2) organic molecules
- (3) biological catalysts
- (4) simple sugars

36 In the cells of the human body, oxygen molecules are used directly in a process that
- (1) releases energy
- (2) digests fats
- (3) synthesizes carbohydrate molecules
- (4) alters the genetic traits of the cell

37 Which statement explains the importance of maintaining a constant internal environment to ensure proper enzyme functioning?

    (1) Changes in pH and temperature will cause the enzyme reaction rate to be too fast.
    (2) Temperature and pH determine amino acid sequences in enzymes.
    (3) Changes in pH will change the genetic instructions of enzymes.
    (4) Increasing the temperature and pH can alter the specific shape of enzymes.

Base your answers to questions 38 through 41 on the information below and on your knowledge of biology.

The Galapagos pink land iguana, *Conolophus marthae* (*C. marthae*), is native to only one of the Galapagos Islands. Its entire range is currently limited to Wolf Volcano on Isabella Island. The iguana was first discovered on this island in 1986. Genetic studies of the animal began sometime later, and it was identified as a species separate from other iguana populations on the Galapagos in 2009. Its population might have been as high as 100 in 1986, but now there might be as few as 10 of the animals left alive.

Other evidence indicates that this species could have diverged from another line of iguanas about 5.7 million years ago. After that, the other line of iguanas diverged into two other species, *C. pallidus* and *C. subcristatus*.

38 In the future, the current population of about ten pink land iguanas will probably

    (1) migrate to new islands in the Galapagos in order to survive
    (2) soon become extinct, because they have little genetic diversity
    (3) undergo evolution by natural selection and survive
    (4) soon become extinct, because they have too much genetic diversity

39 The testing that revealed that these iguanas are a separate species from the other iguanas present in the Galapagos most likely included

    (1) genetic engineering
    (2) cloning studies
    (3) DNA analysis
    (4) the use of paper chromatography

40 One likely reason for the existence of these pink land iguanas today is that their ancestors

    (1) had the same variations as other iguanas but, after a long period of changing environmental conditions, mutated to the pink form when the environment eventually stabilized
    (2) had variations not present in other iguanas that allowed them to live in a particular environment more successfully than the other iguanas
    (3) lived on several other islands long ago, but migrated to Isabella Island around 1980 to have the environment to themselves, without predators to harm them
    (4) found that they were less visible to predators if they made themselves pink to blend in with the plants growing around them

41 Which evolutionary tree best represents the information about the pink land iguana provided in the passage?

(1)

(3)

(2)

(4)

42 The diagram below represents specialized cells in the surface of the leaf of a green plant.

The main function of these cells is to

(1) change the size of the stomate to regulate water loss
(2) close the stomate to keep dust and dirt out of the leaf
(3) directly provide leaf cells with the water involved in photosynthesis
(4) allow newly formed glucose to be released from the leaf

43 Which diagram correctly represents a step in the normal process of human reproduction?

Key
$2n$ = total genetic material of a human cell
n = one half of the total genetic material of a human cell

$2n + 2n \longrightarrow n$

(1)

$2n + n \longrightarrow 3n$

(3)

$n + n \longrightarrow 2n$

(2)

$2n + 2n \longrightarrow 4n$

(4)

June '13 Regents Examination

Part B–2

Answer all questions in this part. [12]

Directions (44–55): For those questions that are multiple choice, record on the separate answer sheet the *number* of the choice that, of those given, best completes each statement or answers each question. For all other questions in this part, follow the directions given and record your answers in the spaces provided in this examination booklet.

Base your answers to questions 44 through 47 on the data table below and on your knowledge of biology. The data table shows the number of breeding pairs of bald eagles in New York State from 1991 to 2003.

**Number of Breeding Pairs of
Bald Eagles in New York State from 1991 to 2003**

Year	Number of Breeding Pairs
1991	15
1993	20
1995	25
1997	35
1999	45
2001	65
2003	75

Directions (44–45): Using the information in the data table, construct a line graph on the grid below, following the directions below.

44 Mark an appropriate scale, without any breaks, on each labeled axis. [1]

45 Plot the data on the grid. Surround each point with a small circle and connect the points. [1]

Example:

Number of Breeding Pairs of Bald Eagles in New York State from 1991 to 2003

Year

46 State *one* possible reason for the increase in the number of breeding pairs of bald eagles in New York State. [1]

_____

_____

Note: The answer to question 47 should be recorded on your separate answer sheet.

47 In which time period did New York State see the largest increase in breeding pairs of bald eagles?
   (1) 1991–1993
   (2) 1993–1995
   (3) 1995–1997
   (4) 1999–2001

June '13 Regents Examination

Base your answers to questions 48 and 49 on the graph below and on your knowledge of biology. The graph shows the size of a population over time.

Population Size

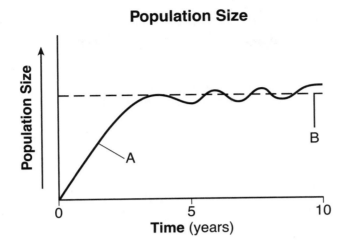

48 State *one* reason for the changes in population size represented by line *A* between years 5 and 10. [1]

_____

_____

Note: The answer to question 49 should be recorded on your separate answer sheet.

49 Which term best identifies line *B* in the graph?
  (1) niche of the species in the environment
  (2) biodiversity in the environment
  (3) carrying capacity of the environment
  (4) number of populations in the environment

Base your answers to questions 50 through 52 on the information and graph below and on your knowledge of biology.

A student conducts an experiment to determine how the amount of light affects the rate of oxygen production in a plant. The graph represents the rate of oxygen produced for one trial, X, in the experiment. By the end of the experiment, the plant had not reached maximum oxygen production.

Relationship of Light to Oxygen Production

Increasing Rate of Oxygen Production

X

Increasing Amount of Light

Note: The answer to question 50 should be recorded on your separate answer sheet.

50 If a student supplies more light than was received during trial X, a bar placed on the graph to represent the results would most likely be

(1) shorter than bar X and placed to the left of bar X
(2) shorter than bar X and placed to the right of bar X
(3) taller than bar X and placed to the left of bar X
(4) taller than bar X and placed to the right of bar X

51 The diagram below represents a cell from the plant being used in the study. Draw an arrow to a cell structure directly responsible for oxygen production in this cell. The tip of the arrow must touch the cell structure. [1]

52 Identify the biochemical process occurring in this cell that produces the oxygen. [1]

Process: _____

Base your answer to question 53 on the information below and on your knowledge of biology.

Botulinum toxin is a protein produced by the bacterium *Clostridium botulinum*. It causes a serious form of food poisoning in humans. In a very dilute form, it is also commonly used to eliminate some signs of aging, such as wrinkles. It does this by preventing nerves from releasing a chemical messenger called acetylcholine into the synapse (space between a nerve cell and a muscle cell). The toxin affects the process that causes the muscle cell to contract and form wrinkles.

53 The diagram below represents a process that is involved in the formation of wrinkles. Complete the diagram by drawing an appropriate structure on the muscle cell membrane that would allow the nerve cell to communicate with the muscle cell.   [1]

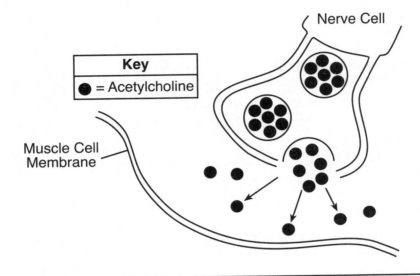

Base your answers to questions 54 and 55 on the scatter-plot graph below and on your knowledge of biology. The graph shows changes in the percentage of vancomycin-resistant bacteria in a population between the years 1983 and 2001.

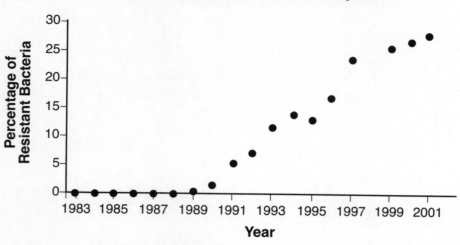

Resistance to Vancomycin

Source: http://evolution.berkeley.edu/evolibrary/article/bergstrom_03

54 Explain why the percentage of resistant bacteria increased over time. [1]

_____

_____

55 State what scientists might do to successfully combat bacteria that are resistant to vancomycin. [1]

_____

_____

_____

June '13 Regents Examination

Part C

Answer all questions in this part.   [17]

Directions (56–72): Record your answers in the spaces provided in this examination booklet.

56 When insects are accidentally transported from one country to a new habitat in another country, the population of these insects often increases rapidly. State *one* environmental factor in the new habitat that would account for this increase in the population.   [1]

_____

_____

Base your answer to question 57–60 on the information below and on your knowledge of biology.

The year 2010 was declared the International Year of Biodiversity. However, significant loss of biodiversity is still occurring. Researchers around the world are working on a variety of ways to protect natural resources. According to an article in *Science News*, March 13, 2010, "reversing the downward spiral of biodiversity will take more than protecting wild places, but that's where scientists are starting."

57–60 Explain the importance of biodiversity to an ecosystem. In your answer, be sure to:
  • state *one* effect of a loss of biodiversity in an ecosystem   [1]
  • identify a source of variation within a species that leads to biodiversity   [1]
  • identify *one* specific ecosystem that has shown a decrease in biodiversity and state *one* cause of the decrease in biodiversity in the ecosystem you identified   [1]
  • identify *one* human activity, other than setting up protected wildlife areas, that has helped to preserve biodiversity   [1]

_____

_____

_____

_____

_____

_____

_____

Base your answer to question 61–64 on the information below and on your knowledge of biology.

Scientists have been experimenting with different forms of alternate energy to help reduce the amount of fossil fuels that are burned. They studied yeast, which convert plant materials into ethanol, a form of alcohol that can be used in automobiles. These experiments were carried out at room temperature. The scientists wondered whether more ethanol would be produced at different temperatures.

61–64 Design an experiment to determine the effect of temperature on ethanol production by yeast. In your answer, be sure to:

- state *one* hypothesis the experiment would test   [1]
- state how the control group would be treated differently from the experimental group   [1]
- identify *two* factors that must be kept the same in both the experimental and control groups   [1]
- identify the independent variable in the experiment   [1]

_____

_____

_____

_____

_____

_____

_____

_____

June '13   Regents Examination

Base your answers to questions 65 and 66 on the passage below and on your knowledge of biology.

Permission to use this third-party content
has not been granted to Pearson.
View content at nysedregents.org.

65 Based on the information given in the passage, state the relationship between the number of cigarettes young males smoke and their IQ. [1]

_____

_____

66 Explain how chemicals present in cigarette smoke are able to enter the body *and* reach the brain. [1]

_____

_____

Base your answers to questions 67 through 70 on the information below and on your knowledge of biology.

The rapidly growing biofuel industry converts resources such as corn plants, vegetable oils, and industrial wastes into products that can be used to power cars and trucks, and heat homes. The increased demand for fossil fuel has led to the construction of factories to produce biofuels. A proposal has been made to build a biofuel factory near Syracuse in New York State.

67 State *one* advantage, other than decreased reliance on fossil fuels, of the increased production of biofuels in New York State. [1]

_____

_____

68 State *one disadvantage* of the increased use of corn for biofuels. [1]

_____

_____

69 State *one* economic advantage of constructing a biofuel factory. [1]

_____

_____

70 State *one* concern that local residents might have about having a biofuel factory in their area. [1]

_____

_____

Base your answers to questions 71 and 72 on the information and diagram below and on your knowledge of biology.

Endometriosis is a condition that occurs in some women, causing multiple cells or layers of cells to grow outside of the uterus. In some cases, these growths can actually cover the entire ovary or cause the tube leading from the ovary to the uterus to be blocked. The diagram below represents the female reproductive system. Two structures, A and B, are labeled.

71 Select structure A or B and indicate your selection on the line below. Describe specifically how the growths that are characteristic of endometriosis at the location you selected could affect the ability of a female to become pregnant. [1]

Structure:_____

_____

_____

72 Select either surgical procedure or hormone therapy and explain why it can be an effective treatment for endometriosis. [1]

Effective treatment:_____

_____

_____

Part D

Answer all questions in this part. [13]

Directions (73–85): For those questions that are multiple choice, record on the separate answer sheet the *number* of the choice that, of those given, best completes the statement or answers the question. For all other questions in this part, follow the directions given and record your answers in the spaces provided in this examination booklet.

Base your answers to questions 73 and 74 on the information below and on your knowledge of biology.

A student observes a red onion cell with a compound light microscope using low, then high power. The two views are represented below.

Low Power   High Power

Note: The answers to questions 73 and 74 should be recorded on your separate answer sheet.

73 The best explanation for the changes observed by the student is that, when switching from low to high power, the

(1) diameter of the field of view decreases
(2) slide was accidentally moved
(3) diameter of the field of view increases
(4) image is inverted and reversed

74 Which diagram represents where the cell should be located in the low-power field of view to be sure the entire cell will be visible after switching to high power?

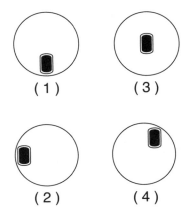

(1)   (3)

(2)   (4)

June '13 Regents Examination

75 Hospital patients are often given intravenous fluids (IVs) to maintain proper levels of water and salts in the body. Great care is used in preparing these solutions. If a manufacturer accidentally prepared a batch of IV fluid that contained much more than the usual amount of salt, harm to the patient could result. The most likely effect on a patient if this incorrectly prepared IV fluid was used is that

(1) water would move into body cells and cause them to burst
(2) water would move out of body cells and cause them to dehydrate
(3) salt and water would both move out of body cells and disrupt homeostasis
(4) salt and water would both move into body cells and preserve homeostasis

76 Which technique could be used to determine the relative number of bases in fragments taken from a sample of DNA?

(1) electrophoresis
(2) cloning
(3) paper chromatography
(4) light microscopy

Base your answers to questions 77 and 78 on the DNA base sequence below and on your knowledge of biology.

AAC–GCC–GTC–CGC–TAG

77 Identify the mRNA codons that would be produced using this DNA as a template. [1]

DNA base sequence: AAC   GCC   GTC   CGC   TAG

mRNA codons: _____ _____ _____ _____ _____

78 If a mutation occurs, leaving 12 bases, what is the maximum number of amino acids that could be coded for by this DNA segment? [1]

_____ amino acids

Base your answers to questions 79 and 80 on the diagram below and on your knowledge of biology. The diagram represents a cell and its changes as a result of two laboratory procedures, A and B.

79 Describe procedure A and explain why it would cause the change shown.   [1]

_____

_____

80 Explain why procedure B has the opposite effect of procedure A.   [1]

_____

_____

_____

Base your answers to questions 81 through 83 on the information and diagram below and on your knowledge of biology.

The circled areas in the diagram represent bird species that are in the same genus, a classification group that includes closely related species. These birds are found on the Hawaiian Islands.

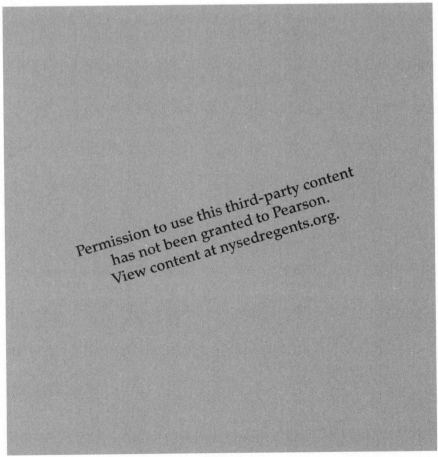

81 Which processes are directly responsible for the presence of the different species of birds shown in the diagram?

(1) mitosis and differentiation

(3) gene mutations and natural selection

(2) gene manipulation and overpopulation

(4) competition and cloning

82 Which two finches are most closely related?

(1) Lesser Koa finch and Nukupuu

(3) Kauai akialoa and Maui parrot bill

(2) Akialoa and Ou

(4) Ou and Greater Koa finch

83 If the Akialoa migrated to an ecosystem occupied by a Greater Koa finch, could both species survive? Support your answer. [1]

_____

_____

_____

84 Identify *one* specific molecule that will increase in concentration in the blood as a result of increased activity of the circulatory system during physical exercise. [1]

_____

85 Before deciding whether a conclusion was valid or invalid, students looked at the results of the entire class. Explain why the results of the entire class were analyzed, rather than just the results of one individual student. [1]

_____

_____

_____